GW00537342

Inspiring outside the box

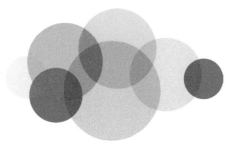

Dr Adrian Burden

Inspiring outside the box

The ten-year backstory to the Malvern Festival of Innovation

Published by Key IQ Ltd
Wyche Innovation Centre
Walwyn Road, Malvern WR13 6PL
email: publishing@key-iq.com

ISBN: 978 1 7391384 0 0

A CIP catalogue record for this book is available from the British Library.

Layout and design by Pippa Sanderson.

Inspiring outside
the box

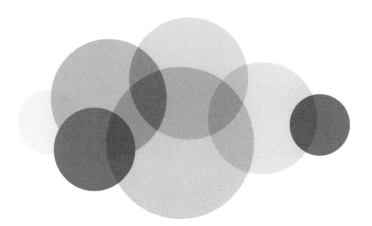

To my wife Emma who put up with all my 'great new ideas' for the
festival each year, and now suffers post-traumatic stress
whenever we visit the Malvern Theatres for leisure!

PHOTO CREDITS

Thanks to everyone who has taken photographs over the years to record the various events recounted in this book. Wherever possible, photographs are credited with the following initials in the captions. AB: Adrian Burden; AS: Alan Smith; Bc: Braintastic; CB: Chris Bassett; CC: Colin Chandler; CM: Cliff McFarlane; CWa: Carl Walker from Wild Edric Media; CW: Chris Winstanley; DB: David Bott; DBS: Dan Barker Studios; DH: David Huckerby from GD PR & Media, now Conteur; DS: Darren Stokes; EP: Emma Philpott; NH: Nicki Hollier; PF: Paddy Fawcett; RB: Robert Bilsland; RH: Rosemary Henderson; RL: Rob Lacey, courtesy of the *Business & Innovation Magazine*; RM: Ruaridh Macdonald from the Beacon Camera Club; SC: Dr Steve Cross; SP: Stuart Purfield; SS: Simon Smith; SW: Stuart Wilkes; TA: Tom Alcott; WR: Wendy Reeves, and ZS: Zoe Smith, Malvern Hills District Council.

A FEW ABBREVIATIONS

Just to save repetition in the text, the following abbreviations and acronyms are frequently used:

EV – Electric Vehicle

IMechE – Institution of Mechanical Engineers

IET – Institution of Engineering and Technology

IoM3 – Institute of Materials, Minerals and Mining

IoP – Institute of Physics

IP – Intellectual Property

JLR – Jaguar Land Rover

MHDC – Malvern Hills District Council

MHSP – Malvern Hills Science Park

MRATHS – Malvern Radar and Technology History Society

NCSC – National Cyber Security Centre

RMS – Royal Microscopical Society

RSC – Royal Society of Chemistry

SME – Small Medium Enterprise

STEM – Science, Technology, Engineering and Mathematics

TSB – Technology Strategy Board (now called Innovate UK)

UKTI – UK Trade & Industry (later Department for International Trade, DIT)

WCC – Worcestershire County Council

WINN – Worcestershire's Innovation programme

WLEP – Worcestershire Local Enterprise Partnership

CONTENTS

FOREWORD

Innovation sometimes involves technology, often involves money, but always involves people. And the path from idea to implementation is sometimes long but always complicated. This makes explaining what it is, how it works and how to get involved to other people a difficult task. Over 10 years ago, with a track record of being innovative himself, Adrian set out to share his passion for, and understanding of, innovation to a community initially based in Malvern, but which rapidly expanded to encompass the UK and the world. This book is the story of that quest and how it developed, but it is more than that. It is also a handbook for others who might want to do the same, and a list of people who shared his vision and were drawn into his quest. Having been "engaged" in the third festival, I was drawn back for many subsequent ones, so I can attest to the fact that Adrian is committed and persuasive and his enthusiasm is infectious. He started with a simple idea, but at every turn, he found ways to broaden the audience, develop the format and extend the reach.

In this book, there are sections on what businesses need to understand to be successful, a tranche on things digital and how and why to engage, but I recommend the parts on getting the message across to schoolchildren and families – a masterclass in drawing future stars into the world of innovation.

So, you can read this book as a story of how to develop a festival series, and it is accessible and engaging. You can also read it as a handbook if you want to run your own festival series (Good luck!). But it contains the names and specialist areas of an important cohort of the UK innovation community, so can be seen as a reference book too. That makes it great value for money!

Dr David Bott, Principal Fellow at WMG, University of Warwick, UK

PREFACE

I started writing this book in the lead up to the tenth Malvern Festival of Innovation in the summer of 2021 to celebrate a decade of the festival and some of the other initiatives I have been running related to innovation and entrepreneurship in my home town of Great Malvern. One of the motivations for writing this all down was to provide a definitive record of what has been achieved and acknowledge many of those who have helped me and participated along the way. Anyone who has organised annual events of this kind will know that it is quite simply exhausting, often nerve-wracking, and at times demoralising.

But as I went back through the archives, I was reminded of why I did it: we've had many eloquent speakers sharing their wisdom and insights, we've had numerous inspiring science communicators, and plenty of dedicated organisations have exhibited and showcased their products and services. It has been fun putting Malvern on the map, helping businesses to progress, and most of all inspiring kids to think about STEM subjects as a career move. Hopefully this retrospective of the festival will make you consider some of the subjects that we covered that remain important today, give you a better understanding of what it is like to stage events in your local community, and maybe encourage you to visit Malvern in the future, particularly if I run the festival again!

Dr Adrian Burden MA(Cantab), DPhil (Oxon), FIMMM, FIET, FRMS, CEng ometime in June 2012, Nick Tudor from D-RisQ Ltd popped his head around the door of my office and said to me and my wife Emma that it would be good to have a high-profile cyber security event in Malvern. Nick and his colleagues had not long moved into our new Wyche Innovation Centre on the Malvern Hills and, as a technology start-up, he was keen to engage with potential customers and showcase the products and services his team were developing.

I remember thinking that a cyber security event was potentially a good idea because Emma had recently formed the Malvern Cyber Security Cluster and there was a lot of interest in this growing industry sector. Moreover, Malvern seemed to be at the epicentre of the UK's nascent cyber security industry in that there was a large number of SMEs in the region. This had come about partly because QinetiQ was active in the sector and shedding staff who were then starting up on their own. Also, down the road to the south in Cheltenham was GCHQ, the UK's intelligence agency, and a similar distance to the west was Hereford with its SAS training camp and links to the defence industry.

INSPIRATION

THEME INNOVATION

However, I felt that we could do better by being a little less focused on a 'sector-of-the-moment'. Instead, how about embracing the ground swell that there was a need to be innovative in general so as to succeed in growing new businesses and competing in the global knowledge-based economy? Back then, the Technology Strategy Board (TSB) was the UK's business and industry facing body and it had started promoting the need to embrace innovation. Indeed, two years later in August 2014 it changed its name to Innovate UK.

> I FELT THAT WE COULD DO BETTER BY BEING A LITTLE LESS FOCUSED ON A 'SECTOR-OF-THE-MOMENT'.

I thus decided that a 'festival of innovation' was what was needed. This ambition aligned well with the fact we had the Wyche Innovation Centre to fill with new businesses and that I had a general interest in science, technology, entrepreneurship and creative design.

Moreover, looking around, there just didn't seem to be a similar festival elsewhere that would be a direct competitor. Cheltenham had its successful Science Festival and Hay-on-Wye just beyond Hereford had its acclaimed Festival of Literature and Arts.

The Hay Festival really interested me because it had begun back in 1988 and was still going strong, attracting high profile speakers to a village quite literally in the middle of nowhere. This demonstrated that with good programming, speakers and audiences would travel to a remote destination to be educated, inspired and informed.

And unlike Hay, Great Malvern had (and still has) good access to the motorway network via the nearby M5, and direct rail services to the cities of London, Oxford, Birmingham and occasionally Bristol. So, it was an easier location to reach.

Malvern also had a natural fit with a festival focused on innovation.

MALVERN'S HERITAGE

QinetiQ was still the largest employer in town, with staff working at the cutting-edge of the defence industry predominantly in computer-related technology such as software systems, cyber security, threat analysis and modelling. But it had also been the site of the development of radar, the invention of touch screens, the invention of passive infrared detectors, amorphous silicon technology and arguably the concept of the integrated circuit itself.

This centre of science had over the years hosted electronics laboratories, clean rooms, semiconductor processing equipment, and much more. To the extent that it was once said that Malvern for some time had the most PhDs per square mile of any non-university town in the UK, and probably more so than some of those with universities.

Also, during the Second World War, the scientists in Malvern working on covert defence technology gave rise to the term 'boffins' after a newspaper referred to them as such in seemingly the first instance of this word.

But Malvern had much more innovation in its heritage, beyond just science and engineering. It had heralded an early form of healthcare tourism

> IT WAS ONCE SAID THAT MALVERN FOR SOME TIME HAD THE MOST PHDS PER SQUARE MILE OF ANY NON-UNIVERSITY TOWN IN THE UK.

with the popular 'Water Cure', in which people would travel from afar to the town to drink and bathe in its spring water to rid themselves of ailments. Even Florence Nightingale and Charles Darwin's daughter Annie had visited to seek rest and recuperation.

Malvern, and the nearby village of Colwall, were also the location in which a paradigm shift in children's schooling took place, with the pioneering of independent private education that continues to this day in Malvern College, Malvern St James, and The Elms. The latter is believed to be the oldest still-running independent school in the UK having been established in 1614.

And the town also has what was until recently the oldest family-owned automotive company; The Morgan Motor Company which produces hand-built sports cars of international repute from its small factory in Malvern Link.

Finally, Great Malvern was no stranger to festivals in general, and so had the venues in which

to stage a potential event of this nature. The Malvern Theatres itself was born out of an art and music festival instigated by resident playwright George Bernard Shaw in the 1930s. Back then, the venue was even called the Festival Theatre of Malvern.

So, this was all well and good; the concept seemed sound, but of course events need to be organised and potential attendees also needed to be informed. So, there was a lot of work to be done to stage a new event and market it as widely as possible.

HANDS TO THE PUMP

Fortunately, in February of 2011, Emma had organised a mini technology expo[1] in the assembly

The precursor to the festival back in 2011; a technology expo in the assembly hall of the Chase School with some table top exhibitors and sixth form entrants to a science poster competition. As I went through the archive, I recognised the representative pictured here (bottom left) from the University of Birmingham. Irina Hoffman is now the Head of Operations at the School of Metallurgy and Materials and I would come to know her in my much more recent role as a Royal Society Entrepreneur in Residence, not realising that we had met several years earlier! (AB)

hall of The Chase secondary school and we'd invited a variety of organisations to take part from around the town and further afield. This had involved hosting a hall full of table-top displays, informing exhibitors about the logistics, getting people in to visit on the day, and even a technology poster competition for sixth form students. Little did we know at the time that this one-off event would be a precursor to a much larger event building on these ingredients.

1 'Successful technical exhibition', *Malvern Gazette*, 24th February 2011.
www.malverngazette.co.uk/news/malvern/8874776.
successful-technical-exhibition/

Things started to take shape over the summer of 2012 as I talked to various venues to discuss what could be done, and a date for early November was set for the inaugural Malvern Festival of Innovation. We decided to stage a two-day event that would bring together business leaders and professionals to network, see what each other were doing, and be exposed to new ideas.

We also decided to 'go-big' from day one by hiring the Malvern Theatres as the venue, partly because it was central to Great Malvern, but also because it was a versatile space with foyers, an auditorium, large hall, meeting room and café. It was also a very respectable venue with helpful and enthusiastic staff keen to work with us on the event.

The Malvern Theatres provided a welcoming venue for the inaugural festival (DH).

As I started connecting the dots in August and September of 2012 it became clear that there was indeed a lot of work to do. I scrambled to put a website together, composed the first @festivalofinnov tweet, and began calling and emailing contacts to compile a programme of speakers and exhibitors.

SERENDIPITY

Several formative things happened during this period which helped shape the festival and the way it was to be curated over the ensuing decade.

Firstly, realising I needed one or two impressive keynote speakers to headline the event, I began looking around and making contact

| | Festivalofinnovation |
| | @festivalofinnov |

The inaugural Malvern Festival of Innovation coming 8th/9th November 2012 - more details soon...

5:39 PM · Aug 22, 2012 · Twitter Web Client

Our first tweet in August 2012 announcing the dates of the first edition of the festival.

with prospective 'celebrity' speakers and soon discovered how difficult it was to reach them, never mind persuade them to join us when I basically had no budget nor any track record.

But I had a lucky break as a contact at the then public body National Endowment for Science, Technology and the Arts (NESTA) suggested I contact Luke Johnson who was the entrepreneur who had made a success of Pizza Express and had gone on to invest in a number of other retail and hospitality businesses as well as having recently been chairman of Channel 4 Television Corporation. I made contact with his personal assistant and soon felt the heat of her very effective firewall as she tried to fend off my enquiry and protect the busy Luke from yet another invitation to speak. But then Luke suddenly jumped in and replied personally, explaining that he actually had a home near Malvern despite living in London, and that he would indeed be keen to help if I could explain a bit more about my plans. I suddenly realised that people's connections with Malvern, past and present, would be one key to making the festival

> I MADE CONTACT WITH HIS PERSONAL ASSISTANT AND SOON FELT THE HEAT OF HER VERY EFFECTIVE FIREWALL AS SHE TRIED TO FEND OFF MY ENQUIRY.

a success, and this fact has proven correct over the years as you will discover.

I have also stayed in touch with Luke and his family since, having dinner together on numerous occasions when he returns to Malvern. He cited the festival in a *Sunday Times* business article[2] rounding up the best start-ups at the end of 2012 giving the event much appreciated national publicity. A few years later, Luke also kindly penned the foreword to my business book *Start to Exit.*

The second fortuitous happening was that I decided to travel to Sheffield to visit MADE: The Entrepreneur Festival in September. There was a link with Luke here too, because he was speaking there and so we arranged to meet up for lunch so he could hear more about my plans. But MADE showed me what could be done; it was a full day of really interesting, experienced speakers including Peter Jones from *Dragons' Den*, a full auditorium of attentive delegates in the City Hall, and a small but interesting exhibition of organisations in the basement. Also, the city had got behind the event with pavement stickers and shop-window poster displays between the railway station and the city centre venue. And there was *The Entrepreneurs' Express* train service from London, that as you will see later, also inspired me.

Thirdly, the planned event seemed to be capturing people's imagination locally and resulted in enthusiastic offers to help out. For example, Artwork Creative kindly designed and donated the festival logo whilst Gillian Davies and David Huckerby at GD PR & Media (now Conteur) kindly offered to be our official professional photographer, working pro-bono as it was our first year.

Finally, we settled quickly on a simple business model which was to finance the event largely with sponsorship from local companies and

Evolution of the Malvern Festival of Innovation Logo, designed by Artwork Creative.

stakeholders, predominantly because this was likely to be the quickest way to secure funds to pay for the cost of venue hire. MHDC, QinetiQ, Malvern Instruments (as it was called then) and a successful local start-up Textlocal all kindly chipped in with very little deliberation. We'd also charge for the formal dinner but offer seats as part of the sponsorship package, and we'd endeavour to make attendance of the talks and exhibition itself free of charge to encourage participation by students, cash-strapped entrepreneurs, and interested members of the public. This inclusivity was to become a cornerstone of the future editions of the festival as we struggled to secure enough financial sponsorship and debated whether to levy charges for attendance to reduce apathetic no-shows.

Innovate Malvern
Community Interest Company

The logo for the social enterprise Innovate Malvern CIC.

At the time, Emma and I were running our technology consultancy business Key IQ Ltd that was also running the newly created Wyche Innovation Centre. In this early stage it made sense to run the event through the same business, but in 2015 created the social enterprise Innovate Malvern CIC (a Community Interest Company) to take the festival forward in later years. ○

2 'Best start-ups: the experts' view', The *Sunday Times*, 23rd December 2012. www.thetimes.co.uk/article/best-start-ups-the-experts-view-kmwdvvzm6cp

2.

Anyone who has read *Range: How Generalists Triumph in a Specialized World*, by David Epstein, will know that many problems are solved by people with knowledge outside the area of specialisation. In other words, having other interests, being multidisciplinary, and learning new skills in other fields can really help drive innovative thinking so as to come up with solutions by analogy through seeing connections and spotting similarities. This relates to the term 'thinking outside of the box'; being a bit unconventional and not blinded by preconceptions.

Epstein's book wasn't published until October 2020, but some eight years earlier I was already convinced by what I would read later, and on our new website I wrote "Touch new products, try new services, glimpse the future. Let your mind freely wander, allow sparks to fly, shift the paradigm, and have your own eureka moment . . .". And this sentiment underpinned the thinking of the festival as a whole; the idea was to come along and be exposed to new things not directly in your line of sight in your day job. To this end, the festival would comprise of broadly themed symposia with fascinating speakers alongside a parallel exhibition

CORE SYMPOSIA

that you could dip in and out of. The exhibiting organisations would showcase a smorgasbord of products, services and business assistance that in turn would broaden people's horizons and might just help them make connections so they went away with new insights to help improve something in their own organisation.

What has been most disappointing over the ensuing years is just how few people seem to get this! At the outset I naively thought local employers would seize the opportunity and encourage (no, insist that) their staff took a morning, afternoon or even whole day out of their routine and went up the road to the festival. But this was not actually to be the case; the fact the subject matter was fairly broad and may not have been of immediate direct relevance to the day job meant few people understood what they might get out of taking advantage of fantastic speakers descending on the then-termed 'World Class Worcestershire' to share their knowledge. Instead, local policy makers harped on about emerging technology trends and new business opportunities without actually taking the time to immerse themselves in the topics presented on their doorstep, and so-called high-tech innovative companies kept their blinkers on and their staff missed out on some truly mind-expanding presentations.

2012'S AMBITIOUS START

Emma and I curated a full two days of talks including a day of parallel streams in an attempt to fit it all in. The festival opened with a plenary talk from Professor Peter Dobson, Director of Begbroke Science Park at the University of Oxford. Peter had been my college tutor whilst I did my D.Phil. (PhD) in Oxford, and he had collaborated with Raychem Ltd that had also sponsored me as a student. We had stayed in touch over the years because he, like me, was really interested in applied research, commercialising technology and understanding how to navigate the choppy waters as a technology start-up. Therefore, he was a fitting first speaker, outlining the difference in cost and complexity of bringing a new manufactured product and a new intangible service to market.

The morning of Thursday 8th November continued with the Cyber Security symposium, a subject area that back then was starting to become important but was certainly not mainstream like it is today. If you remember, it was initially suggested that the festival be one centred on cyber security, and so with the growing Malvern Cyber Security Cluster that Emma had formed, it was certainly justified in being the focus of a key session.

Welcoming the first visitors to the festival at the registration desk in the Malvern Theatres entrance foyer, and me with my opening slides on stage in the auditorium. (DH)

> ## SO-CALLED HIGH-TECH INNOVATIVE COMPANIES KEPT THEIR BLINKERS ON AND THEIR STAFF MISSED OUT ON SOME TRULY MIND-EXPANDING PRESENTATIONS.

We opened with a keynote from retired Col. John Doody, an expert in the field and local resident whom Emma had involved in the cluster. We also featured some of the local companies active in the area, with Elliott Atkins, the Head of Cyber Intelligence at QinetiQ, Dr Simon Wiseman the CTO of Deep Secure, Ian Whiting the MD of Titania and of course Nick Tudor, Founding Director of D-RisQ who had planted the idea of an annual cyber security event in our minds earlier that year. We also had Lt Col Ian Buchanan speak about cyber policy at the Ministry of Defence so as to provide a military and government view of the subject.

Later in the afternoon, we changed topic and finished the day off with the Digital Media symposium. Once again, Emma and I had delved into our address books and pulled together a fascinating mix of speakers who travelled from around the country to join in. Andrew Humphries,

Dealmaker for the UKTI's Global Entrepreneur Programme spoke about digital clusters, a concept that was actually quite new and in which Malvern was beginning to feature as a recognised cyber security cluster. Jennifer Sheridan, CEO of TOGEVA, spoke about her journey from digital artist to technology entrepreneur; Alistair Shortland the founding CEO of Textlocal explained why businesses should embrace mobile messaging; Mark Stanger visited from Coventry's Serious Games Institute to explain the emerging role of electronic gaming in education; and Dr David Hardman MBE outlined the changing landscape in science parks and business real estate as the idea of 'virtual places' began to emerge. This latter talk was ahead of its time given that we have now lived through numerous virtual meetings in the growing metaverse as a result of the Covid-19 pandemic.

We had one speaker, Danny Meany, Chairman of New Media Partners who was ill and so couldn't join us, highlighting the risks of disruption to the programme from this kind of uncontrollable issue. Although this was a great shame, we also discovered that as some speakers talked for longer than timetabled, there was also the problem of sessions overrunning, and so an absent speaker helped to bring us back on the schedule.

The day was rounded off with a fascinating talk from local friend Paul Farrer, a self-taught TV and film music composer who had on-going lucrative returns from, amongst other things, the theme tune to the popular television programme *The Weakest Link*. He explained the challenges of being creative under the pressure of a looming time deadline, and as you'll read later, he also spoke at TEDxMalvern on this subject a few years later.

Next day, we ambitiously staged talks running concurrently as parallel sessions in the auditorium (the cinema) and a seminar room (the hospitality suite). This worked well in terms of enabling us to cover a lot of ground, but it divided the audience and meant the numbers in attendance looked

lower. But the day started off well with a double-bill plenary in the main auditorium which was, thankfully, very well attended. Luke Johnson opened with his talk about innovation in business and his experiences over the years of being an entrepreneur. He was by now Chairman of his investment company Risk Capital Partners, chair of the new national initiative StartUp Britain, as well as being a director of numerous other businesses both large and small.

NOT MANY SMALL TOWNS CAN LAY CLAIM TO HAVING A SPORTS CAR MANUFACTURER IN THEIR MIDST.

His talk was followed by local businessman Charles Morgan, the then Chairman of the family-owned Morgan Motor Company who gave a great presentation about the history and future plans of the carmaker, highlighting how design plays an important part in differentiating their products. Not many small towns can lay claim to having a sports car manufacturer in their midst; Maranello, the home of Ferrari in Italy is one of the few others that I think has some similarity.

The two streams that followed were a business symposium (that was the forerunner to the Business of Innovating theme we had in later years) and a Materials & Devices symposium that we were compelled to host given that both Emma and I are materials scientist graduates.

Dr Mark Yeadon, a very capable patent attorney who had been a senior research scientist alongside me at the Institute of Materials Research & Engineering (IMRE) in Singapore, talked about the role of intellectual property (IP) in business and wealth creation. This presentation was followed by Ellie Runcie, a Director at the Design Council whom I had met at an edition of VentureFest in Oxford and who provided some excellent case studies illustrating how design impacts product success. Dennis Yeates then stood in at the last minute for his colleague Dawn Harford from Artwork Creative to discuss the importance of branding and marketing; remember they had kindly designed our festival logo too.

Top: Lisa Loudon pitches her pop-up food outlet to the attentive investor panel; from left to right Luke Johnson, Chris Boulton, Giovanni Finocchio and Mark Reilly.
Bottom: Giovanni, one of the fire-breathing dragons, grilling an entrepreneur. (DH)

Meanwhile across the venue, Del Stark had travelled down from Scotland to talk about nanotechnology, Rowena Innocent spoke about R&D teamwork at Malvern Instruments (now Malvern Panalytical), Richard Horne from Heber Ltd explained recent developments in the real-time control of devices including the use of the new Raspberry Pi

computer and the emergence of the Internet of Things, and Dr Cliff Jones the CTO of locally founded ZBD Displays spoke about bistable liquid crystal display (LCD) technology for low power retail signage. He later moved away from Malvern, but returned in a later year to speak at TEDxMalvern.

After lunch we convened a panel of investors (Luke Johnson, Chris Boulton, Giovanni Finocchio from Midven, and Mark Reilly from IP Group) to listen to short pitches from entrepreneurs. This format worked surprisingly well, as each presenter explained their concept and funding need live on stage in a very limited amount of time. They were then grilled by the panel before the audience had the opportunity to field a question. It was an enjoyable session in which to watch a few different approaches to pitching and then directly connect with the entrepreneurs afterwards to collaborate. Adomas Bukauskas presented a web platform that would facilitate international e-commerce, Chris Ollivier and his colleague James Eadon pitched a novel games and puzzles company called Captica, Lisa Loudon described her pop-up mobile cookery concept of food explorer days for youngsters at local outdoor events or parks, and then stunt bike rider and designer Mike Singleton finished the session with a competent pitch about his innovative electric trike.

After the pitches, we then returned to the business symposium and focused on the growth, export and exit stages of a venture. Nigel Walker, from what was then known as the TSB explained the different financing options for a business. Carolyn Parker followed from the University of Warwick's International Institute for Product and Service Innovation outlining how collaborating with academia can be beneficial to innovative businesses, and then Steve Dunn explained the Growth Accelerator initiative that was running in the UK back then. Linda Smith, later the founding CEO of Worcestershire's technology accelerator BetaDen in Malvern, was at the time Head of International

Trade at the local UKTI and she explained the assistance available for businesses wanting to export and grow globally. Finally, Dr Mark Reilly, from the IP Group whom Emma and I had originally met whilst we were living in Singapore, talked about business planning strategies for a trade sale exit or stock market listing.

Meanwhile, the Sustainability and Environment symposium was taking place in the Hospitality Suite across the foyer with Emma chairing whilst I had been hosting the session just described. This highlighted another disadvantage of the parallel symposia; I couldn't been in two places at once and both sessions were equally fascinating.

We had the CEO of Asia BioBusiness Dr Andrew Powell, who had also travelled the furthest by coming in from Singapore (although not specifically for this event), speak about risk communication in innovation. He highlighted the importance of frank, honest discussion to present both the pros and cons about new technology, something of great importance today as organisations deal with fake news and conspiracy theories. Mike Woollacott, the MD of Greenwatt Technology, then presented about renewable energy technology which is top of the agenda a decade later. Tom Jarret from UK Flood Barriers explained how to be innovative in a conservative market at a time when his work was of growing importance as food plains were being built upon and flood defences were starting to be installed around the UK. We were also fortunate to welcome Simon Bond from the University of Bath's Innovation Centre who spoke about start-ups in cleantech.

Local expert Michael Goodfellow-Smith then explained his work in improving sustainability of businesses. As you will read, Mike would become a valued supporter of the festival in later years helping me with a number of sessions on the green economy. We also heard from John Turvill, Director of C-Zero on ways to produce

biomethane sustainably, and Katy Boom from the University of Worcester explaining how to prepare students for the future environmental sustainability challenges.

And as I write this, recalling that full line-up back in 2012, I think how relevant each of those talks would still be today, and indeed how anyone that listened to those speakers ten years ago will have come away with glimpses of where the world

RECALLING THAT FULL LINE-UP BACK IN 2012, I THINK HOW RELEVANT EACH OF THOSE TALKS WOULD STILL BE TODAY.

was indeed heading. Back then, we were sensing the future importance of cyber security across the home and business, we were wrestling with how best to support entrepreneurs with IP, growth, export and financial assistance, we were aware of environmental issues before the currently accepted climate emergency, and we predicted the rise of importance of software-as-a-service and virtual digital environments in which to work and learn. We had attracted over thirty-five varied and interesting speakers to participate and they had each brought fascinating insights and experiences to life for our benefit.

As one attendant kindly fed back to us: "The quality of all speakers was very impressive and a real coup having them travel to Malvern. The presentations I attended were pitched at the right level, were thought provoking and achieved a great balance to an audience no doubt comprising both specialists and generalists."

2012'S EXHIBITION

The talks were not all you could enjoy at the inaugural two-day event in the Malvern Theatres.

The cyber security pavilion in the upper foyer of the Malvern Theatres, including (from top) Titania, borwell and D-RisQ. (DH)

We also filled the Forum Theatre and the Upper Foyer with table top-exhibitors. These were classified into innovative technology and service companies, falling in line with the subjects covered by the themed symposia described above, and companies or organisations supporting innovation.

The expo showcased over 60 quite diverse organisations that delegates could chat with, and gain a better understanding of what they did or how they could help, and some of them were national bodies like the Intellectual Property Office, UKTI, and Design Council. It was also good to see a number of universities from around the region and some businesses that at that stage were small and upcoming, but soon to grow rapidly (like IASME Consortium, Textlocal, Titania, and Versarien).

> WITH VENUES BOOKED, SPEAKERS TRAVELLING FROM AFAR, EXHIBITORS COMMITTING TO PARTICIPATE, AND VISITORS COMING WITH HIGH EXPECTATIONS, THE SHOW LITERALLY MUST GO ON.

THE BAPTISM OF FIRE

In addition to the two-day symposium, we also hosted an evening formal dinner which is described in a later chapter. The festival had been fun to organise, but hard work to pull together. The issue with events like this is that there is a very clear, immovable deadline. This has the advantage that once it's done, it's over, but the disadvantage is that you can't delay things if there are slips or

The main exhibition in the vast Forum Theatre in the Malvern Theatres, along with the UKTI's very apt and iconic poster Innovation is Great (Britain). (DH)

hiccups during the runup. With venues booked, speakers travelling from afar, exhibitors committing to participate, and visitors coming with high expectations, the show literally must go on.

And there is a lot to do which, unless you've organised a large community event yourself, you'd be forgiven for not appreciating. Speakers need to be invited, and many that are asked are either unavailable or can't commit until nearer the time. The programme has to be fluid and adaptable as different people respond, and speakers may need tailored travel assistance or hotel accommodation. In parallel, exhibitors are being approached, and as happened in this first year, the take-up was greater than expected which meant we extended the venue hire to include the more costly and spacious Forum Theatre. The key to efficiency was in providing clear information so that questions were minimised; with on the order of a hundred different entities being firmed up for speaking and exhibiting in this first year, I quickly realised there was little time to respond to each if they had individual queries and concerns.

The main challenge was also the marketing; people needed to know the event was on. Back in 2012 we spread the word through social media, informing our contacts in local businesses and

community groups, using organisations that sent out newsletters, and through the local press. The problem with event marketing is it is never enough and there is always more one can do, so it has to be scheduled over a few months leading up to the event with a flurry of activity just as everything else demands attention in the final few weeks.

And the level of activity, as the event approaches, reaches fever pitch in the final few days. I didn't appreciate this until Emma and I were still up at midnight on the eve of the first festival finalising name badges, collating attendance lists, assembling slide decks, and responding to email enquiries, having earlier hand-packed delegate bags and loaded the car with banner stands, programmes, event supplies, laptops, audio-visual kit, and so forth.

And when you are on a shoe-string, you don't have a team of employees setting up. We had a few very helpful volunteers who mucked-in, but we pitched up with a car fully loaded outside the venue at 7:30am and had to make sure things were ready to welcome exhibitors, then speakers, and then visitors in a timely fashion. And, believe me, not all speakers send slides in advance despite numerous requests, and others have last minute changes to upload on the day anyway. In one case an eminent speaker who shall remain nameless arrived with a memory stick of photographs which needed to be compiled into a PowerPoint presentation minutes before we were due to kick off!

However, we got through it all and recorded that over 400 people attended the event. As was said in our follow-up press release, Peter Urey from London based Fearless Innovation Management commented "The list of guest speakers was a Who's Who of luminaries from the world of innovation in business." Mark Yeadon from Leeds based Yeadon IP said "The Festival was a gem of a conference. An enviable line-up of speakers with very meaningful insights into the world of innovation." Chris Bocock, then Chief Executive of MHDC stated "Malvern Hills District Council were delighted to be able to support Key IQ in delivering the first Malvern Festival of Innovation. We believe that this year's event provides a strong basis for a successful annual event for Malvern that will help to promote the Malvern area and inspire future innovation within our businesses and community."

And to round it off, the festival was also recognized as a High Impact Event by Global Entrepreneurship Week UK.

Global Entrepreneurship Week UK High Impact Event 2012 award.

You can view the video of highlights from back in 2012 on the festival's YouTube channel, including appearances from a much younger-looking me, John Doody, Paddy Fawcett, Linda Smith, Ellie

Runcie and others that I have mentioned above at youtu.be/EwqIUeQICeI

BACK IN THE SADDLE FOR 2013

One thing that you quickly learn about committing to an annual event is that not long after one completes you actually have to think about the next one. I had a rule not to think about it until at least after the New Year, but then you soon have to start worrying about venue hire, sponsorship, getting dates in people's diaries and constructing at least a framework programme on which to base the next event on.

And so, in early 2013, the festival planning began again. Given that I had decided to proceed in the summer with the first one, it actually felt like I had the luxury of time on my side. The issue of course was that the festival was not really my day job; it was an extra activity that I'd squeezed in alongside everything else I was doing.

On this occasion, as you'll read later, we added a schools' event and a family day to the programme, but the main content was still aimed at businesses, entrepreneurs and professionals.[3] To this end we repeated the two days of symposia in the Malvern Theatres with two parallel sessions of talks and an even larger exhibition.

I managed to encapsulate the philosophy of the festival on the front cover of the printed programme by writing: "Malvern has long been associated with innovation; both in terms of business and technology. In the shadow of the Hills private school education was pioneered, the UK's first mineral water was bottled commercially, medical tourism in the form of the Victorian-era Water Cure was established, the Morgan motorcar is handcrafted and sold worldwide, radar was developed, liquid crystals for flat panel displays

---

3 'Second year of celebration of brightest ideas', *Malvern Gazette*, 22nd October 2013. www.malverngazette. co.uk/news/10752613.second-year-of-celebration-of-brightest-ideas/

were created, and touch screens were conceived. Apparently, the word boffin was originally derived to affectionately describe the 'brain boxes' working on technical military projects in Malvern during the Second World War.

"But neither Malvern, Herefordshire & Worcestershire, the Midlands, nor indeed the UK can rely on past heritage for future success and prosperity. Today we need to innovate more than ever: the way we do business, the way we use resources; the way we live. We need new ideas to stay competitive, new technologies to improve lives, and new insights to lead the way.

"Being creative and having good new ideas is far from easy. You need to build on what you already know, be exposed to things you would not normally come across, and be guided as to how best exploit your concepts.

"That's why we have brought together over 30 speakers to tell us the latest about industries key to our future: cyber security, engineering & manufacturing, environment & sustainability, technology for tourism, and how to start and develop a business linked to the knowledge economy.

"And it is why we've convened over 70 exhibitors to showcase innovative products & services and to offer their help and support in developing and protecting your own ideas. Thank you for coming to the festival. We hope you'll leave with expanded horizons. . . ."

I couldn't have put it better today, nine whole years later.

In the main auditorium we started with Dr Tim Cook, the former head of ISIS Innovation (now Oxford University Innovation) who had been instrumental in shaping the university's technology transfer office. Tim, whom I had first met after a talk he gave at the University of Padova when I lived in the city a few years earlier, talked about the challenges of realising economic value from good ideas and how the University of Oxford tackled this problem.

We then split into the flagship Cyber Security symposium and what I termed the 'The Business of Innovating' to look across commercial themes and help all kinds of businesses and entrepreneurs succeed. The cyber security session featured Graeme Hackland (yes, his real surname) from the Lotus F1 team who spoke about IT risk

THE LIST OF GUEST SPEAKERS WAS A WHO'S WHO OF LUMINARIES FROM THE WORLD OF INNOVATION IN BUSINESS.

management, Dr Colin O'Halloran the co-founder of D-RisQ, Nigel Davies from QinetiQ's secured navigation team, Andy Williams from Titania, Giles Smith who was the Deputy Director of Cyber Security at the then Department of Business, Innovation and Skills (BIS), and finally Dibble Clark from the local cyber security company 3SDL (now Meta Mission Data). Dibble talked about the skills gap and their new apprenticeship scheme in collaboration with the local comprehensive school The Chase, something that was timely given the growing number of cyber security companies in the region and the fact that we were now specifically engaging school students within the festival.

Meanwhile, across the hall we had Andrew Reith from the Intellectual Property Office explaining the role of IP in a business, Mike Newnham talking about product development (someone who later became a long-term resident of the Wyche Innovation Centre running his innovation consultancy businesses from our hot-desk zone), and Jeremy Redfern from Parkinson Wright solicitors highlighting commercial law, before he in turn introduced his case study featuring Tony Bennett from Coomber Electronic Equipment and Russel Walker from Atwell International.

After a networking lunch we heard Ian Glover, President of Bloodhound SSC 1k, deliver a very inspiring talk about the Bloodhound Supersonic Car challenge and the advanced technology that would enable such high land speeds to be achieved. Emma would later get to know Ian in his role as President of CREST in the world of cyber security. Staying with the public engagement and engineering, Clive Beale from the Raspberry Pi Foundation then took to the stage to talk about the relatively new pocket-sized computer called the Raspberry Pi. This presentation provided a great insight into the ambitions for this venture, and as you'll read later Clive kindly stayed overnight to participate in our new schools' event next day.

These two plenaries then led us into the Engineering and Manufacturing symposium in which Pete Baynham from GE Aviation talked about how innovative R&D was managed at his company. This was followed by a review of developments in wireless communication from Steve Braithwaite of ASH Wireless, before Jon Wells (Head of Design at the Morgan Motor Company) compared modern design methods with traditional manufacturing approaches in the context of the automotive industry. In parallel, across in the hospitality suite, James Cooksey the Director of Growth Capital at Santander UK's Corporate and Commercial arm explained the role of innovative financing for fast-growing knowledge-intensive businesses. Santander was a Gold Sponsor this year, and so arguably the first household name to come on board and support the festival in this way.

Next day, we had been fortunate to attract another influential and experienced speaker to open the proceedings, with Dr Frances Saunders, the President of the IoP, echoing Tim Cook's earlier words by talking about her insights into translating innovative technology into a viable business. This

From top to bottom: Ben Fletcher from Renault UK explaining the new world of electric vehicle motoring, Chris Walklett in good spirits after his finance workshop, and Dr Frances Saunders President of the Institute of Physics chatting with delegates in the café after her presentation. (SP)

led to another set of parallel sessions: Environment & Sustainability alongside the continuation of the Business of Innovating session.

Professor Ravi Silva from the Advanced Technology Institute at the University of Surrey, with whom I'd worked as a postdoc on electronic thin films, travelled up to talk about the green energy challenge; a talk that would resonate as much today as it did in 2013. We then had a double act from Andrew Hieron and Ben Fletcher who were head of Renault's new electric vehicle programme in the UK and defining how the novel Renault Zoe was being launched on to the UK's roads. Andrew was our neighbour's brother, and he had kindly agreed to be roped in after we'd had dinner with them one evening and I had been expounding how well the first year's festival had gone!

Paul Isherwood then talked about sustainable projects in the foods and drinks industry, based on his experience of being Head of Technical and Quality at SHS Drinks, the company down the road in Gloucestershire behind the brands of Bottle Green and Shloer. The session was rounded off with a topical presentation about the climatic and environmental issues of shale gas, delivered by Dr Rachel Westwood from Keele University.

Across the foyer, Chris Walklett from Bishop Fleming had provided a finance and accounting workshop on the lifecycle of a technology business highlighting the role of R&D tax credits. Linda Smith returned for a second year by hosting a growth and export workshop with Dr Roger Chandler talking about his company Keynetix Ltd as a case study.

After lunch we welcomed Hazel Moore, the founder of First Capital, to speak about how best to pitch to an investor. Hazel had studied Natural Sciences, specialising like myself and Emma in Materials Science, just a couple of years ahead of us, so it was great to have a scientist turned investor speak on this subject. Hazel then sat on the pitching panel alongside local finance coach Mike Hankins, local business consultant Bob Brown and speaker Chris Walklett whilst a series of brave entrepreneurs pitched their ventures for some grilling and critical feedback.

The day was still not over as we followed with the Technology for Tourism symposium focusing on the role of innovative technology in promoting tourism. This topic built on a forum we had begun hosting monthly at the Wyche Innovation Centre that brought together technology developers and tourism industry promotors, which is also a key sector in and around Malvern. The line-up included Mike Brooks who had created a smart phone app to help walkers interpret the history and geology along the route of the Geopark Way, Dr Chris Parker the Head of GeoVation Outreach at Ordnance Survey launching their 7th national GeoVation Challenge on the theme of 'How can we encourage active lifestyles in Britain?', and Alastair Shortland who followed up on his previous year's talk about text messaging to explain its role in engaging the visitor in the tourism and hospitality sectors.

Meanwhile, Andrew Tyrer from the TSB was next door explaining to delegates how the UK's Innovation Vouchers and support grants could support business growth before Ellis Pitt from the Design Council looked at the role of advanced design and design right protection in successful product development.

And as in the inaugural year, we also staged an exhibition of companies in the Forum Theatre and upper and main foyers. A number of organisations had returned from 2012; like the Design Council, the Intellectual Property Office, QinetiQ and Malvern Instruments, and we had some new names including Brand Refinery, Bishop Fleming, Areca Design and UnLtd meaning over 75 organisations were on show. We estimated that over the two days we'd attracted over 500 people to the business events, and of course as you'll read later, we had more attendees to the schools' day, family day and evening dinner, so the festival was gaining traction[4].

4 'Festival of Innovation builds on its successes', *Malvern Observer*, 13th November 2013. malvernobserver. co.uk/news/festival-innovation-builds-successes-3279/

Highlights of the festival are available to view online, mentioning some of the other subevents and initiatives detailed later in this book: youtu.be/G06ds-qCSrQ. We also heard from some of our sponsors and supporters about their view of what innovation means: youtu.be/ PWV922P54Sc. And in 2013, just before

The view of the array of exhibition stands in the Forum Theatre, with delegates chatting at the IMechE stand and Ellis Pitt from the Design Council at the Morgan Motor Company exhibit. (SP)

the event kicked-off, the festival was a finalist in the 2013 Visit Worcestershire Awards for Excellence. My recollection is that the Pershore Plum Festival pipped us to the post!

HEADING FOR A HATTRICK

For 2014, we decided there was scope to add in an extra day to the core programme and host events across Wednesday, Thursday and Friday. However, part of the reason for this was that we decided to dispense of the parallel sessions which were dividing the audience, and we also decided to rein in the exhibition to be just contained within the foyers. The Forum Theatre was quite large to fill, expensive to hire, and believe it or not some people hadn't realised there were exhibitors in there in the previous years (despite signage around the venue and a floor plan in the printed programme!).

We also brought the event forward by a month so that it would run in the first week of October[5]. This was mainly driven by Innovate UK's plan to hold an innovation event in London in November on the same days that we would normally run the festival. It seemed silly to try to compete, especially as we aimed to involve Innovate UK in our own event to give it some national clout. October was also a better time to engage schools before half term and we sensed that it was also a good time to attract a business audience with the clocks not having changed and the weather being a little warmer. In short, there are always pros and cons with event dates, and I've found it is best to try to stick with a pattern so that it becomes established in people's calendar.

Once again, preparations started with trying to secure sponsorship. This year Bishop Fleming and Santander both agreed early on to return as Gold Sponsors, and we managed to get none other than HP onboard as well. We also secured Lockheed Martin as a Platinum Sponsor, but oddly we had trouble engaging with the local company QinetiQ who were conspicuous enough in their absence to result in a Twitter thread discussing this.

This year, we also arranged some VIP Networking Breakfasts co-hosted by sponsoring

5 'Festival of Innovation set for return', *Malvern Observer*, 24th September 2014. malvernobserver. co.uk/news/festival-innovation-set-return-5850/

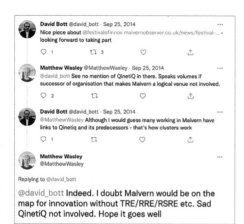

David Bott @david_bott · Sep 25, 2014
Nice piece about @festivalofinnov malvernobserver.co.uk/news/festival-... - looking forward to taking part
♡ 1   ⎀ 3   ♡   ⬆

Matthew Wasley @MatthewWasley · Sep 25, 2014
@david_bott See no mention of QinetiQ in there. Speaks volumes if successor of organisation that makes Malvern a logical venue not involved.
♡ 2   ⎀   ♡   ⬆

David Bott @david_bott · Sep 25, 2014
@MatthewWasley Although I would guess many working in Malvern have links to Qinetiq and its predecessors - that's how clusters work
♡ 1   ⎀   ♡   ⬆

Matthew Wasley
@MatthewWasley

Replying to @david_bott

@david_bott **Indeed. I doubt Malvern would be on the map for innovation without TRE/RRE/RSRE etc. Sad QinetiQ not involved. Hope it goes well**

Twitter thread ahead of the event querying the fact QinetiQ did not seem to be involved. They did actually participate at the schools' day, but they did not sponsor the event in 2014.

organisations in the Malvern Theatres' café ahead of the festival's exhibition opening. This came about because of a somewhat surprising occurrence the previous year. Harrison Clark Rickerbys, a local law firm, sent me an invitation to their Malvern Festival of Innovation Networking Breakfast to be held from 7:30am at the Bistro Café in the Malvern Theatres which was scheduled to take place in the venue whilst we were setting up the exhibition! This had been arranged without consultation, and although it was great that they wanted to be involved with our event, it transpired the Malvern Theatres had thought the session was being organised with our blessing! It sounded like it was an official part of our programme to "mark the opening" of the festival with their own welcoming speakers. They had also arranged HSBC as a sponsor, despite one of our Gold Sponsors being a competitor bank: Santander.

So, we pre-empted any repeat in 2014 by bringing what was admittedly a good idea, if not an added complication to arrange in parallel with all the other things that go on in the first few hours of an event. The first official VIP Breakfast was actually hosted by SME Solicitors, with Harrison

Clark Rickerbys having their turn the next day ahead of the cyber security session. Numbers into the café area were necessarily limited, but we could host up to 50 people and give them an opportunity to network and catch the beginning of the festival before they headed to their office.

We kicked off in the auditorium on Wednesday 1st October with the Advanced Engineering & Manufacturing symposium. Dr David Bott delivered the opening plenary on the Epidemiology of Innovation; a thought-provoking piece on how innovation spreads through a business community or cluster, and the similarities of the mechanics with the spread of disease. I had contacted David because at the time he lived not far away in the Worcestershire countryside, and I had briefly bumped into him at a TSB Launchpad event in London. He became an ardent supporter and friend of the festival, helping me over the years to hook sponsors and speakers. You may have noticed that he has also kindly penned the foreword.

David was followed by Pete Rose whom I'd got to know through winning some mentorship from a HP business competition. He had travelled up from Swindon a few times to meet me, and helped with our consultancy business at the Wyche Innovation Centre, whilst also taking a keen interest in the Malvern Cyber Security Cluster and how this might develop nationally. He kindly linked me to a colleague based in Malvern who was working on some projects with county councils around the country, including Worcestershire, and so was keen to sponsor the festival. Sadly, Pete Rose passed away from an illness in August 2021, at the time he was Deputy Chief Executive at NHS Digital and a key player in the nation's response to the pandemic[6].

Gordon Hollingworth from the Raspberry Pi foundation was due to speak next, but a mix-up became apparent when I frantically phoned him

---

6 Obituary for Pete Rose at NHS Digital, 10th August 2021. digital.nhs.uk/news/2021/pete-rose-obituary

from outside the venue an hour or so earlier, which meant that he actually spoke the following day. He was the Director of Software Engineering, playing a crucial role in getting the firmware to work on the stripped back computer board, and interestingly he had lived and worked in Malvern as an apprentice at the site now occupied by QinetiQ.

Before the networking lunch, Chris Garfit from Santander spoke about funding support in the manufacturing sector and the bank's Breakthrough programme that could assist aspiring businesses to grow.

The afternoon session featured a keynote from John Perkins CBE, the then Chief Scientific Advisor at the UK government's Business Innovation and Skills (BIS). He talked in general terms about the future and promise of the manufacturing sector in the UK before highlighting the findings of his recent review of engineering skills. We then heard from Robin Walker MP (for Worcester). It is unusual to have an MP from a neighbouring constituency speak at an event, unless they hold another office function in their portfolio such as being a minister for trade. On this occasion, Harriett Baldwin MP had been unable to join us because of another commitment and so she was happy for Robin to give some opening remarks on her turf instead.

The afternoon then featured Ian Burnett from JEMI UK who was very active in the semiconductor industry. I had first met Ian when we were sourcing second-hand materials processing equipment at a display technology start-up in Oxfordshire before I moved to Singapore. Ironically, I had visited the QinetiQ site in Malvern with Ian to take away some plasma deposition equipment when they were closing their cleanroom facilities. That had been my first-hand introduction to Malvern's tech scene!

The last two talks of the day focused on subtractive manufacturing at Mazak and additive (3D printing) technology courtesy of Malvern Instruments. The latter was developing particle analysis techniques that would help optimise materials for rapid prototyping using 3D printing techniques.

The next day's Cyber Security symposium was once again one of our busiest days. Earlier in the year, Emma and a number of Malvern's cyber security companies had been featured on Peter Day's BBC Radio 4 *In Business* programme, so the topic was still extremely well-suited to the festival[7].

Clockwise from top left: David Bott with his opening keynote, followed by the late Pete Rose speaking about innovation and big data, Professor John Perkins CBE answering audience questions on the future of manufacturing in the UK, and Sarah Macdonell speaking about 3D Printing technology. (SW)

We heard from our Platinum Sponsor Lockheed Martin, Mike Gadd from the Civil Aviation Authority, and Prof Harold Thimbleby at the University of Swansea. Harold explained how medical devices were becoming more at risk from cyber security issues, giving an example of how a pacemaker that sent data back to the physician could be compromised to the detriment of the patient's health. Bob Rose,

7 'Cyber Town Malvern', BBC Radio 4, 16th January 2014. www.bbc.co.uk/programmes/b03pmbjg

Innovate UK's Severn Valley Cyber Launchpad that Emma and I had been helping to manage. During the session we heard from Babble IT, Payara (formally C2B2), D-RisQ, Infinite Precision, PixelPin and Westgate Cyber.

Our keynote speaker the next morning, at the Business of Innovation session was Lee Strafford, the founder of Plusnet. He gave an inspiring talk about what it was like to start and grow an IT business that eventually became a household name taking on the likes of BT as an internet service provider. This recounting of an entrepreneur's journey gave me the idea for the Startup Stories sessions that we hosted separately in later years. Unfortunately, Lee was not feeling well, so he departed soon after his talk rather than staying on to sit on the pitching panel later in the day.

The morning continued with a number of high calibre speakers providing fantastic insights; Professor Fiona Lettice looked at innovation trends and practical examples of responsible

Top row, L–R: Emma opening the cyber security symposium in the auditorium, with Rich Palk providing a keynote from Lockheed Martin.
Second row, L–R: Gordon Hollingworth explaining a Raspberry Pi computer and Nigel Walker introduces the Severn Valley Cyber pitches (in the bottom row, L–R), including Geoff Anderson from PixelPin, Colin O'Halloran from D-RisQ and Dominika Tasarz from Payara. (SW)

Director Security at ADS Group, also spoke about supporting SMEs, and used the opportunity to launch a partnership with the new UK Cyber Security Forum that Emma had been progressing[8].

A highlight of the afternoon was an innovation showcase of the businesses that were part of the

Clockwise from top left: Lee Strafford, founder of PlusNet, and Prof Fiona Lettice from Norwich Business School. After lunch we had entrepreneurs pitch their business, including Andrew Vincent from CompareHospitality, as well as Nick Brown and John O'Sullivan from SpreadServe. (SW)

8 'ADS and UK Cyber Security Forum announce partnership', 3rd October 2014. www.adsgroup.org.uk/blog/innovation/ads-uk-cyber-security-forum-announce-partnership/

innovation processes before Chris Parker from GeoVation hosted an open innovation workshop featuring Roland Harwood who provided an interactive session with the audience. And ahead of the entrepreneur pitching session, Neil Fogarty delivered a high energy talk about the lifecycle of a start-up, adapting to change within an organisation, and how to promote a culture of innovation.

During each of the three business days, and the Family Day that followed, we hosted exhibitors in the upper and lower foyers of the theatres. This was a smaller area than we occupied in the first two years, and we generally had different organisations on the stands each day depending on the theme of the symposium. Occasionally some of the organisations, particularly the sponsors, attended multiple days and so this complex allocation had to be arranged. Because we weren't hiring the entire theatre venue all night,

as this would have been prohibitively expensive and there were evening shows on as well, some of the tables had to be cleared each evening and set up again next day. There were also some areas that could stay set up, and so this too had to be planned; a moving feast as different organisations

Below: Morgan Motorcar on display outside the Malvern Theatres in Priory Park.
Opposite: Platinum sponsors Lockheed Martin on display on the exhibition. (SW)

signed up and had their own requirements as to which days they were attending or supporting!

Over five hundred people had attended the three days of sessions at the Malvern Theatres, boosted further by a matinee performance at the venue during the first day which meant we had some extra footfall from people passing through the exhibition that may not otherwise have visited.

You can watch highlights from the entire week, including the schools' day and family day here: youtu.be/W4PzgCer18Y, with background about the motivation for the festival from Emma, another appearance from Paddy Fawcett, some comments from Samantha Murphy at the Royal Society of Chemistry, as well as insights from some of the cyber security exhibitors including Simon Banks from Somerdata, John Davies from Pervade Software, and Rich Palk from the platinum sponsor Lockheed Martin.

MORE ADAPTING

In 2015, with Innovate Malvern CIC incorporated to take the festival forward, the Herefordshire and Worcestershire Chamber of Commerce chose to schedule their Business Expo event in the same week as the festival. They had traditionally held a spring gathering at the Three Counties Showground, attracting their local member businesses to exhibit. The previous year they had decided to make the expo biannual, and had held one late summer only to discover that it is not good timing because people tend to be away on holiday when things need organising. So, they selected the Thursday of our week, and I decided to meet with them to see if we could collaborate rather than compete.

The result was that, on the Thursday, we'd hold the Business of Innovating session in the main seminar room at the Three Counties Showground, hopefully complementing their exhibition and attracting more people to our session as they boasted a footfall of about eight hundred to their event. Because of this, we

rescheduled our cyber security symposium from the Thursday to the Friday[9].

Firstly, though, our Wednesday session at the Malvern Theatres was focused on agricultural technology[10] which I titled "Agri-tech: food and drink for thought". This was an emerging industry very relevant to the rural farming counties of Herefordshire, Worcestershire and Gloucestershire. We invited Mark Stansfeld, the Chairman of Giffgaff and the chair of WLEP, to open the event with a talk about telecommunications and how this sector can drive high tech industries like agri-tech forward.

Then we had another hugely informative, and yet rather poorly attended, session with talks from Professor Simon Blackmore on robotic agriculture as being pioneered by Harper Adams University, a talk on the internet of things being applied to farming from Dr Simon Kampa at Senseye, the role of IT and data in farming from Animesh Mishra at Quickbird, a reprise from Mike Woollacott on smart rural power grids, a review of food and drink sustainability from the Cool Farm Alliance, and then a fascinating talk about bioponics and vertical farming from Alexander Fisher at Saturn Bioponics. It was such a shame that the speakers had relatively few people in the audience despite agri-tech being one of WLEP's priority areas for Worcestershire according to their five year plan!

The next day, we were alongside the Chamber Expo. Our opening keynote was another hard hitter; none other than Sebastian Conran whom David Bott had helped me to entice along. He gave a fantastic talk about design thinking, and yet many of the business delegates in attendance of the Business Expo missed out on the opportunity to hear all about it. As they did when Chris Vagges,

9 'Event in Malvern looks to the future of business and technology', *Malvern Gazette*, 22nd September 2015. www.malverngazette.co.uk/news/13775883.event-in-malvern-looks-to-the-future-of-business-and-technology/

10 'Drones could lead an agricultural revolution', *Malvern Observer*, 2nd October 2015. malvernobserver.co.uk/news/drones-could-lead-an-agricultural-revolution-9969/

Top row, L–R: A disappointing attendance in the auditorium for the Agri-tech symposium, despite one row of seats filling before the start with guests from MHDC.
Middle row, L–R: Mark Stansfeld Chair of the WLEP opens the session with a keynote from Prof Simon Blackmore following.
Bottom row: Alice Hutchings from Saturn Bioponics chats in the exhibition. (ZS)

from the Worcestershire success story G-Tech, spoke about design practices in the domestic goods industry using their cord-free vacuum cleaner as a case study.

During the session, we then heard from Birmingham's serial entrepreneur Simon Jenner talk about his experience in growing creative businesses, Kevin Smith on financing strategies and who has gone on to write a number of business books, before Emma spoke about cyber security and its role in protecting business from crime and fraud.

David Bott also stood in at the last minute to give a talk about the grant funding landscape and how best to tackle it as a business seeking research and development support. This was in place of Modwenna Rees-Mogg who had to cancel her appearance late in the day due to illness.

After lunch, we hosted another of the popular entrepreneur pitching sessions with Dr David Bozward from the University of Worcester sitting on the panel alongside David Bott and Simon Jenner.

The session had worked, but the attendance had not been any better by being co-located with the Business Expo. It looked like our regulars had turned up but that we had not attracted many newcomers from the event downstairs. In future years, we'd just return to our usual format at the Malvern Theatres and demonstrate that we could host a well-attended cyber security day even if there was another business event a few miles down the road.

Our Cyber Security & Big Data symposium went ahead on the Friday, with Harrison Clark Rickerbys hosting a breakfast briefing[11], followed by Phil Smith the Chief Executive of Cisco UK & Ireland as our headline speaker. Once again David Bott had been instrumental in persuading Phil to speak, and indeed for Cisco coming on board as a much-appreciated Platinum Sponsor. Phil's talk was, as

you might expect, highly informative, delivered effortlessly as he walked around the stage with an iPad in hand acting as his slide previewer and remote control.

After the keynote, we had a showcase of talks from a selection of SMEs from the UK Cyber Security Forum, including Surevine, Abatis UK, Pervade Software, Echosec, Panaseer, Digital Shadows, Crossword Cybersecurity and GeoLang all contributing. The UK Cyber Security Forum CIC was another social enterprise that Emma and I had founded to coordinate and grow the cyber security clusters around the country, with one being the increasingly popular Malvern Cyber Security Cluster that was meeting regularly at the Wyche Innovation Centre.

This year, QinetiQ also returned as a Platinum Sponsor, and Brian Lillie their Chief Technology Officer gave a keynote about the cyber skills landscape and whether it was keeping up with

---

11 'Malvern recognised as the centre of cybercrime fighting', *Malvern Gazette*, 22nd October 2015. www.malverngazette.co.uk/news/business/13889374. malvern-recognised-as-the-centre-of-cybercrime-fighting/

Clockwise from top left: Guest speakers Sebastian Conran, Chris Vagges, and Simon Jenner. Joel Keller from MHDC talking with delegates about the Malvern Small Business Forum. (ZS)

Top row, L–R: Simon Smith from MHDC, Emma, Harriet Baldwin MP and me outside the Malvern Theatres; and a full cyber security exhibition in the main foyer.
Middle row, L–R: A full auditorium for the symposium and Emma introduces the day.
Bottom row, L–R: Phil Smith from Cisco presents the keynote; and after the session in the foyer with Simon Smith, Emma, Phil Smith and the Chief Executive of MHDC Jack Hegarty. (ZS)

demand or hindering innovation in the sector. Harriet Baldwin MP also joined us this year to say a few words about importance of the cyber security industry to the region and the UK in general.

We ended the day with a panel debate hosted by Stuart Wilkes featuring Nick Tudor, David Bott, Paul Sherwood from Codethink, and Edmund Sutcliffe from Opus Novum. The discussion centred around whether networks and IT systems could ever be secure and how we were to deal with the increasingly complex threats from malevolent actors. The discussion would be as valid today as it was back then.

The cyber security symposium had been really busy, with a group of Masters in Cyber Security students coming from the University of Warwick as part of their induction week. This kind of engagement was win-win: apart from boosting numbers so that both the upper and lower levels of the auditorium were full, it also meant students learnt about the cutting-edge status of their chosen industry sector, and exhibiting businesses had the opportunity to meet potential recruits or future industry influencers. In later years, the University of Warwick would return with new cohorts, and we also welcomed groups of fresh computing undergraduates joining us from the University of Worcester.

THE 2016 RETHINK

As we embarked on the planning for the fifth festival in 2016, we reflected once again on the generally poor attendance of the themed symposia other than the ever-popular cyber security day. This year, we decided to shift the cyber security day back to the Thursday, and reduce the core symposia at the Malvern Theatres back to two sessions with the Business of Innovating on the Friday. But we extended the programme elsewhere with a launch evening at the start of the week and a Startup Stories event in a smaller neighbouring venue. You can read about how these took shape in later chapters[12].

The Cyber Security & IoT (Internet of Things) symposium kicked off with another VIP Breakfast, this year hosted by IntaPeople with some short talks about the cyber skills gap. Emma had managed to attract a speaker from the new National Cyber Security Centre (NCSC) to deliver the opening keynote, which despite the necessarily silhouetted

profile on the online programme certainly attracted delegates to hear more.

The new NCSC was not to be confused the National Cyber Skills Centre (also an NCSC for a little while longer) that had been started at the Malvern Hills Science Park. This initiative was unfortunately now withering on the vine through lack of vision, despite all that was happening around it in the world of cyber security. And despite a succession of talks we'd heard over the years at the festival on the urgent need to address a skills shortage in the industry. This reinforces my view that if you have policy makers and stakeholder purporting to understand an industry, they should get out to events on their doorstep and find out what they don't know. I still believe the first NCSC could have made waves for Malvern and been a key part of the UK's ecosystem; after all the skills shortage in cyber security and IT in general still hasn't gone away!

The cyber security talks from SMEs then followed in quick succession; Duncan Sutcliffe from his family-owned insurance business dropping a laptop live on stage to dramatically highlight the risk of information loss, Marc Wickenden showing a video of taking down an armed drone, and Cevn Vibert highlighting the risk to critical national infrastructure through an offensive cyber attack. All sobering stuff!

The day also included talks from D-RisQ, Advent IM, Tranchulas and MathEmbedded, as well as a talk from a member of the RAF defensive cyber operations team, and a first glimpse of the new Cyber Essentials scheme that was to dominate Emma's life in the coming years and become pervasive amongst the UK's business landscape. We also heard the first blockchain talk on secure identity, delivered exuberantly by Irra Ariella Khi.

This year had also been a tricky one to organise because our daughter had dropped out of school suffering with acute anxiety, and so Emma was spending most of her time supporting her at home.

---

12 'Week long festival of innovation in Malvern', *Worcester News*, 29th September 2016. www.worcesternews. co.uk/news/business/14773086.week-long-festival-of-innovation-in-malvern/

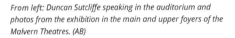

From left: Duncan Sutcliffe speaking in the auditorium and photos from the exhibition in the main and upper foyers of the Malvern Theatres. (AB)

I curated and organised most of the festival, and on the cyber security day itself, Emma and I both attended the morning, but I had to return home at lunchtime so that Emma could stay and host the rest of the day. Family always comes first, but the show had to go on too, so we learnt to juggle even more than usual this year.

The next day was our Business of Innovating session, with Kevin Baughan, the Chief Development Officer at Innovate UK providing the keynote on the UK's innovation economy. Kevin was an ex-colleague of David Bott's, and once again I was indebted to David for persuading Kevin that he should visit Malvern. This year we also had Wynne Jones IP as a Platinum Sponsor, spearheaded by Dr Jayne Nation who had been very supportive and enthusiastic in the leadup to the festival. We had an intellectual property session with some of their partner organisations: Jim Robertson focused on patents, Paul Gordon from Willans solicitors talked about resolving disputes and James Geary from Randall & Payne highlighted R&D tax reliefs and the Patent Box scheme. This was a very informative session for any knowledge-based business, but based on audience numbers there were either few such businesses in the region or all the business leaders knew what they were doing and weren't in need of any more insights.

Before lunch we had Dr George Windsor from Nesta present on innovation analytics, looking at the UK's economic activity and trying to make sense of innovation data. This was followed by another insightful talk from Mike Webster of TheOverworld, talking about branding, new product development and the customer experience.

> **FAMILY ALWAYS COMES FIRST, BUT THE SHOW HAD TO GO ON TOO.**

After lunch, the stars finally aligned for Modwenna Rees-Mogg to speak, having been scheduled for the two previous years but circumstances transpiring to work against us. Modwenna, married to the brother of the politician Jacob Rees-Mogg, is an expert investor who had lots of advice on how to pitch at various stages of business growth. She then kindly joined the panel alongside Neil Anderson, Kevin Baughan, and Jayne Nation to hear four entrepreneurs present their business. Once again, a fun, informal session that was pretty nerve-wracking for the participants!

SIX YEARS AND COUNTING

In 2017 Worcester and Malvern were highlighted in the *TechNation* report with the festival and the

Wyche Innovation Centre getting a mention, as well as two notable cyber security companies Titania and IASME Consortium[13]. With national recognition growing, we persevered with the two-day business day format in the Malvern Theatres for one more time[14]. The cyber security day still attracted crowds, but the more general Business of Innovating day was a struggle. The exhibition also tended to fill the upper and main foyers on the cyber security day, and we limited the business day to the main foyer.

The Cyber Security symposium had the added dimension of AI (artificial intelligence) this year and BAE Systems and Yoti both came on board as Platinum sponsors. You must appreciate that it is much easier to write this sentence than it is to achieve it; raising sponsorship is a gruelling disheartening task, as often those that have supported a previous year have a new agenda, a new representative, or a new set of financial constraints to navigate, meaning there is a constant need to cultivate new contacts and explain to them the benefits of being part of the festival.

Tim Pullen from BAE Systems gave a great opening keynote about the role of AI in cyber defence and security. Colin O'Halloran from D-RisQ followed this up with an interesting talk on using swarm intelligence to improve network cyber security. As usual, we had a full day of speakers, with Jamie Akhtar and Thomas Seidling from CyberSmart describing their journey on the GCHQ Accelerator programme, Stuart Laidlaw from Cyberlytic explaining how AI could be used to detect cyber security threats, and John Abbot from Yoti explaining how the future of identity management

was both crucial and also rapidly changing to adapt to new challenges. My colleague Tom Alcott introduced BlockMark Technologies' certificate service on the blockchain too, after rousing the audience to an after-lunch group sing-along which was, it has to be said, a first for the festival.

Clockwise from top left: Some of the Business of Innovating symposium speakers: Kevin Baughan, Jim Roberston, Mike Webster and Modwenna Rees-Mogg. (AB)

To try to increase the audience attendance at the Business of Innovating session, this year I had invited Emma Jones MBE from Enterprise Nation to give the opening keynote. She travelled on the early train (the Innovation Express no less) from London Paddington, gave a slick highly informative talk about strategies to launch and grow a new business and then had to dash back to the station to get to another appointment. Those that were in the audience were full of praise afterwards, just a shame a few more hadn't come along to benefit.

And our second speaker of the day, another of David Bott's introductions, was Rashik Parmer MBE, an IBM Distinguished Engineer who gave a very insightful talk about digital disruption now and in the future. After a break, Lorraine Stone from the WLEP gave an update on the new 5G testbed for Worcestershire and how businesses

13 TechNation 2017 report.
technation.techcityuk.com/cluster/worcester-and-malvern/

14 'Festival makes Malvern a hub of innovation', Malvern Gazette, 11th August 2017. www.malverngazette.co.uk/news/15468369.festival-makes-malvern-a-hub-of-innovation/

could use it to their benefit[15]. John Morton, a serial tech entrepreneur then shared his experience of growing new tech-oriented businesses and how business leaders could harness data to grow more effectively and efficiently.

This year Harrison Clark Rickerbys returned, this time as a Palladium Sponsor for the day which was a great help. Previously they had been more aligned and interested in the cyber security day, but during this year they had formed the Three Counties Defence and Security Expo (3CDSE) inspired, I am reliably told, by the festival and its cyber security day. Their event was first held in Hereford, but later moved to the Three Counties Showground and has been growing since. Being very defence and armaments focused, it does attract attention from protesters which thankfully is not a concern for our festival.

Their team provided a triple-bill of helpful presentations; Jon Whitbread spoke about raising funds to start and scale, Kate Lees focused on the value of patent protection and design right protection, and then Robert Cobley gave some case studies of exploiting business ideas through to commercial reality.

After lunch, we welcomed Polly Barnfield OBE, the founder of Maybe who recounted some of her journey as an entrepreneur and talked about innovation in retail technology to help keep high street commerce alive; a problem that post-Covid is as relevant today as ever. Neil Ricketts, the CEO of Versarien, then gave a fantastic presentation about the lessons he'd learnt pitching his high technology business to numerous audiences over the years. Versarien is a business that had, and continues to have, a meteoric rise. They actually exhibited

back at the first edition in 2012, after I invited them along having read that they were the London 2012 UKTI Startup Games Overall Winner. Fast forward to 2017, and Neil had already taken the company public on the Alternative Investment Market (AIM). They had also won numerous customers and development partners along the way for a quite diverse range of applications for the graphene materials that the company was pioneering. His presentation was a masterclass in pitching, negotiating, holding your nerve, and growing your business quickly.

Clockwise from top left: A fantastic line-up of speakers at the Business of Innovating session in 2017 with Emma Jones MBE, Rashik Parmer MBE, Polly Barnfield OBE, and Neil Ricketts (whom at the time of writing does not have a gong, but ought to one day for his services to industry). (AB)

We then held another elevator pitching session, with Neil, Polly, Beryl Cuckney and Martin Cordey sitting on the panel. Despite its popularity with the audience, this was the last occasion we held the pitching session as it was always hard to find entrepreneurs willing to participate. To date we had always managed to attract a critical mass, but I didn't want to keep trying my luck.

---

15 'Malvern at the forefront of new 5G revolution', *Malvern Observer*, 27th September 2017. malvernobserver.co.uk/news/malvern-at-the-forefront-of-new-5g-revolution/

'5G trial is superb news for county', *Malvern Gazette*, 27th September 2017. www.worcesternews.co.uk/news/15561454.5g-trial-is-superb-news-for-county/

CYBER SECURITY & QUANTUM COMPUTING

In 2018 we just held one business event in the Malvern Theatres; the cyber security session with a quantum computing twist[16]. We continued to hold other symposia in smaller venues on other days, as you'll read in the following chapter, but I decided it was an uphill battle to get enough people along to attend events on business in general as there just wasn't the appetite in Malvern or the surrounding area to justify the cost or effort.

But we had a good Cyber Security symposium with a fair attendance from business professionals and students. The day started with a VIP Breakfast courtesy of Infosec People, and then we had Professor Tim Spiller, Director of both the York Centre for Quantum Technologies and the Quantum Communications Hub, talk about the implications of new quantum technologies on cyber security. This is a subject we will hear so much more about in the future, and it was pleasing to have it featured at the festival.

This keynote was followed by Dr Roberto Desimone from BAE Systems, back as a Palladium Sponsor, expand on the theme with insights from an industrial perspective on how quantum computing algorithms could be used to improve and optimise cyber security threat assessments. Dr Caroline Clark, whom I'd got to know on the Industrial Advisory Board at the School of Physics at Bristol, then spoke about building a quantum technology business from start-up in the form of KETS Quantum Security based in Bristol.

This was followed by Emma who squeezed in a talk on IASME's new Community Security Operations Centre (SOC) to help protect vulnerable people and organisations from cybercrime. This development had come out of some training

of neurodiverse individuals in Worcester in collaboration with the UK Cyber Security Forum. There was also a timely update about Cyber Essentials by Chris Ensor from NCSC.

After lunch, we welcomed Professor Sir John McCanny CBE who visited from Northern Ireland but had many friends and acquaintances in Malvern. He gave a really interesting overview of the economic growth in and around Belfast as a result of its cyber security cluster and the research and innovation programme at the Centre for Secure Information Technologies (CIST) that the city hosts.

Outside the auditorium there was also the usual exhibition of cyber security companies and organisations on display. We limited it to just the main foyer as some had complained previously that it was too quiet and out of the way to be located in

Some of the 2018 keynote speakers, including (top row, L–R) Professor Tim Spiller, Dr Roberto Desimone, (middle row, L–R) Dr Caroline Clark and Sir John McCanny CBE. (bottom row) Table top exhibits in the sunny main foyer. (AB)

16 'Rise of the quantum computer on Malvern Festival of Innovation agenda', *Malvern Observer*, 17th September 2018. malvernobserver.co.uk/news/rise-of-the-quantum-computer-on-malvern-festival-of-innovation-agenda/

the upper foyer. Frankly it was easier, and cheaper, to just focus on the main foyer, so we went with it particularly as we had just the one business event in the Malvern Theatres now.

A BUMPER YEAR

2019 was a good year. It was before the pandemic, and we had secured an enthusiastic, forward looking Platinum Sponsor. When we had first started the festival, we had quite low levels of sponsorship with Platinum being the top level at £2,000. Gold, Silver, and Bronze were then below this. In reality, we needed quite a few sponsors to

> **JESS SPOKE CONFIDENTLY ON STAGE IN FRONT OF A FULL AUDITORIUM ABOUT HER WORK, WHICH A FEW YEARS EARLIER I WOULD NEVER HAVE DREAMT WOULD HAVE BEEN POSSIBLE. IT WAS WORTH STAGING THE DAY JUST FOR THAT PROUD MOMENT!**

cover the costs of the event, particularly as it grew, and so when we formed Innovate Malvern, we also expanded the range of sponsorship options to cover days or topics, as well as to cover the week of events.

As a result, I revised the levels with more precious metals (I am, after all, a materials scientist)

and so the original Platinum level became Palladium; top for sponsoring one day or a topic. Then we had much higher levels for the recognition across the festival week and the Malvern Science in the Park event that we had also started to run during the year. These levels were Rhodium, Iridium and Platinum.

Of course, despite many people telling me that our original sponsorship levels were far too low and we could raise tens of thousands of pounds of sponsorship with ease from big organisations, the reality, as you might expect was very different.

But the upcoming start-up called 'business mix' (yes, all in lower case) out of London was the exception to the rule who were excited by the festival and came on board as a fully-fledged Platinum Sponsor[17]. This brought with it the early relief that we could stage a great event without the usual worries of securing sponsorship at the eleventh hour. But it also brought the added pressure that one organisation was committing a lot to the festival and so it needed to be a really good event that brought them return on their investment and left them happy they had been a part of it.

In the end, we had a great festival with many events spread across the week[18]. The core symposium was just the cyber security day at the Malvern Theatres, but it was a busy session and business mix had the prime exhibitor location in the centre of the main foyer.

The cyber security theme this year was Securing SMEs and we had talks from the Global Cyber Alliance, the insurers AXA, NCSC, Avast, and Intel. We also heard from smaller businesses

---

17 'Bringing together innovators at the Malvern Festival of Innovation', *Startups Magazine*, 18th September 2019. startupsmagazine.co.uk/article-bringing-together-innovators-malvern-festival-innovation

18 'Festival in Malvern showcases science wonders', *Worcester News*, 7th October 2019. www.worcesternews.co.uk/news/17951819.festival-malvern-showcases-science-wonders/

Top row, L–R: Jamie Akhtar and Thomas Seidling returned with their double act from CyberSmart. Jess Burden making her debut on stage to talk about a new service offering from IASME Consortium.
Middle row, L–R: Melanie Oldham from Bob's Business explains the human behavioural aspect of cyber security and NCSC provided an update on the UK's cyber security landscape.
Bottom row, L–R: Cyber networking and the Cyber Expo from above. (AB)

COVID-19

I had just started planning 2020's festival when we went into lockdown in late March. The pandemic was a shock to many businesses, but not least the events industry. For us, the festival was not a money-making livelihood, but the uncertainty made organising anything very difficult. As we approached the usual festival dates over the summer there was an inkling of hope that some kind of in-person or hybrid event might be possible, but with very little sponsorship and plenty of uncertainty, I had decided if we did anything it would be on a small scale in a small venue. As such, we didn't hire the Malvern Theatres and we didn't organise a cyber security or mainstream business event. As you'll read in the next chapters, we hosted a few virtual sessions so as to at least keep the festival alive[19].

INNOVATION ON THE HILLS

Our tenth edition of the festival was scheduled for October 2021, and the pandemic rumbled on to the extent that I left detailed planning as late in the day as I could to reduce exposure to risk of things not running and being faced with large bills for venue hire, etc[20].

As such, we didn't run a cyber security session this year either, partly because the centre of mass in the cyber security landscape was shifting. Cheltenham and Gloucester had become more

like CyberSmart, Bob's Business, LuJam, and IASME Consortium.

Included in the line-up was my daughter speaking alongside her colleague Jonathan Ellwood about IASME's progress with their CyberSOC and low-cost cyber security monitoring solution. Jess, whom you may recall had suffered from extreme anxiety at school, had since been diagnosed as being autistic, but had gone on to train in cyber security with a cohort of neurodiverse individuals. She had then started an apprenticeship in IT infrastructure and networking whilst working at IASME. Jess spoke confidently on stage in front of a full auditorium about her work, which a few years earlier I would never have dreamt would have been possible. It was worth staging the day just for that proud moment!

19 'Covid-19, Innovation-20', *WLEP News*, 24th September 2020. www.wlep.co.uk/Covid-19-innovation-20/

'Pandemic won't stop Malvern Festival of Innovation going ahead', *Business & Innovation Magazine*, 29th September 2020. www.businessinnovationmag.co.uk/pandemic-wont-stop-malvern-festival-of-innovation-going-ahead/

'A virtual celebration of innovation in Malvern as annual festival goes online', *Malvern Observer*, 3rd October 2020. malvernobserver.co.uk/news/a-virtual-celebration-of-innovation-in-malvern-as-annual-festival-goes-online/

20 'Science in focus as festival of innovation returns to Malvern', *Malvern Gazette*, 1st October 2021. www.malverngazette.co.uk/news/19616183.science-focus-festival-innovation-returns-malvern/

active with events (such as those organised by their Cynam cluster) and bigger national cyber security events, like Cyber UK organised by NCSC, were dominating. Both Emma and I felt that it would be hard for us to compete and put on a worthwhile event at the festival.

So, having been involved in the BetaDen accelerator programme with BlockMark Technologies, and the scheme having progressed on to its fourth cohort, I tabled the idea that we revive the showcase format at the theatres but feature as many of the BetaDen companies as possible. BetaDen had not had an in-house live showcase since their first cohort because the pandemic had got in the way, and they had been making noises about a multi-cohort event to catch up. So, to me, it made perfect sense to collaborate and use the festival to host an Innovation on the Hills showcase session bringing BetaDen companies, and others that wanted to be involved, together.

In the end the collaborative process was like pulling teeth, but the day itself was great because many of the BetaDen alumni and present cohort leapt to support the event. Emma also mobilised her IASME contacts to add another dimension to the session so that IASME's technology partners and certification bodies could meet in-person and catchup. To round it off, I had also persuaded another world class speaker to join us.

David Rowan, the founding editor of *Wired UK* magazine and the author of *Non-Bullshit Innovation*, agreed to speak. I'd met him at the London Midland Labs accelerator programme showcase a few years earlier, and his fast-paced talk about winning formulae for organisations trying to succeed through innovation was fascinating and instructive. After a couple of previous attempts to secure him; before the pandemic he was really busy on the speaker circuit and then the pandemic itself got in the way, he travelled up from London for the afternoon to give the opening talk and sign copies

Elevator pitches from: First row: Jon Wells (Worcester Scientific), Ian Drury (Prizm); second row: Matt Young (Plinx), James Thomas (JET Engineering); third row: Paddy Fawcett (Invizio), Romeo Morgado (I4S); fourth row: Paul Rhodes (WellGiving), Vincent Borgraeve (Flowide); fifth row: Tom Alcott (BlockMark Technologies), Omolola Adeyemi (Crossword Cybersecurity) and sixth row: Linda Smith (BetaDen). (AB)

of his book. Once again, the vast majority of the region's purportedly innovation-led businesses missed out through unattendance. This reinforced my view that, after ten years of trying, offering the advantage of unique insights that some people and businesses elsewhere around the world would pay handsomely for was probably a lost cause here.

The rest of the afternoon was a success too; I think many simply enjoyed the opportunity to be in a small well-attended exhibition to talk with like-minded business leaders and technologists after over a year of no trade shows or conferences. We were certainly one of the first events to risk organising and re-opening after the bulk of the pandemic, and indeed just over a month later the Omicron variant swept the UK and made events like this prohibitively difficult again for another six months. ⭘

Left: Guest speaker David Rowen pictured with me and his book Non-Bullshit Innovation *(TA). View of the main foyer (below) and upper foyer (above) showcasing many of the BetaDen businesses, The IASME Consortium, and their technology partners. (AB)*

ON THE FRINGE

As the festival grew, so we added other events to the programme comprising talks, panels, and presentations about business and technology away from the main venue of the Malvern Theatres. These were still largely aimed at business professionals, but were open to all and depending on the subject they attracted other members of the public including students and those that had retired.

But before we did this properly, there were two notable occasions where we had what I would term fringe events as they weren't organised by me or Emma, but rather someone else took some of the strain.

The first was actually at the outset in 2012 when Richard Henson, a lecturer at the University of Worcester in IT and a shareholder of IASME Consortium whom Emma was now working with, suggested running an evening session on cyber security. This was held in a room at the then South Worcestershire College on the Wednesday evening before the main event started, and neither Emma nor I could attend as we were tied up trying to get everything we hadn't thought of done in time for the next morning. But feedback indicated that

MORE SYMPOSIA

it went well and we were grateful that there was already interest at this early stage to work alongside the main festival.

The second notable event was in 2015 when the Malvern Hills Electric Automobile Association (ElectrAA) organised an Electric Vehicle Innovation Showcase in the Malvern Theatres and Priory Park on the Sunday, the day after the festival would otherwise have finished. As such, it became part of the main programme, but Jim Murphey, Dan Wild, Scott Edy, and their team did all the leg work of organising the speakers, arranging the venue, putting together the afternoon's programme, and

even securing a sponsor in the form of the Institute of Advanced Motorists (IAM, now called IAM RoadSmart). We helped to market it and brought it under the festival umbrella as it was an excellent addition to line up that year.

They had arranged for some early examples of electric vehicles (EVs) to be on display in Priory Park behind the Malvern Theatres, both from car retailers and EV enthusiasts. Examples included a Tesla Model S, Renault Zoe, BMW i3, Nissan Leaf, and local company Indra's e-moped. I was fascinated by what I saw, but at the time real world range was still limited, despite Tesla being ahead of the pack by starting to roll out their dedicated network of Superchargers in the UK.

During the afternoon there were also talks in the upper foyer of the Theatres with presentations

Tesla, Renault Zoes and other electric vehicles lined up in Priory Park. Indra's electric moped also generated a lot of interest. (AB)

about the considerations of migrating from petrol (and diesel) to electric, the various tax breaks that could help make EVs more affordable, as well as a panel discussion in which the audience were invited to ask any burning questions about owning and driving an EV. Today, as I write this, EVs are suddenly becoming mainstream with more models available from a growing menu of manufacturers, and EV sales starting to outstrip internal combustion engine (ICE) sales. I also now drive an EV, and have to say it is a world of difference in performance and convenience. Range is still a problem for those wanting to make extended road trips, and charging infrastructure in the UK has a lot of catching up to do.

THE CONTINUED BUSINESS OF INNOVATING

You will already have read that the Business of Innovating symposia, derived originally from general business sessions on starting and growing knowledge intensive ventures, were core to the festival and tended to be part of the main programme at the Malvern Theatres alongside relevant exhibitors.

However, in 2019 we changed the format into a series of 'fireside chats' and held it in the neighbouring Coach House Theatre which was a smaller venue and more suited to the size of audience we were attracting.

The idea for the format came from my attendance of Startup Grind in Silicon Valley earlier in the year in which the guests generally sat on stage and chatted about their business experience rather than making a more formal PowerPoint presentation. This approach was well received by the audience, and suited the intimate setting of the Coach House Theatre. We made use of our two red tub chairs from the Wyche Innovation Centre reception, and I splashed out and ordered two very smart cushions adorned with the festival logo.

As business mix were our Platinum Sponsors this year, they also played a helpful role in the line-up, with their associates and colleagues featured in the programme. We started with business mix's Chief Operating Officer Vicky Young chatting with Graham Dodgson about the role of intellectual property in business and a discussion of some case studies to illustrate his points. Then Emma chatted with Hilarie Owen, author of *We Lead*, a title published by the same house as my book; Adam Jolly's Novaro Publishing. I will introduce Adam properly later and explain how he ended being involved in the festival on a number of occasions. Hilarie has had lots of experience working with successful business leaders, many of them female, and understanding how they evolve and react to the changing landscape.

This discussion was followed by another member of the business mix team, Jon Downing, speaking with Etienne Smith from MOHARA. The conversation was about developing new products and successfully bringing them to market, particularly on how to be steered by customer needs (the market pull) rather than your own 'technology push'.

David Bott returned to the festival's stage this year to chat with public relations and marketing communication specialist Claire Cunningham. She had worked with David when he was at the TSB (now Innovate UK) to help technology entrepreneurs to better explain their 'wares' before, during and after commercial development projects, so her insights were practical and valuable.

Sophie Ficek and Gemma Ryall, two human resources (HR) specialists that worked with business mix, talked about the people element of businesses and provided some tips to help your business grow by getting the best from your team. This was an area we hadn't covered much in previous years, but motivated and rewarded staff make a huge difference to how well a venture succeeds.

Finally, we wrapped the afternoon session up with business mix CEO David Page chatting

with Garrick Jones and Paul Ashcroft; the co-authors of the book *Alive: Digital Humans and Their Organisations* also published by Novaro. Paul and Garrick also run the Ludic Group together,

Fireside chats on stage at the Business of Innovating session in the Coach House Theatre, featuring (clockwise from top left) Vicky Young & Graham Dodgson, Emma Philpott & Hilarie Owen, and David Page, Garrick Jones & Paul Ashcroft. (AB)

assisting companies to think creatively about digital transformation and build new capabilities.

Even though the venue only has a small ante room, we also managed to squeeze in a few table-top exhibitors, including the Malvern Book Cooperative and Novaro Publishing so people could buy copies of the various books. And business mix were there too, of course, so they could engage with attendees and get the most out of their sponsorship of the festival.

We also segued into an evening Startup Stories session with pork-filled rolls and other refreshments out in the courtyard. One episode that sticks in my mind is how David, chatting with Paul and Garrick in the last slot of the day, stated how a particular discussion point could be debated later over a glass of wine. Realising we had soft drinks and beer to accompany the refreshments, and that our lead sponsor obviously had a preference for wine, I frantically texted my colleague Wendy sitting in the audience and helping with the event, to dash out and get some bottles of red and white. She did so, with her usual efficiency before the session ended, and no one was any the wiser about the hastily amended drinks options.

STARTUP STORIES

Although the Business of Innovating sessions were informative and useful, I always think that a lot can be learnt from the entrepreneur who is in the thick of it, been there, done that, and had to solve problems on the fly. It is far less theoretical and often far more interesting. As I mentioned earlier, listening to Lee Strafford talk about his journey founding and growing Plusnet in one of these symposia gave me the idea to have a sessions dedicated to these war stories.

So, in 2016, I decided to use the Coach House Theatre as the setting for three entrepreneurs to 'tell their story'. This was actually the first occasion that we used this venue, and the fact that it seats eighty comfortably, but with a capacity of about a hundred people made it well suited as a less expensive venue than the main Theatres for smaller, more niche, sessions.

The first year featured local tech entrepreneur Alistair Shortland telling us his story of growing and exiting TextLocal. Alistair had already spoken on two occasions at the festival about text messaging services for marketing, but this time he told his personal story and listening to him I knew instantly the subject matter and format for this new session was a winner.

He was followed by Nick Holzherr whom I'd met at a Birmingham 'Silicon Canal' event, and he was able to recount his colourful experience of starting a number of businesses and competing on BBC's *The Apprentice*. And then, another successful local entrepreneur and star of BBC's *Dragons' Den*, Neil Westwood talked about the Magic Whiteboard story which included investment from Dragons Theo Paphitis and Deborah Meaden. Neil is one of

The inaugural line up for Startup Stories in 2016 with (clockwise from top left) Alistair Shortland, Nick Holzherr and Neil Westwood, before they all sat on a panel session to answer questions from the audience. (AB)

those unassuming guys who recounts past events with ease and humour.

We then had an opportunity to network over finger-food, drinking Friday Beer from a new local brewery formed from some ex-QinetiQ employees;

> THIS TIME HE TOLD HIS PERSONAL STORY AND LISTENING TO HIM I KNEW INSTANTLY THE SUBJECT MATTER AND FORMAT FOR THIS NEW SESSION WAS A WINNER.

no better liquid refreshment for a start-up event! We actually made the event free and used sponsorship to cover the venue and refreshments. This was because if we charged for tickets, we'd need to get a temporary license to be selling the beer as part of the event. Keeping it all free meant all of this added bureaucracy would be avoided.

In 2017, we continued with the series highlighting the trials and tribulations of being an entrepreneur, and also had another member of Birmingham's Silicon Canal tribe along to speak. This time it was the enigmatic Mike Bandar, talking about his experiences both with his own ventures, but also helping others. He was also notable for commuting to work by kayak along one of said 'silicon' canals!

Then we heard a quite different story from Sue Shackleton, a member of the local Malvern

More start-up stories from (clockwise from top left) Mike Bandar, Sue Shackleton and Jamie Turner. (AB)

Small Business Forum who had helped to start a business making and selling clocks that help children learn to tell the time. This was a story of a product-based business with staff in both hemispheres, along with insights into design, overseas manufacturing, and order fulfilment. Sue included discussing the challenges and advantages of having your team working across different time zones; very fitting for a clock business!

We concluded the session with a classic start to exit story from Jamie Turner, the co-founder and Chief Technology Officer of Worcester's online address service provider Postcode Anywhere, later called PCA Predict. We heard how the business began, how they troubleshooted IT problems and grew the business, before selling for a cool

£66 million (eventually, having turned down a similar sized offer previously).

In 2018 Claire Cockerton was scheduled to come up from London to speak, but that morning she messaged me to say she was feeling unwell with the flu. As an event organiser, this is the kind of message you don't want to receive less than twelve hours before the event, particularly when you are already in the thick of it with the rest of the day's programme. Fortunately, Mike Goodfellow-Smith was chairing the Environment and Sustainability session and so I collared him to see if he could put something together for that evening! And, knowing Mike as I do, he pulled a great talk out of his hat. He spoke about his entrepreneurial background in the sustainability sector and his experience helping other ventures in this space make a start through various accelerator programmes he'd been involved with over the years.

This was followed by the co-founder and Chairman of crowdfunding company Seedrs, Jeff Lynn, another unassuming and super-friendly guy who kindly travelled up from London for the event. His style was to sit on a chair centre stage and just chat through his experience, highlighting how they

In 2018, we were joined by (clockwise from top left) Mike Goodfellow-Smith, Jeff Lynn and Ella Stearn. (AB)

overcame regulatory hurdles in their business and in turn how they helped numerous start-ups find funding and grow.

And our final speaker was local social media influencer Ella Stearn, describing how she started her business and has gained followers from around the world as she helps other businesses build marketing traction through targeted campaigns. Ella was also an early example of a digital nomad, working whilst she travels.

During 2019, after aforementioned pork, wine and beer in the Coach House Theatre courtyard, we hosted Startup Stories for the fourth time. Our first speaker was Jane Garrett, then working at the Quantum Technology Enterprise Centre at the University of Bristol. I had met her whilst sitting on the Industrial Advisory Board at the School of Physics, and although Jane was helping other very high technology businesses start and grow, she had also had experience running a company that did a reverse takeover on the Alternative Investment Market (AIM) which was a topic we'd not covered before either!

We then heard from Melissa Snover, a fast-paced super-slick presenter and business entrepreneur based in Birmingham who had started a 3D-printed sweet business and was now about to launch a 3D-printed personal nutrition business. We were lucky to get Melissa, as normally very busy, she had almost had to pull out because of a heavy business-launch timetable during the same week coupled with a sore throat and chance she'd lose her voice. My solution was to make the trip as painless as possible for her; paying for a taxi to pick her up from home, drive her to the venue, and then whisk her back home again for an early night, moving her talk to an earlier slot in the programme to make the logistics work. It was worth the effort, as the talk was very well received by the audience, and I'd narrowly avoided another hole in the proceedings.

We wrapped up the evening with local entrepreneur Paul Hawes who had started Smartbox Assistive and grown it into a very successful family business to help people with

SHE HAD ALSO HAD EXPERIENCE RUNNING A COMPANY THAT DID A REVERSE TAKEOVER ON THE ALTERNATIVE INVESTMENT MARKET (AIM) WHICH WAS A TOPIC WE'D NOT COVERED BEFORE EITHER!

disabilities to communicate. He had sold the business just over a year earlier, when he was originally due to speak at the festival but a personal commitment had meant we re-scheduled. His talk

The 2019 line-up for Startup Stories was (clockwise from top left) Jane Garret, Melissa Snover, and Paul Hawes. (AB)

was another inspiring story, this time highlighting how a well-executed exit could still be tarnished by the competitions watchdog.

In 2020, we held Startup Stories as a virtual event. We nearly managed to hold it in person, but rising cases of Covid proved problematic, and we had to resort to a Zoom studio in the boardroom at the Wyche Innovation Centre. We had booked the Coach House Theatre in anticipation, and even worked with Jack Wratten at Bloom.Space next door to provide enhanced Wi-Fi for a streamed hybrid event. But in the end, I deemed the risks too high and didn't want added complications of being responsible for hosting a super-spreader event!

Nicky Godding kicked off from her home in the Cotswolds, telling the story of how she and business partner Kirsty Muir had started the *Business and Innovation Magazine*. The magazine was now a regular media partner of the festival, and I had met Nicky and Kirsty just as they launched at a business dinner in Birmingham a few years earlier. I attended as a guest of David Bott's colleagues at the University of Warwick, illustrating once again how connections lead to more connections. As this was a virtual event, we have the recordings from the session available on our YouTube channel, so you can hear what Nicky had to say here: youtu.be/ g0EhQhpl4_A.

I was joined in the studio by Chris Pinder, an entrepreneur who is very active in the Malvern community, who spoke next about his own venture experience. He had started an audio-visual equipment business at university which had gone

Chris Pinder from HD Anywhere braved the Wyche Innovation Centre studio and joined me in person behind a Perspex screen for the virtual Startup Stories. You can see me taking the photo on the laptop screen! (AB)

on to grow very successfully since, and enabled him to support local initiatives like new premises at the stadium of Malvern Town Football Club: youtu.be/34zaoy7xttQ.

We then went live to London to connect with Claire Cockerton, whom you'll recall had been ill a couple of years earlier and kindly agreed to speak this year instead. The session took the form of a virtual fireside chat, and we heard about Claire's entrepreneurial career spanning from Toronto to London: youtu. be/VApMpiqLbr0.

INNOVATION INSIGHTS

The plan had been to hold another Startup Stories session in 2021, but I just couldn't get the line-up of entrepreneurs I needed to make the programme fit. Various things conspired against me, like unavailability of prospective speakers on the date and I think a general nervousness to travel to the event with the on-going Covid uncertainty.

As a result, I changed the emphasis and title to 'Innovation Insights' to be a blend of entrepreneurship and supporting the growth of innovative businesses. We started with Ian Sterritt who had a wealth of experience about how intellectual property helps knowledge-based and tech-intensive businesses grow, giving examples of what valuable IP is from the perspective of the entrepreneur founder.

Dr Maddy Nichols, visiting from Bristol, then illustrated how Spin Up Science works with scientists and other technically-grounded founders to inject business acumen into their venture. This was a great talk on how clusters and business communities can be seeded and the type of support that brings benefit.

I had then lined-up Nick Tudor to speak about his experience of starting and growing D-RisQ, which if you remember began life in our Wyche Innovation Centre and then grew into bigger space at MHSP. Nick, who had spoken on a similar subject at one of

Clockwise from top left: Ian Sterritt talked about IP before Maddy Nichols discussed supporting tech entrepreneurs and Nick Tudor highlighted the importance of cashflow. (AB)

my convened Tech Entrepreneurship seminars at the University of Birmingham, tells a great story of the pressures of watching cashflow like a hawk and dispels many of the myths of getting rich-quick in the grind of growing a technology-based business.

This year, we then decamped next door to Bloom.Space as there was more room to network and eat food; the Coach House Theatre being concerned about such an activity in their limited space with Covid still in the air.

Once again, the programme of speakers had been great and the buzz afterwards as people chatted and shared ideas rewarding. But audience numbers were not large and, despite Covid, I felt many people who would benefit from the session in local businesses, local accelerators and local government organisations had let an opportunity on their doorstep slip by again. It's not a case of getting horses to drink the water, but more getting them to understand the need to go to the water in the first place.

ENVIRONMENT & SUSTAINABILITY

The theme of environment and sustainability grew in importance over the decade recounted. We featured it as a session in the first edition back in 2012, although it was a parallel session in the hospitality suite rather than the main auditorium. One of the speakers was Mike Goodfellow-Smith who later invited me to talk about the festival at

a local chapter meeting of the Royal Academy of Arts. There I explained some of the progress we had made in the event since he had first presented, and he and his wife Julia, both busy in the sustainability and energy efficiency sector were keen to get involved.

So, in 2018 Mike and Julia's company Quest for Future Solutions were listed as a supporting organisation and they helped to put together the programme for a session. Rather than hold it at the Malvern Theatres, I decided the Coach House Theatre would be a better venue, and so we hosted the event as a morning session followed by some networking over lunch.

> IT'S NOT A CASE OF GETTING HORSES TO DRINK THE WATER, BUT MORE GETTING THEM TO UNDERSTAND THE NEED TO GO TO THE WATER IN THE FIRST PLACE.

Between us, we assembled a really interesting line-up; Professor Chris Rogers from the University of Birmingham spoke about future-proofing cities and what was needed to consider to make them more sustainable and efficient. Then, another contact from within Mike and Julia's network, Dr Louise Pryor, spoke about insuring for climate change and innovative approaches to dealing with the challenges. Henrietta Stock, who couldn't join us in person, then provided a pre-recorded talk about progress to decarbonise the UK's electricity supply.

Following this, Tonya O'Donnell explained the innovative work of a local family-owned engineering company called RIFT Technology.

They had developed magnetic actuators and motors that were very efficient by effectively creating a series of small nested motors within one assembly; something that would be useful for electric vehicles and numerous other machines and appliances in a world where green electricity would be the dominant power source. RIFT also kindly sponsored the event which helped us to hire the venue and lay on some refreshments in the coffee break and over lunch, whilst also ensuring the event was free for all to attend.

The speakers and team outside the Coach House Theatre. From L-R: Louise Pryor, Chris Rogers, Tonya O'Donnell, me, Julia Goodfellow-Smith, Mike Goodfellow-Smith and Allan Walton. (CB)

I had then invited Professor Allan Walton from the School of Metallurgy and Materials at the University of Birmingham where I was visiting a day a week as an Entrepreneur in Residence. He was leading some fascinating work on extracting and recycling magnetic materials from old devices; many of said materials are in short supply, sourced from mines in conflict areas or are sourced and refined in

ways that seriously damage the environment. Allan would go on to spin the work out as a commercial venture in Birmingham and I expect we'll hear much more about this company in the future.

Mike, who ably chaired the event giving me a welcome break from introducing speakers, also felt the same frustration as me about the small audience turnout. I had forewarned him that despite intensive marketing, getting people to turn up, listen and learn was an eternal challenge. It was one of the reasons I wanted to host the morning in the smaller Coach House Theatre venue rather than the main Malvern Theatres.

But despite his disappointment, he was still up for helping again the next year, and so in 2019 we had another Environment & Sustainability symposium on the Friday morning of the week. Once more, Mike kindly chaired the session and we managed to open the day with some introductory remarks from our local MP Harriett Baldwin.

Anna Bright from Sustainability West Midlands then set the scene with a talk about what was happening in the West Midlands. Professor John Bryson, a Malvern resident from the University of Birmingham, followed with a presentation about how citizen-led initiatives can help places to more readily meet the needs of their residences.

Beverley Nielsen, an energetic and enthusiastic face in the community with many hats, then spoke about her experiences helping entrepreneurs develop sustainable and responsible businesses as Associate Professor/ Executive Director of IDEA (Institute for Design & Economic Acceleration) at Birmingham City University (BCU).

Beverley has been a sympathetic ear over the years, sharing my frustrations of getting everyone to sing from the same hymn sheet in Malvern in terms of promoting the town and its technology businesses. She also understood the challenges of staging an event like the festival, having herself been the hands-on organiser of the Birmingham Made Me festival in the past.

Our next speaker was Marvin Tabi, CEO of WESAF Energy, one of the ventures in the business mix portfolio, working to create a viable cane-to-biofuel business model in off-grid rural communities in Africa, and first off in Cameroon. This talk gave an insight into what needs to be done on the ground thousands of miles away from Malvern in a location where the relatively poor have an increasing demand for energy, and yet need to be encouraged to think about sustainability and their future impact on the environment.

Our penultimate speaker after a lunch break was Philip Mossop who had founded WasteCollection. com and at the time was very close to a deal that would see him sell the business and exit. On the face of it, he would have made a great contributor to Startup Stories, and in fact he had spoken in my Tech Entrepreneurship seminar series at the University of Birmingham on this very topic. However, Philip is actually an eloquent speaker about the issues of waste, recycling and the circular economy, and this talk covered more about the sustainability projects he'd been involved in and what would soon become more of his focus for the future.

AS YOU WILL HAVE GATHERED, STAGING EVENTS WITH SPEAKERS IS NOT WITHOUT THE RISK THAT THE INTENDED PROGRAMME HAS TO BE RE-WORKED AT THE LAST MINUTE.

Tom Levitt, author of *The Company Citizen: Good for Business, Planet, Nation and Community* was the final speaker of the day. When I invited him to participate, it transpired he'd actually been a science teacher at the comprehensive school in Wootton Bassett just a few years before I'd attended, so was interested to hear who'd taught me. His talk highlighted that business needs to make tackling environmental and sustainability issues at the heart of their activity, but in doing so it was often found to be worthwhile rather than simply a drag on the bottom line.

The 2019 Environment & Sustainability speakers; *first row:* Harriett Baldwin MP and Anna Bright; *second row:* Beverley Nielsen and John Bryson; *third row:* Marvin Tabi and Philip Mossop; and *fourth row:* Tom Levitt. (AB)

We also featured this environmental and sustainability theme in 2020's virtual event, having all the speakers join on line over Zoom, rather than in person at the Coach House Theatre that we had booked in anticipation. At the time I was participating in the BetaDen accelerator programme and so had seen another cohort member, Tom Fenton, speak about his building energy performance monitoring solution at Veritherm and how conventional measurement methods were getting it badly wrong. The result was a significant performance gap between what was being stated and the much worse carbon emissions from buildings in reality. So, I invited Tom to kick the session off, and being virtual, the presentation was recorded and is available to watch: youtu.be/ Ud771ReWJNA.

The second speaker was Professor Louise Manning from the Royal Agricultural University down the road at Cirencester. Her talk focused on food supply chain challenges in terms of making the systems smarter with better data transparency whilst enhancing efficient food production: youtu.be/ VdUnUMfagGk.

Then we went west to Aberystwyth University to hear from Dr Rebecca Charnock about the work being done there within the AberInnovation research park on circular economies and sustainability: youtu.be/ubfpnNCbRtl.

Our final talk was from Dr Mark Broomfield who had recently had his book published, titled *Every breath you take: a user's guide to the atmosphere.* I'd received a proof copy from his publisher a few months earlier and enjoyed the read; a good mix of fact and dry wit about the cause and effect of air pollution: youtu.be/J_Q61KHS_p4.

AUTO ADVANCES

For some years I had been trying to think how to better involve the Morgan Motor Company in the festival, and in 2017 we decided to host one of the sessions at their premises. They have a visitor centre which had also been used as a venue for various business events that I'd been to in the past, so I thought it would make a nice change to have an event towards Malvern Link rather than in Great Malvern.

As it happened, we were not able to use the main visitor centre venue as they had tours booked, but we did use an adjacent seminar room. It was a slightly strange room as it had a supporting pillar right in the middle, but with a serving area at one end, it was actually ideal for the numbers we expected and the networking buffet lunch we planned as part of the session.

We started the day with Hugo Spowers, an understated yet inspiring individual who had brought along his Rasa two-seater hydrogen fuel cell car to display outside. He outlined his journey of designing, making and testing hydrogen-powered cars and why they offer so much promise for the future of the motorcar. He had actually collaborated with Morgan about a decade earlier on the Morgan 'LIFEcar' fuel-cell powered concept EV.

As you will have gathered, staging events with speakers is not without the risk that the intended programme has to be re-worked at the last minute. We had originally hoped to hear from the Chief Technology Officer of Morgan as an introductory talk and welcome, but ironically (as we were on site) he was called away into another meeting and so we didn't actually hear anything from Morgan during the symposium!

We had also hoped to hear from Mike Schooling and his company Indra, working on electric vehicle conversions and innovative charging solutions to use the car battery pack as domestic storage for peak consumption. But, when the time came, he was snowed under with work so thankfully Nick Tudor of D-RisQ stepped in to talk about testing complex software for the transport industry, and in particular the challenge for rolling out fully autonomous systems (such as self-driving cars). I

think Nick wins the prize for having talked at the highest number of different events and venues at the festival.

David Bott meanwhile wins the prize for the most suggestions and introductions to speakers; Professor Paul Jennings being one who continued the session with a further presentation on the future of autonomous connected vehicles. He elaborated on the challenges outlined by Nick, but also explained how they were testing different scenarios at WMG at the University of Warwick in dedicated simulators.

The presentations were followed by a networking lunch, where I later learnt that a certain Jack Wratten was chatting to newly recruited Christine Butler at the MHDC. Jack was using the festival as a good reason to visit Malvern to see if it might be a place to relocate to from London, and he was persuaded by Christine to consider putting a co-working space into Malvern based on his

Top: The Morgan Three-wheeler alongside our welcome sign at the Morgan Motor Company.
Bottom: The RiverSimple Rasa hydrogen-powered car parked up next to another Morgan in the carpark. (AB)

experience of operating one in London. Since then, he has set up Bloom.Space in The Grange between the Malvern Theatres and the Coach House Theatre, a venue we have gone on to use for the festival. Jack has contributed greatly to the local community by helping new businesses grow and connect in his facility, but also mentoring start-ups in BetaDen. It is this kind of anecdotal outcome that has made the festival so worthwhile; simply measuring numbers of attendees does not itself indicate much socio-economic value.

After the lunch, attendees had the opportunity to take a free factory tour of the Morgan Motor Company, which was for many a highlight of that year's festival. Thanks go to their Chief Executive Steve Morris for enabling this to happen as part of the day.

LITTLE DID WE KNOW AT THE TIME THAT THIS WAS TO BE AN IMPORTANT LANDMARK IN WHAT WOULD BECOME BLOCKMARK GEMS.

BITCOINS & BLOCKCHAINS

In June 2017, I had co-founded BlockMark Technologies with Tom Alcott. We had embarked on creating a new business out of blockchain technology, and this fast-moving field was generating a lot of interest as the seminal bitcoin cryptocurrency gave way to next generation blockchain platforms like Ethereum and a surge of new 'Initial Coin Offerings' (ICOs). So, in 2018, I felt it was time to have a symposium devoted to blockchain.

Mark Robinson set the scene with an introductory talk about blockchains in general and some of the terminology that is used in the field. The session generated a lot of interest and the Coach House Theatre was almost full despite torrential rain and high winds battering the town outside.

Dr Neil Pennington then took the reins to give some examples of where blockchain technology

can be used, in particular for energy supply and in financial technology (fintech) applications. Neil had been involved in a number of really interesting projects over the years trying to prove the benefits of decentralised systems in a variety of scenarios, and he used these as illustrative case studies in his talk.

Another much-touted use case for blockchain technology is to improve supply chain visibility and accountability, and so Eleanor Matthews was our next guest speaker who had come up from Oxford to explain this application.

Tom then had a slot to explain some of BlockMark Technologies' research and development into certification on the blockchain, and to launch our new non-fungible tokens (NFTs) comprising algorithmic or generative art in the form of gems. These were based on templates from our artist-in-residence Paul Farrell, who also joined the session to learn more about this emerging technology that he had suddenly found himself involved in.

Tom had arranged for some examples of the NFTs to be printed on large boards and mounted in enormous picture frames. We had a launch photo with Paul and our coder James Brewer, and little did we know at the time that this was to be an important landmark in what would become BlockMark Gems. Initially, we had named them CryptoR0x, the 0x being a nod to

The launch of CryptoR0x (later BlockMark Gems) NFTs with (from L–R) Tom Alcott, myself, Paul Farrell, and James Brewer.

Clockwise from top left: Me chatting with Dan Barker to open the Thriving Three Counties Podcast Live, before Dan spoke with Lucy Barkas, Kristo Shivachev (DBS) and Ruth Allsopp (AB).

the naming convention of Ethereum addresses, but we later rebranded. And, having started the NFT project in autumn 2018, with not just proof on the blockchain, but also this launch photo on Twitter, we were later to generate interest from the NFT 'archaeology' community looking for 'old' examples of NFTs!

Our next slot focused on another blockchain platform called Hyperledger Fabric for which IBM had become a key promotor. Peter Cripps provided an overview of the framework illustrated with examples of where it was being tested and deployed. We then wrapped up with a talk from Melissa Tate of DOVU who were commercialising the use of blockchain in transportation; particularly to improve efficiency and collect valuable data about customer behaviour. Their Chief Executive Officer Irfon Watkins was due to speak, but Melissa

IN ESSENCE, THERE NEEDS TO BE A SUFFICIENT POTENTIAL AUDIENCE THAT WILL MAKE THE EFFORT TO COME ALONG.

kindly stepped in when Irfon needed to travel overseas at the last minute. The company still exists, but has shifted its focus to carbon offset data management.

THRIVING THREE COUNTIES PODCAST LIVE

Dan Barker, an active member of the local Malvern Hills Business Forum before the Covid pandemic, had filmed the Innovation Shorts that we staged in the Theatre of Small Convenience in 2019 (more on that later). He had left the paid security of aerospace industry to start his own business of photographing products to help businesses with their marketing, and along the way had begun broadcasting a weekly podcast featuring successful business professionals from Herefordshire, Worcestershire and Gloucestershire.

I had had the pleasure of being one of the early participants[21], and suggested that we do a live session in the Coach House Theatre in which he chat with three guests in half hour slots and record them for a special edition of his podcast. Dan was up for the challenge, and to kick the session off, I would turn the tables and interview Dan about his career background first before he welcomed his own guests. Listen to recording here: podcasts. apple.com/ro/podcast/from-engineering-to-photography-my-story-dan-barker/ id1549243672?i=1000538652821

Although not a huge live audience, the session went really well as a 'fireside chat' format on stage in the intimate surroundings of the Coach House. Dan initially interviewed Lucy Barkas, who I'd known as a fellow Entrepreneur in Residence at the University of Worcester a few years earlier: podcasts.apple.com/ro/podcast/passion-for-people-leadership-lucy-barkas-live/ id1549243672?i=1000539662248.

Dan's next guest was Kristo Shivachev whom he had interviewed before in one of his regular slots, and this time discussed some of the highlights of his work in design and supporting students keen to follow a similar career path to his: podcasts. apple.com/ro/podcast/a-rising-tide-lifts-all-boats-kristo-shivachev-live/ id1549243672?i=1000540093163.

The final guest was one I had suggested to Dan would be of interest; Ruth Allsopp who had

worked in cyber security at Titania and had since gone on to help run the Worcester foodbank: podcasts.apple.com/ro/podcast/from-corporate-to-charity-ruth-allsopp-live/ id1549243672?i=1000540847540.

THEMATIC POTENTIAL

Not surprisingly, the most successful themes, both as core symposia at the principal venue and as additional topics during the week work best when they are of local or regional relevance. In essence, there needs to be a sufficient potential audience that will make the effort to come along. Good candidates are those topics where industry is working nearby (in the case of Malvern: cyber security, automotive manufacturing, etc), there is an emerging popular interest with some local activity (blockchain, agritech, tourism, etc) or there is lots of curiosity from business and the general public (environment and sustainability).

I really enjoyed curating the various sessions and learning more about the themes both during the preparation and through being in the audience. I think we could have done more on agri-tech and fintech, and it would have been interesting to have covered energy solutions as well as medical technology (med tech), but it only really works if you have a captive audience wanting to hear about these topics. Just me sitting in the audience doesn't cut it! ○

> # IT ONLY REALLY WORKS IF YOU HAVE A CAPTIVE AUDIENCE WANTING TO HEAR ABOUT THESE TOPICS. JUST ME SITTING IN THE AUDIENCE DOESN'T CUT IT!

21 Thriving Three Counties Podcast, Episode 24, 4th June 2021. podcasts.apple.com/gb/podcast/ successfully-exit-a-tech-startup-overseas-adrian-burden/ id1549243672?i=1000524186049

4.

Before the Festival was conceived, Emma had had the idea of a dinner to celebrate Malvern's long-running involvement in cutting-edge technology. She was quoted in the *Malvern Gazette* saying "There is an impressive list of technologies that originated in Malvern, some of the more famous ones including liquid crystal displays (LCDs), radar, thermal imaging, flat panel speakers and millimetre wave scanners. The dinner will be a celebration of all these achievements and to honour the great minds, lateral thinking, risk taking and experimentation which made them possible.[22]"

As such, we organised a dinner at Malvern College on the 11th March 2011. It proved to be a popular and enjoyable evening, with Professor Peter Raynes from the University of Oxford, and an inventor of LCDs, joining us as the after-dinner speaker. Harriett Baldwin MP also attended and had an opportunity to speak about the government's support for technology research and development. We also had a static display from Malvern's Historical Society (later to become MRATHS) which included a number of fascinating artefacts linked to defence research at the now QinetiQ site.

So, the fact that this event was so well received gave us both the confidence and the experience to include a formal dinner at the same venue in the festival's programme. Malvern College is a great

22 'Celebrate Malvern's involvement in technology', *Malvern Gazette*, 2nd Feb 2011. www.malverngazette. co.uk/news/malvern/8825718.celebrate-malverns-involvement-in-technology/

FORMAL DINNER

setting because it has the old school feel with its late nineteenth century architecture around the campus, and yet we hosted the dinner in their well-equipped Gryphon Room within their relatively new sports centre complex.

TABLE 16

The inaugural festival formal dinner will be remembered for not just Tim Harper's after dinner talk on nanotechnology, but because of table 16 at the back of the room. Consisting of a few of our guests and volunteers, they surpassed themselves with a fight almost breaking out over a disagreement and heckling during the speech. But luckily Tim was a consummate professional who actually enjoys a bit of audience feedback! I had known Tim for a number

of years as we bumped into each other at electronic display conferences, materials events and business plan competitions. Emma also worked with him and his technology consulting business in Singapore. He has since gone on to commercialise graphene technology and electric vehicles here in the UK.

PRELUDE TO A PUBLISHING DEAL

Over the ensuing years, we repeated the annual dinner and had a variety of interesting after-dinner speakers join us to share their insights. As the organiser, I had the enjoyment of chatting with them over dinner and finding out more about their career and work.

In 2013 I invited Adam Jolly to speak. I had been introduced to him by Mark Yeadon and had recently

Clockwise from top left: Some members of the infamous Table 16 in front of the QinetiQ display at Malvern College. Tim Harper speaking after dinner about the impact materials science on our lives and me rounding up the evening in front of a full house. (DH)

festival one meets many intelligent and driven people, but David, who was one of the founding fathers of the mobile operating system Symbian, stood out as super-smart and spoke at a break-neck pace about the Future of Innovation – Visions and Nightmares. He is also, I think, the only person I've met with a rare three letter Twitter handle; @dw2.

Anne Lise Kjaer, author of *The Trend Management Toolkit: A Practical Guide to the Future*, joined us in 2016. We were fortunate in being able

contributed a chapter of *The Innovation Handbook* that he had edited for Kogan Page. Over dinner I learnt that he was planning to start his own boutique publishing venture focused on a business audience, and we discussed my book idea called 'Start-up as you mean to go on' which was to be about the things you can do early on in a business to help scale and exit in the future. A few years later, Adam's company Novaro Publishing published my book *Start to Exit: How to maximise the value in your start-up* as its first title in what has since become an interesting and growing series of business books. Evidence of how events like this can make lasting connections.

A FLOCK OF FUTURISTS

Futurist Richard Watson joined us the following year, and as author of *Future Files: A Brief History of the Next 50 Years* and founder of the organisation What's Next? he gave a fascinating talk about the current technological and societal trends, making some predictions about where innovation would lead us over the next decade. I realised that there was a whole profession based on futurism which would become a rich seam to tap for the festival in the future.

So, along those line, in 2015 I invited the Chair of London Futurists David Wood to speak. At the

Malvern
Festival of Innovation

Formal Dinner

8th *October 2015*

www.festival-innovation.com
@festivalofinnov #InnovateMalvern

Menu from the formal dinner in 2015.

to slot into her schedule, as she had to catch the last train home in order to fly out of London the next day for an overseas business trip. Her trend forecasting agency works with lots of household name brands like Sony and Ikea, so to have her insights presented in Great Malvern was a treat.

ADDING VARIETY

Our speaker the next year was quite different. Duncan Sutcliffe, managing director of our insurer Sutcliffe & Co, introduced me to Newall Hunter, a cyber security IT specialist, drone pilot, and an intrepid explorer who was about to head off on an unassisted solo mission to cross the Gobi Desert on foot. His talk was all about the equipment, the preparation, and the technology that would help him. A few weeks later he set off, but had to abort the mission early for his own safety; he

had explained there were certain points along the journey where there would be no turning back or any chance of rescue if things went wrong, so he had to be very disciplined in assessing the risks ahead of time.

We hosted another much sought-after speaker in 2018. Hilary Sutcliffe from SocietyInside had just

Seated guests ready for dinner in 2018, with one of the IASME Consortium tables in the foreground including my daughter Jess seated with colleagues Giselle Pearson, Ben Davenport, Wendy Barker, Yvonne Charrot, Tim Charrot & Lynne Thomas. (RL)

been appointed co-chair of the World Economic Forum Global Future Council on Values, Ethics and Innovation. She kindly travelled to Malvern to speak about gene editing, artificial intelligence and robotics, and highlighted our opportunity to learn from the mistakes made with past technology introductions like genetically modified foods.

A BEST LAID TABLE PLAN

During that evening I sat on the table with two visitors from London, David Page and Vicky Young, who had made contact just a few weeks earlier about their company business mix sponsoring the festival. I had explained over the phone that being so close to the event, they might not get as much benefit from the exposure as they could with a bit more time, for example if they sponsored the next

Top L–R: Dinner guests Dr Louise Pryor who was speaking the next day at the environment and sustainability symposium, Trevor Thomas, Sir John McCanny who spoke earlier in the day as a keynote at the cyber security day, and Dr Richard Chisnall a long-time supporter of the festival.
Middle, R–L: Emma with her colleague Stephanie Coates.
Bottom, L–R: Rosemary Henderson from our media partner Business & Innovation Magazine, *myself and guest speaker Hilary Sutcliffe. (RL)*

year. However, as they were travelling to the festival to kick its tyres and attend the dinner, I thought it would be good to seat them on the top table and have the opportunity to learn more about their work. This strategy paid dividends because they enjoyed their visit to Malvern so much that business mix, as I mentioned earlier, became our headline Platinum sponsor for 2019.

And as such, their CEO David Page was our after-dinner speaker that year too, giving an insightful talk about the challenges of climate change and how it was imperative that the community of innovators take steps to tackle the problems as soon as possible. They also used the platform to launch their new operational partnership with The Green Hub.

In 2020 we didn't hold a formal dinner because of the Covid pandemic. Although people had been able to gather in pubs and restaurants over the summer, by the autumn it was looking touch-and-go what would be permitted indoors, and a large gathering of people for a dinner was not something we thought we could plan. And indeed, as the entire festival went virtual that year, a virtual formal dinner however innovative that might have been, was not attempted!

THE CURVE-BALL AT TEN

But in 2021, we returned with a vengeance. Because of the uncertainty and continuing concern about Covid, we didn't expect to attract as many guests to the dinner and so chose the smaller venue of the Dame Laura Knight Suite at the Mount Pleasant Hotel. However, there was definitely an appetite

(pun intended) to get out and enjoy a work-related dinner as we managed to seat 75 which was pretty much capacity.

And the highlight was the after-dinner act (yes, act) from Beatrice Freeman who mixed her cyber security experience (she'd attended the Malvern Festival of Innovation previously as a delegate and exhibitor), her new career in stand-up comedy and her love of opera. Only at a festival like this could you be talking over dinner about STEM education, blockchain technology, enterprise policy, and then drinking coffee to the sound of an aria.

Ahead of time, we had agreed a very modest appearance fee to compensate a bit for Beatrice's time joining us at the festival, and then a few days later as the world was opening up to some post-Covid travel and events, she was approached by her agent to speak at a cyber security event the same evening in Switzerland. The proposed fee was over an order of magnitude higher, demonstrating her growing reputation on the speaking circuit and highlighting how fortunate we were to have her join us. And to her credit, Beatrice turned down the other job and honoured her arrangement with us, for which I was very grateful. ○

Bottom left: The fantastic business mix delegation (from L–R) Rob Beardmore, Sangeeta Parmar, Jon Downing, David Page, their guest Frank, Vicky Young, Lucy Downing and Marvin Tabi). Opposite: The colour-coordinated BetaDen contingent (from L–R) Jenny Rohde, another guest, Clive Summerfield, Linda Smith, Hannah Ross and David Sidaway. Bottom right, L–R: Harriet Baldwin MP, Councillor Sarah Rouse and the then Chief Executive of Malvern Hills District Council Jack Hegarty. (RL)

5.

In 2012 the festival was focused on a predominantly business audience both in terms of the two days of themed symposia and the formal dinner. But I've always had a keen interest in promoting STEM (science, technology, engineering and mathematics) subjects to children because I firmly believe that having knowledge in these subject areas offer great career opportunities. I also think that these subjects really come to life at work and the way they are taught in school does not always do them justice; they are often perceived as hard, dry and boring.

My interest in STEM at a young age was kindled by the fact my father was an engineer in the RAF and so he would occasionally take me to work open days where I would see the insides of aircraft, hangers and air-traffic control towers. This looked like an interesting world of avionics, mechanics, hydraulics, electronics, and a varied day job of making, testing and fixing.

The other thing I remember was having a glossy early 1980s annual report from the UK's Science & Engineering Research Council (SRC / SERC, now EPSRC). I remember reading

NEXT GENERATION INNOVATORS

this at about the age of ten or eleven, and then again from time to time at senior school. I'm not sure how I ended up with a copy but it had reports of research being undertaken from around the country, including nuclear fusion, supercomputing, radio astronomy and particle physics. Accompanying the articles were photographs of big-ticket equipment and scientists working alongside. Seeing these facilities linked to the physics and chemistry I was studying at school inspired me to want to work in a science laboratory, and guided me to pursue these subjects at A-level and later University.

A PILOT

And so, in 2013 I decided to add events aimed at inquisitive children; an event for schools and also a family day which I'll describe in more detail later. The schools' event came about because two stars aligned:

The then Honorary Secretary of The IET Hereford & Worcester, Brian Middleton, had approached me about the on-going need to encourage school children to consider STEM careers and whether the festival could help with this. And, in parallel, a local friend Adela Ward who worked in the events team at Malvern College had overseen our 2012 formal dinner and had suggested the school could get more involved in the festival and had approached Darren Stokes, their Head of Design & Technology.

In early March of that year Darren, Adela, myself and a representative from the IET Lyndon Baines held a meeting to discuss the possibility and came away with a tentative plan. Darren was keen to showcase his computer design suite, Lyndon was up for some hands-on engineering like a ball launcher, and I had almost confirmed the Director of Education from Raspberry Pi as a speaker at the main event and thought a Raspberry Pi workshop would also be great if we could get some kit.

It was agreed that the morning would comprise the three activities over three hours aimed at final year primary schools, with a capacity of 54 students split into classes of 18. The sessions would then repeat in the afternoon in similar sized groups this time for students from the first three years of secondary school. We were referring to it as a fringe event, with Lyndon and The IET taking a lead, and in mid-June we had the idea to call it the Next Generation Innovators event within the festival. Linda Scott from the STEM Ambassador Network at

WE HAD BEEN GREATLY OVERSUBSCRIBED, WITH 375 APPLICANTS FOR THE 108 AVAILABLE PLACES.

the University of Worcester was also brought into the loop and she offered her team's support too, and John Palmer the Curriculum Leader for IT and Computing at The Chase School was also involved.

The planned activities were some hands-on Computer-Aided Design in Malvern College's CAD

suite, hosted by Darren and some of his older students, a Raspberry Pi session, and a ball-launching workshop hosted by the IET. The IET also created a poster to attract volunteers from within the membership network, and with numerous meetings with the ad hoc committee of organisers, the sub-event was taking on a life of its own.

By mid-September, I had briefed Clive Beale, the Director of Education at the Raspberry Pi Foundation, and he agreed to bring along Raspberry Pi computers and resources for the workshop as well as help out on the day. John had a family bereavement, so Paddy Fawcett who had started the Little Pi Shop business out of the Wyche Innovation Centre, stepped in to support the workshop. Clive also arranged to courier over one hundred Raspberry Pis so that each attendee could go away with one after the event![23]

I didn't manage to get across to the event as I was tied up in the Malvern Theatres all day with the main symposia. But it all went really well, with nine primary schools attending from across Herefordshire and Worcestershire in the morning, and nine senior schools after lunch. The main problem was that holding the pilot in the St Edmund Hall venue meant we could only host six students from each school, so it was generally those whom already had an interest in STEM or were doing well at school that were 'rewarded' with the trip out to the event. We had been greatly oversubscribed, with 375 applicants for the 108 available places.

Feedback from the event included the following from Cradley primary school "Would you pass on our thanks to everyone responsible for the event last week. Our 6 pupils thoroughly enjoyed themselves and Rebecca who accompanied them commented on how well organised everything was." And this feedback from King Charles I School

23 'Innovative event aimed at inspiring students to embrace universe and technology', *Worcester News*, 6th November 2013.www.worcesternews.co.uk/news/business/10788084.innovative-event-aimed-at-inspiring-students-to-embrace-universe-and-technology/

in Kidderminster, "Just wanted to thank you for all the hard work you put into the event at Malvern College on Friday. My students all enjoyed it and it was an excellent opportunity for them to see innovative technologies in action and try them out." St Barnabas CE Primary took the time to write afterwards saying "just wanted to thank you so much for the STEM festival last week. Our children had an amazing time and came back inspired and enthused wanting to tell their peers about the workshops. Needless to say they were delighted with their goodie bags, particularly with the Raspberry Pis! The staff felt it was such a positive experience and a great opportunity for them, they made contact with teachers from our local High school and are now in conversation about the possibility of a computing club. So thank you once again for the careful organisation which enabled everyone to have such an interesting morning. Please pass our thanks on to everyone who contributed."

LIKE A BIG BANG NEAR ME

Soon after the event I was contacted by Sue Hodgson-Jones (soon to be Sue Verdeyen) who had attended the festival on various days and dropped in to see the schools' event in action too. Her partner Paul Verdeyen had exhibited at the festival and was also very supportive of the event and its goals.

> OUR CHILDREN HAD AN AMAZING TIME AND CAME BACK INSPIRED AND ENTHUSED WANTING TO TELL THEIR PEERS ABOUT THE WORKSHOPS. NEEDLESS TO SAY THEY WERE DELIGHTED WITH THEIR GOODIE BAGS, PARTICULARLY WITH THE RASPBERRY PIS!

Sue had previously organised a Big Bang Near Me day at the Three Counties Showground which was a local version of the Big Bang science fair for schools that is held annually in Birmingham. She was keen to collaborate to see if the next school event could build on both our experiences and engage more students in the large Severn Hall at the Three Counties Showground where she was the Education Officer and a STEM Ambassador.

And so early in 2014 we brought together the IET, IoP, IMechE, RSC and some other potential stakeholders to start planning a larger Next Generation Innovators event. Sue kindly took a lead on the event and helped to bring in some of her agricultural contacts as exhibitors, whereas I helped to bring in other STEM-related businesses and organisations from my network. Sue worked with her events team to layout the hall with about 40 exhibits, and we had over four hundred students from local schools register with the assistance of the STEMNET team that Linda Scott managed at the University of Worcester.

Stills from the highlights video of the festival showing (clockwise from top left) the CAD workshop, Raspberry Pi workshop, and ball launch engineering challenge in action at the fringe event in Malvern College. [DH]

Not long before the event, I had the opportunity to attend a TeenTech event in Bristol which was an initiative organised by Maggie Philbin (who used to present BBC's *Tomorrow's World* when I was at school). I had met Maggie at an event that she was compering earlier in the year, and she was interested in what we were doing in Malvern and said that we could potentially turn it into a TeenTech branded event in the future. So, I had a look at some of the things they do at their event and the kind of organisations they attract which was very insightful, particularly the attention to detail and quality of engagement.

The larger hall compared to the pilot venue the previous year also gave more space for some of the activities and a wider variety of exhibits, which included a Bloodhound Super Sonic car workshop, some Alpaca from The Cob House with wool processing demonstrated alongside, and a repeated run of timetabled Raspberry Pi workshops. Another highlight included hands-on exhibits about cyber security and cyphers from GCHQ's outreach team and a hands-on exhibit from local particle analysis company Malvern Instruments[24].

We also had a young inspiring entrepreneur called Jamie Dunn join the event and give some talks to students. He had originally been planning to attend the main event and sit on our pitching panel, but another commitment got in the way. Diane Aston from IoM3 visited to give two talks about the different materials used in the world around us, bringing various sample for students to handle and discuss.

The whole day went very well, running in parallel with the Cyber Security symposium across town. I didn't manage to get over to see the event in action, so it was testament to Sue for running such a tight ship and pulling it off. Sue and Paul came to

Top: Paul Verdeyen demonstrated the new Ultimaker 3D-printer and allowed students to handle various printed artefacts.
Second and third rows: Groups of students had a go at making and racing 'rocket-powered' cars, and others worked on hands-on Raspberry Pi computing exercises.
Fourth row: There was also opportunity for students and teachers to walk between displays and engage with the exhibitors. (SW)

24 'Malvern's Next Generation Innovators', Malvern Instruments (now Malvern Panalytical), 7th October 2014. www.materials-talks.com/malverns-next-generation-innovators/

The Severn Hall at the Three Counties Showground partly set-up the evening before, and then the next day with the event in full swing and the immersive dome cinema fully inflated. (AB)

the formal dinner that evening as our guests, which they thoroughly enjoyed despite being exhausted from the full-on day. I think it took all weekend for them to recover!

BACK TO THE FUTURE FOR 2015!

In 1985, the blockbuster film *Back to the Future Part II* featured time travel to 21st October 2015, a few days after the planned festival for this year. Innovation and futurology are closely linked, but often we don't predict things correctly. We still don't have hover-boards and flying cars, but we have made enormous leaps with the Internet and smart phones.

Sue had shown that the format at the Three Counties Showground worked well. I decided that it would be better to hold the event on a separate day to the main event, meaning that I could then be more involved in it rather than trying to be in two places at once. This was also the year that the H&W Chamber of Commerce decided to organise their expo event in the same week, so actually the venue would not be available later in the same week any way, and so it was agreed that we could run Next Generation Innovators on the Tuesday, clear that evening to allow the venue to set-up the expo the next day ready for the Thursday event (when we would also be back running the Business of Innovating session upstairs in the seminar room).

By the end of April, planning was underway with 900 student and 90 teachers from 20 schools having registered to attend, but still few commitments from any exhibitors.

We had been unsuccessful in securing a small grant from the British Ecological Society to support the event, but the IMechE said they would sponsor an inflatable dome theatre in which an immersive science show could be regularly screened. This kind of financial support is crucial if the event is to have an engaging programme from some professional organisations that specialise in STEM content.

This year, both Sue and I were determined to feature more about agriculture, horticulture and agritech. Sue was well connected to the agricultural organisations in the region through her work with other events held at the Three Counties Showground, and she really wanted them to engage

The Fab Foundation UK bus with students from Dyson Perrins school (ZS) and inside the bus with Paul Verdeyen speaking to a group from Malvern St James school for girls. (AB)

with the student audience at our event. This was also the year I was hosting the AgriTech symposium (the day after the schools' event) at the Malvern Theatres, so it was hoped we could get some of those participants interested as well.

In the end we had about fifty exhibitors, with Cargill and Worcestershire Beekeepers' Association being the only one from the world of agriculture.

However, we had a good mix of exhibits and activities including some hands-on workshops, exhibits, talks and technology demonstrations.

Paul Verdeyen was working with the Fab Foundation UK (FabLab) initiative and they were equipping a bus as a mobile showcase to visit schools and events like ours. It was touch and go whether the bus would be ready in time for the festival, but Paul managed to get it along, although it didn't quite look like the wrapped high tech showcase he was hoping for! Nevertheless, it was a good addition to the event and parked up outside the hall with a variety of equipment on board that Paul talked to various school groups about during the day.

Dr Jonathan Hare talks about fullerene C60 molecules in a packed seminar room (left) and later helps on the Royal Society of Chemistry stand in the main expo (AB)

One of the day's talks was from Dr Jonathan Hare who returned to Malvern from having presented at our first family show in 2013 (more on that later). He delivered a presentation up in the seminar room titled 'Wonderful Molecules' about carbon allotropes and their chemistry, as well as helping on the RSC stand in the main exhibition area. Diane Aston also returned from the IoM3 to deliver her materials presentations, writing after the event "Thanks for a great day yesterday. . . . My first group of year 7, 8 and 9 were great and all my reservations about working with such a big group of year 6 were unfounded as they were absolutely fantastic. Please pass on to the school what a pleasure they were to work with and how impressed I was with their ideas!"

Within the main hall, alongside exhibits, we also had some talks and workshops in small groups.

The hall was extremely noisy though, so it wasn't the ideal location for presentations. Jason Stanton from Cyber Security Challenge talked about cyber security and decoding ciphers, Ellis Pitt from the Design Council ran a product design workshop with brainstorming and post-it notes. The IET repeated their popular Raspberry Pi workshops as well.

To try to get more corporate buy in to our schools' initiative, we arranged for some VIP guests to visit during lunchtime, having some buffet food laid on in one of the side rooms. Guests included Paul Walker the MD at Malvern Instruments who went on to become a key supporter and trusted advisor of our initiatives, Mike Ashton CEO at the H&W Chamber of Commerce, Chris Vagges from G-Tech who would speak later in the week at our Business of Innovating session, Anna Hopkins from Northrop Grumman, and Councillor Rebecca Massey who was helping us to promote the festival more widely.

After I had given a brief introduction over lunch, the VIPs had the opportunity to tour the exhibition with me and see for themselves the breadth of activities on offer. The inflatable dome showing

ALL MY RESERVATIONS ABOUT WORKING WITH SUCH A BIG GROUP OF YEAR 6 WERE UNFOUNDED AS THEY WERE ABSOLUTELY FANTASTIC.

the educational film *Back to the moon for good* was a hit with multiple groups of some fifty students being accommodated in succession throughout the

Clockwise from top left: Jason Stanton addresses a group of students about cyber security and Ellis Pitt hosts a product design workshop. The IET hosted a large Raspberry Pi workshop (CC) in which students spent about forty-five minutes on a hands-on coding exercise to control LEDs using python. (AB)

day. Mario Di Maggio and Robert Bilsland coped remarkably well keeping the tech working, corralling the students in and out, and fitting as many into each screening as possible to avoid disappointment.

TAKING THE REINS

In 2016 Sue left the Three Counties Showground and she and Paul later that year moved overseas to Portugal to start a new life tending olive trees and developing a holiday rental business. Thank goodness I had got more involved in the organisation of the Next Generation Schools' day the previous year, as this time I had to sort it all out in its entirety.

First of all, I had to negotiate the venue hire, as Sue had managed to include it previously within her

Some highlights from the exhibition hall included:
Top row, left: Revathi Timms' Avatar 3D exhibit demonstrating additive manufacturing (AB).
Top row, second from left: Revathi photographed with the Dyson Perrins students (ZS).
Top row, right and second from right: Groups of students engaged at the Code Club stand.
Middle row, left: Energy Simple stand and (middle row, second from left) Worcestershire Schools and Business stand (all AB).
Middle row, second from right: Malvern Instruments demonstrated particle size analysis using laser scattering.
Middle row, right: Sara Lukic from QinetiQ ran a Lego Mindstorms robotics obstacle course.
Bottom: Finally, Mike Schooling brought along Indra's electric motorbike and explained how petrol engines were being replaced by electric motors in vehicles. (all ZS)

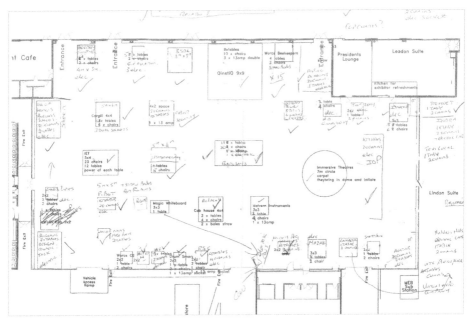

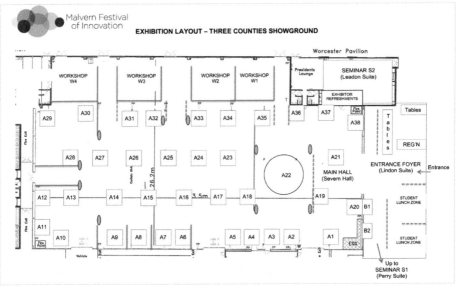

Sue's working exhibition plan from the previous year and how it evolved in 2016 to include more sound-friendly workshop zones down one side.

educational remit but this was no longer possible. We came to an agreement in which we contributed some cash and the Three Counties Showground also sponsored the event. Because our event was large, we were effectively using the main Severn Hall as well as the main entrance foyer (Lindon Suite), small Seminar Room (Leadon Suite) and larger upstairs seminar room (Perry Suite). We also needed lots of tables, chairs, electric sockets and some audio-visual equipment, so ended up with a fair deal given how much support we needed from their team on the day.

We had also decided to limit the day to school years 7, 8 and 9 (that is those in the first three years of senior school education when they will start to make their GCSE choices, called 'KS3' or 'Key Stage 3'). By not trying to cater for the younger primary school student, it was possible for talks and organisations to be better tuned to the students' level of understanding of STEM subjects and where they would be in their learning curriculum.

This year built on the previous year's formula developed so ably by Sue. I had her old exhibition plan and some of her contacts and set about convening the exhibition, workshops, and talks. I decided to structure the timetabled activities to be on the hour every hour for simplicity, and cater for about twenty students at each workshop location. Because the hall was so noisy, we came up with the solution of having an area divided by wooden baton and fabric screens which helped to separate out some of the workshops and deaden some of the noise.

It also became clear just how tricky the timetabling was. Many aspects only get finalised in the last few days, with schools changing their attendee numbers, some schools dropping out, exhibitors still finalising their requirements and so forth. This year we had nearly forty exhibitors, ten workshops, and three speakers to entertain some seven hundred and fifty students and their seventy teachers and teaching assistants. Schools planned to arrive and depart at different times depending on their transport arrangements and distance from school, and in the mix we also had half a dozen home educated students with their parents. The aim was for each student to hear at least one main science 'lecture', attend one or two workshops, see the *Future Moon* show in the dome and have time to tour the exhibition under their own steam. I found myself sorting out and then re-sorting out the timetable right up to the eleventh hour.

In terms of speakers, we had Professor Marcus du Sautoy OBE from the University of Oxford, whom you'll read later had given a talk about his new book at our launch evening. He kindly stayed the night and gave a talk titled 'The Number Mysteries and other Mathematical Curiosities' to a room of nearly 200 students before heading off to London to fly to a conference in the United States. It was great to have such an inspiring speaker reinforce the 'M' in STEM.

We then welcomed Orla Murphy, the 2015 IET Young Woman Engineer of the Year, visiting from JLR to speak about the future of infotainment, and a career that brings together music & engineering. She was a fantastic role model for the students in the audience, particularly the girls who may have not realised how appealing a career in engineering can be. Orla actually gave her talk twice during the day to make her trip more worthwhile and so I could make sure more students got an opportunity to hear from her. You can see a brief interview between Orla and Zoe Smith from MHDC at the festival here: youtu.be/nS5cDcP7zGw.

Our third speaker was the fascinating zoologist Adam Hart, Professor of Science Communication at the University of Gloucestershire, who had written a light-hearted popular science book titled *The Life of Poo*. His talk was all about the world of helpful bacteria, providing a much-needed biological element to the proceedings.

In amongst our room of exhibitors, we had many of our supporters and friends return. This included the Imagineering Foundation, IoP, IET, IMechE, RSC, Avatar 3D, QinetiQ and Malvern Instruments. We also had some welcome newcomers including the Peter Jones Foundation who was collaborating with Beryl Cuckney in

Left: The full seminar room with Marcus du Sautoy way up front in the distance.
Right: Adam Hart presenting later in the day all about bacteria and how useful these micro-organisms are in our lives (think healthy gut, making cheese, decomposing sewerage, and so on). (AB)

Malvern to deliver lifechanging entrepreneur workshops to young adults within the care system who had not had the opportunity or support to secure meaningful employment. We were also attracting a good mix of universities as well, with this year including University of Bristol, University of Gloucester and University of Worcester.

It's always nice when you get positive feedback from an event, and occasionally I'll stumble across a blog or article on a school website where an attendee has written about their day out.

Amelia Lane, in year eight, from RGS Worcester school wrote "When we got to the fair we were given time to explore and look around at the various stalls. We saw a mini show about Mathematics and logic with lots of interesting facts and many interactive things to do. We took part

WE COULD SCAN IN A WHOLE PERSON, SWAP THEIR HEAD FOR AN ANIMAL AND FINALLY PRINT THIS ON A 3D PRINTER. IT WAS REALLY COOL!

in a mini lottery and a session of musical chairs to demonstrate patterns in nature. After the show we went to a Computing and IT workshop. We could scan in a whole person, swap their head for an animal and finally print this on a 3D printer. It was really cool! The trip helped us to discover new interests and we learned about choosing the right GCSE options for different career possibilities."[25]

And Bishop Perowne school actually took the trouble to get an article printed in the *Worcester News* about their day out. Their head teacher was quoted as saying "Giving our students the opportunity to attend events likes this is all about improving their understanding of how science, maths and technology work together. Our school motto is Endeavour Forever, so being able to bring to life what students are learning in the classroom is important. They all thoroughly enjoyed the day and it really highlighted the kind of exciting and

Top: Revathi Timms returned with her 3D-printer; (middle) IMechE were on hand again with their big stand of tactile engineering exhibits adjacent to the inflatable dome cinema (bottom) that they sponsored once again. (AB)

25 www.rgsw.org.uk/worcester/rgs-news/malvern-festival-innovation-amelia-lane-year-eight/

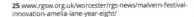

This year made good use of the space in the hall with a Morgan sportscar on display and a fleet of different electric vehicles courtesy of ElectrAA, including the new BMW i3 which Dan Wilde bravely brought along for students to inspect. (AB)

Returning companies engaging the students with their hands-on exhibits and demonstrations; from top left: Malvern Instruments, QinetiQ and Western Power. (AB)

innovating careers that are available to them in these fields."[26]

UP, UP AND AWAY

Our highlight this year was the launch of a weather balloon with a Raspberry Pi payload, kindly arranged by Nick McCloud[27]. Despite the preparation (including the need to file a 'fight plan' with the civil aviation authority to have permission to proceed), we didn't really know until the morning if the weather would be suitable. In the end the sun shone and the wind dropped sufficiently for a spectacular launch from outside the main hall watched by a group of students and their teachers. Then, with a Raspberry Pi on board, a stream of telemetry and photographs was beamed back to a computer in the exhibition space so that its progress could be tracked in real time.

Some new supporters: Clockwise from top left: the Peter Jones Foundation promoting entrepreneurship, the Institute of Biomedical Sciences[28], and industrial equipment supplier Laser Lines represented by our local friend Peter Smith who kindly brought some kit along to see what our schools' day was all about. (AB)

The balloon was also chased on the ground by a retrieval team, having located themselves somewhere downwind to stand a chance of getting to the landing site relatively quickly. The weather forecast was used to predict the route and a small release mechanism was primed to drop the payload by parachute during the flight, as the computer and accessories

26 'Bishop Perowne students visit Malvern Festival of Innovation', *Worcester News*, 21st October 2016. www.worcesternews.co.uk/news/14816566.bishop-perowne-students-visit-malvern-festival-of-innovation/

27 'Balloon launch will help build students' tech skills', *Malvern Gazette*, 18th September 2017. www.malverngazette.co.uk/news/15541463.balloon-launch-will-help-build-students-tech-skills/

28 'IBMS members at Malvern Festival of Innovation', *IBMS news*, 17th October 2016. www.ibms.org/resources/news/ibms-members-promote-science-at-malvern-fair-of-innovation/

were relatively expensive. Eventually the balloon itself would burst or deflate and be lost elsewhere. However, it didn't go to plan, as the payload didn't release properly and it ditched somewhere in the English Channel a few hours later[29].

The empty hall as the setting up begins and the preliminary arrangement of furniture the evening before in preparation for exhibitors arriving in the early morning. (AB)

Rhys Phillips, research engineer at Airbus Group and an honorary lecturer at the School of Physics & Astronomy at Cardiff University talks to a

full room of students: Thunderbolts and lightning, are they really frightening? His Van de Graaf generator was at the ready. (AB)

The weather balloon launch courtesy of Nick McCloud and the subsequent real-time tracking out over the English Channel. (AB)

Other than that, this year's schools' event was very much along the lines of previous years. We arrived late afternoon the day before to set up the venue with the able help of John Elliott and his team at the Three Counties Showground. This year we brought along our coloured gazebos from Malvern Science in the Park, adding more colour to the venue and helping to break up the space within the hall.

Our speakers this year included Nick giving an introduction to the weather balloon launch, Rhys Phillips from Airbus on lightning strikes and aircraft construction (with some very eye-catching static discharge demonstrations), as well as Linde Wester a doctoral student from the University of Oxford who introduced the students to world of quantum physics. These mind-expanding talks are probably nothing like the science covered in the classroom, and yet they are really interesting topics with relevance in the real world and linked to fascinating careers. Students will have seen the weather forecast on the television or mobile apps probably without giving much thought to how the data was collected, kids will fly in a plane on holiday without understanding the construction of aircraft and what happens if you fly through a thunderstorm, and many students (and teachers) will be blissfully unaware of quantum technology and the likely impact this will have within a student's lifetime. Not only that, but meteorology, aerospace engineering and quantum physics are related to the mainstream school subjects of geography, physics and chemistry, yet I bet it wouldn't be obvious to many.

29 'The balloon goes up for successful Festival of Innovation in Malvern', *Worcester News*, 10th October 2017. www.worcesternews.co.uk/news/15587164. the-balloon-goes-up-for-successful-festival-of-innovation-in-malvern/

Meanwhile, downstairs in the smaller seminar room, my colleague Tom Alcott introduced students to blockchain technology and the concept of digital money, whilst Emma stood in at the last minute to talk about cyber security because Diane Aston from IoM3 unfortunately fell ill on her way to us and had to turn around and return home.

This year we had a bumper exhibition with the IoP bringing a small inflatable dome cinema as a planetarium to go alongside the usual main dome that this year alternated shows titled Journey to Infinity and Journey to Mars. We also spilled out into the entrance foyer this year with some of the exhibitors, so there was a lot going on. Daden wrote a blog about their day offering virtual reality immersive learning workshops to students[30].

Newcomers included the RAF, Gordon Coppock and his bicycle generators, and mining equipment company Komatsu. These three had all participated in the Malvern Science in the Park event you'll read about later, and so it was evident that the two events were synergistic and made it easier to populate the show with quality exhibits. We also welcomed the Quekett Microscopical Club with their light microscopes, and the Cheltenham Science Group with their hands-on science experiments extracted for the day from their venue in Cheltenham.

Worcester City also supported the day, partly because an ardent supporter Amanda Lloyd had changed jobs from MHDC to the city council and got them onboard from the inside[31].

ADA LOVELACE DAY

Our Next Generation Innovators event on 9th October 2018 coincided with Ada Lovelace Day, an

Newcomers to the schools' day Cheltenham Science Group, Gordon Coppock, Komatsu, the Quekett Microscopical Club, RAF, Imaginify, and Legrand. (AB)

official celebration of the achievements of women in STEM. Richard Henson and Christine Swan rose to the occasion dressing up as Charles Babbage and Ada Lovelace to arrive by Tardis and perform a sketch about their history and achievements.

This was also the year that MHDC created National Boffin Day[32] in 2018, a nod to the term that was coined for those clever scientists that worked on radar technology in Malvern during and after the Second World War, and hence to celebrate intelligence, innovation and creativity in all its forms. MHDC created a quiz to find out what boffin you were most closely related to, and decorated their stand with our *Big Bang Theory* cast cut-outs.

30 https://dadenblog.blogspot.com/2017/10/fieldscapes-at-malvern-festival-of.html

31 'Interactive event hopes to encourage more to study 'difficult' subjects', *Worcester News*, 5th October 2017. www.worcesternews.co.uk/news/15578980.interactive-event-hopes-to-encourage-more-to-study-difficult-subjects/
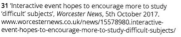

32 'Malvern festival set to celebrate boffins everywhere', *Malvern Observer*, 5th October 2018. malvernobserver.co.uk/news/malvern-festival-set-to-celebrate-boffins-everywhere/

Simon Smith and Gemma Ranford from MHDC on the National Boffin Day Stand. (AB)

This year was also a bumper year for recognised weeks and 'years of' in the world of science and technology. Firstly, it was UK's designated Year of Engineering and so an ideal opportunity to promote this discipline. It was also Rail Week to promote the wide range of careers

And some of our returning favourites all engaging students with their eye-catching exhibits and interesting activities. This time Revathi brought along a 3D printer for chocolate, the IoP inflated a planetarium, and the IET were back with an updated raspberry Pi workshop. (AB)

Richard Henson, a Senior Lecturer from the University of Worcester, appeared as Charles Babbage and Christine Swan an experienced computer science teacher and visiting lecturer at Birmingham City

University, played Ada Lovelace. (RM)

Celebrating the Year of Engineering with Imagineering, IMechE, the IET, GE (all RM), Legrand and Mazak. (AB)

in the rail industry, World Space Week (usually coinciding with our festival being an annual event early in October), and Biology Week (also an annual early October event). And on top of that October is also usually European Cyber Security Month, so there were plenty of hooks that we could hang our activities off.

We also had another good line-up of speakers and workshops. Dr Ozak Esu who was the winner of the IET's Young Woman Engineer of

Some exciting new exhibits this year included the hydrogen fuel call powered car driven down from the University of Birmingham's Chemical Engineering department and pictured with their PhD student Sam Sogbesan, and the Herefordshire and Worcestershire Earth Heritage Trust pictured here with their outreach manager Beth Andrews. (RM)

Charles Penny helped us recognise Rail Week with his tabletop rail engineering demonstration. (RM)

the Year award in 2017 spoke about her career in electronics and electrical engineering. Sonal Bhadane joined us from Elekta Ltd and spoke about medical physics technology, advances in radiation therapy and oncology. Then in the smaller seminar room, we had talks from Alastair

Top row: Up in the Perry Suite Dr Ozak Esu spoke to a full house about electrical engineering, and Sonal Bhadane explained how radiation therapy is being developed to better cure cancer. (AB)

The exhibition hall was busy as usual, this year with a new colourful dome cinema acting as a focal point and playing From Dream to Discovery: Inside NASA. We also had some of our popular exhibitors return, including Dave Watson from Cheltenham Science Group, Gordon Coppock with his pedal-power bikes, and the RAF. (AB)

Shortland on his entrepreneurial TextLocal story that started in his spare bedroom, Tom Alcott on blockchain technology, and Dalim Basu on careers in computing. And workshops included Marie Jenkins exploring the mindset of an entrepreneur and the University of Birmingham School of Physics providing a hands-on activity to build exoplanets and calculate the Goldilocks Zone for some known planetary systems beyond our own solar system!

using a range of different materials, the Extreme Robotics Laboratory came with drones and robots, and their Human Interfaces Technologies Team also joined in with virtual reality kit to try.

Some of the broad range of hands-on activities and investigations taking place around the exhibition hall. (RM)

Dr Chris Hamlett from the University of Birmingham and the Discover Materials initiative led a series of workshops to protect eggs from damage, with live drop-testing to evaluate the students' entries. (AB)

BIGGER AND BETTER

With business mix being our Platinum Sponsor in 2019, we were able to ensure a packed programme of exhibitors and speakers once again for the Next Generation Innovators event. Through business mix connections, we had BatFast, a cricket simulator activity which was really popular and added sports science to our coverage.

Through my Royal Society Entrepreneur in Residence connections at the University of Birmingham, we had Dr Chris Hamlett run a workshop on protecting eggs dropped from height

Left: David Page, CEO of our Platinum Sponsor business mix chats to some students, and the BatFast cricket simulator drew in the crowds. (AB)

Our two headline speakers Yasmin Ali (left) and Philip Moriarty. (AB)

Celebrating the centenary of the Women's Engineering Society we welcomed Yasmin Ali, a chartered chemical engineer, who spoke about her work in energy innovation. And Professor Philip Moriarty visited with his electric guitar and suite of physics experiments to present his fantastic interactive talk titled 'Universal Harmonies: When Physics Meets Music Meets Maths'.

In the exhibition hall this year we had a new Tesla Model 3 courtesy of a member of ElectrAA, and Indra were back demonstrating their EV-to-grid technology that allows you to power a house (or, in the case of the event, a popcorn machine) by taking stored energy back out of your parked car at peak energy times. We also had Goodfellow, a major materials company, join us with their technical manager Dr Aphrodite Tomou also speaking about materials science to groups of students in the seminar room. Other newcomers this year included Neoperl, a plumbing components manufacturer, NMITE (New Model Institute for Technology and Engineering) which was being set up as a new technical university in Hereford, and Cyber Discovery.

New Tesla Model 3 fully electric vehicle, Indra and their car-powered popcorn dispenser, Goodfellow, Neoperl, NMITE and Cyber Discovery. (AB)

GOING VIRTUAL

You'll read later that in 2020 the Covid pandemic meant that we broadcast a virtual Malvern Science in the Park event in the summer. In the case of the festival, it became clear quite quickly in the planning stages that although schools were expecting to be back after the summer holidays, they would be grappling with making up for lost time and coping with a resurgence of Covid cases. And hosting a

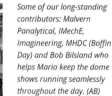

Some of our long-standing contributors: Malvern Panalytical, IMechE, Imagineering, MHDC (Boffin Day) and Bob Bilsland who helps Mario keep the dome shows running seamlessly throughout the day. (AB)

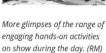

More glimpses of the range of engaging hands-on activities on show during the day. (RM)

crowded in-person student event was not going to be feasible, especially as most organisations were still working from home and unlikely to want to exhibit either.

So, I decided to host a half-day virtual session and encourage schools to watch from their premises using Zoom and Facebook Live as the means to link up with speakers and broadcast to an audience. I also thought that we could take advantage of the situation by having some virtual visits to university and company laboratories, as they could join us from their site and provide a tour of some of their equipment. For many school students this would be a unique opportunity to see a STEM workplace and perhaps understand what it would be like to work in such an environment.

I set up again in the boardroom at the Wyche Innovation Centre and acted as host to introduce the speakers and in some cases chat through topics with them.

The first talk was from my colleague Tom who talked about blockchain technology. He was down the corridor in the same building, so a good one to start with in case there were any technical hitches. As we recorded the whole session, you can watch his talk here: youtu.be/GTvTXz411Es.

Janina Neumann, a bilingual graphic designer, then joined from down the road in Gloucestershire. Last year, she and her colleague Dr Carla Brown had kindly run a workshop on branding and business ideas with exercises focused on the Grand Challenges outlined in the UK's Industrial Strategy. This was an opportunity to hear more about her career and some of the things she had learnt along the way: youtu.be/ EOiXauGF50M.

Then we joined Chris Gell at the University of Birmingham in the Extreme Robotics Laboratory where they do state-of-the-art research on robots; including improved handling of objects, better machine vision for automated control, and systems for use in harsh environments like nuclear waste plants. Chris provided some background to all of this and then showed some of the robotic systems in their lab which I'd had the opportunity to tour before Covid when I had my entrepreneur in residence office just down the corridor from them. youtu.be/PEeT2eytjMk.

Whilst Chris was on, we were trying to troubleshoot some technical issues with our next speaker who was not able to get her device to connect properly over Zoom so that we could hear her through her microphone. This meant that we seamlessly jumped to our next planned segment whilst we worked out a solution in the background!

So, we returned a bit closer to home and had a tour of some of the test and development facilities in Malvern Panalytical courtesy of senior development scientist Dr Alex Malm. As they usually bring an example of particle size measuring equipment to

> THIS MEANT THAT WE SEAMLESSLY JUMPED TO OUR NEXT PLANNED SEGMENT WHILST WE WORKED OUT A SOLUTION IN THE BACKGROUND!

the schools' day event, it was great to see behind the scenes in the R&D labs where the team works and where apprentices or graduates might spend their day if they worked for the company. youtu.be/w8sYvmV5GfU.

With technical issues resolved (slides emailed to me and hastily cued up locally, and a different device used to connect), we were then joined by another friend and supporter of the festival Marie Jenkins. Marie had recently completed a degree in entrepreneurship as a mature student at the University of Worcester, and in fact I had first met her there when I helped as an entrepreneur in residence at the business school. Marie had also delivered workshops with the students at the schools' day on the mindset of an entrepreneur, so it was great to have her insights into goal setting, the importance of positivity, and how to develop solutions-focused thinking: youtu.be/IDMy7CCoLVA.

After Marie, we had a presentation about what a career in cyber security might look like from Emma Kirby and how students could embark on such work in the future. This was based around the Cyber Discovery schools programme that has content to help school-aged students explore cyber security issues and improve on their digital skills: youtu.be/3oacn_sgOsM.

The IMechE were keen to be involved and Kevin Blacktop, the chairman of the Worcester area committee who also worked at the Birmingham Centre for Railway Research and Education, was joined online by his colleague Stuart Hillmansen. They spoke about the HydroFlex project to develop and test the UK's first mainline hydrogen-powered train: youtu.be/rs0W8G4fQ_o.

After this I then had a chat with Dr Carla Brown about her career as a microbiologist before going on to lead an educational gaming start-up. Carla had participated at our previous year's live schools' event and delivered the STEM workshop with Janina, but had since moved back to Scotland to focus on her a business. This was a great opportunity for students to hear how you could train in one science discipline, travel around the world to work in different countries, and move into different roles including that of being a tech entrepreneur: youtu. be/_nvAEG-OUao.

As chair of the Industrial Advisory Board of the School of Physics at the University of Bristol, I

had got to know a number of staff there and been encouraging them to exhibit at previous editions as part of their outreach activity. This year, we were able to take students into a state-of-the-art surface science and materials analysis laboratory to give them an insight into university research and the kind of expensive equipment that is used. Dr Gary Wan was our remote host: youtu.be/pOlm31L5s-w.

Some of the day's speakers dialling in from their work and home: Top row, L–R: Tom Alcott and Janina Neumann; second row, L–R: Chris Gell with a robot and Alex Malm with a particle suspension; third row, L–R: Marie Jenkins and Emma Kirby; fourth row, L–R: Carla Brown and Gary Wan; and fifth row: Janaki Shanmugam. (AB)

Finally, we were able to travel halfway around the globe to Singapore to hear about the Institute of Materials Research and Engineering, and some of their facilities and research too. Dr Cedric

Clockwise from top left: University of Birmingham's student racing car, University of Wolverhampton's STEM Response Team, Regional Cyber Crime Unit (RCCU) discussing cyber security, and exploring different materials with Goodfellow. (RM)

Troadec, whom I used to know when I worked out there, was still in place and able to persuade one of the scientists in his team to stay up late and join us. Dr Janaki Shanmugam talked about some of the facilities she uses in her research: youtu.be/dxZQygwu4Hg.

We then wrapped up in time for a late lunch. We had a modest turnout during the morning with various schools watching the Facebook stream live from their classrooms, and of course the various videos have been watched since on YouTube

BACK AT THE THREE COUNTIES SHOWGROUND

Early preparations for the 2021 edition of the Next Generation Innovators went well in that there was a good level of interest from exhibitors to participate again in person and for speakers to come along and give up some of their time presenting to students. I was concerned that schools may find it difficult to take time out of the classroom having not long reconvened after the Covid lockdown, and so kept a watchful eye on any Covid resurgence as schools returned after the summer in September.

At its peak we had over seven hundred school students and their teachers registered to attend from about fourteen different schools from around the region. Then, as we went into the hectic final few weeks of preparations, timetabling and committing to various expenses, the schools started to drop like flies. Covid certainly played a part, with stated reasons including "Unfortunately, we will not be attending this year due to concerns around different schools mixing", "Given the rising numbers of COVID cases both in our school and in the county, we feel that it would be wise to cancel our trip", "Our school has had a Covid-19 outbreak and have taken the difficult decision not to attend the festival this year". Then we had some other reasons too: "Having spoken at length with senior management and the Career Lead, due to staff restraints, we have to withdraw our interest

in attending this event", "Sadly I am no longer able to take students out of school on this date due to clashes with other events", and the one that wins the prize was "I was really hoping to bring a group with me, but I just haven't had any time to organise the admin this end, I'm really sorry!?"

Suddenly I was left with a hall full of exciting exhibits and virtually no schools planning to attend. I frantically opened it up to primary schools and contacted other senior schools to see if they would like to come if they hadn't registered or indeed bring more classes if they could. Malvern St James girls' school was the only one that rose to the challenge and brought another year group with them at very short notice. They were delighted because they could bring the year that missed out in 2020 because of Covid.

Unfortunately, as much as I'd hope it wasn't the case, this reflects the difference between a private school and a state school; the latter find it too much trouble to organise and drop out at the last minute, whereas the former seizes the opportunity and makes the most of it to the benefit of their students. Ironically it is the state school students that would benefit most from such an event on their doorstep because they have less resources at their disposal to promote STEM subjects during the academic year.

Then, on the day itself, we had three further no-shows from schools and over all less than 200 students and teachers in attendance. For those that did make it, it was a great opportunity to take part in lots activities and talk at length with scientists, engineers, entrepreneurs, designers and people in different careers. But it left me embarrassed that so many had kindly come along to interact with school students and so few were in attendance.

It is also expensive to stage; we spent nearly £5,000 on venue hire, activities, speaker costs, lunches, first aid cover, etc and I cover this through year-long efforts of securing sponsorship. It is by far the most complex day to organise, probably

Lots of hands-on activities (RM)

But as you'll see from the photographs we had some great participants, including keynote speaker Dr Anna Ploszajski who travelled up from London to talk about materials and some of the contents of her new book *Handmade: A Scientist's Search for Meaning Through Making*. We switched to the smaller seminar room as we didn't have enough students to fill the main room we'd used in the past, but the advantage was a more intimate talk with school students which Anna still delivered on two occasions during the day.

We had a good mix of exhibitors and workshops; I'd arranged for the Bloodhound Education workshop to return this year and IMechE co-hosted The Bugatti Trust and UBRacing so had a great static display. This year I parked my Tesla Model 3 up opposite Indra's exhibit to fill some space and ensure we had a good EV exhibit. Some of the regular local technology companies returned too, like QinetiQ, Mazak, and Malvern Panalytical[33]. And new to the day were the STEM Response team from the University of Wolverhampton who provided videos last year, and IASME Consortium engaging about cyber security[34]. ○

accounting for over a third of my time for the whole festival, which for 2021 would have equated to about 150 hours. I write more about costs later, but a benchmark volunteer rate that is used is £15 per hour, so this is a further £2,250 for my time. In reality, if I consult for a business, I charge out at more than £175 per hour, so you can do the mathematics! But the point is that with over 100 volunteers onsite for the day too, there is an inordinate amount of goodwill invested in this event and over the years I don't believe it has been fully appreciated. Schools get to bring their students along for free and yet you wouldn't believe how many drop out at the last minute or never turn up without an explanation! As I'm not planning such a session this coming year, it will be interesting to see if anyone notices.

33 'Malvern Festival of Innovation 10th Anniversary!', Malvern Panalytical Blog, 2nd December 2021. www.materials-talks.com/malvern-festival-of-innovation-10th-anniversary/

34 'Science on the agenda as Festival of Innovation returns to Malvern', *Malvern Gazette*, 17th October 2021. www.malverngazette.co.uk/news/19650793.science-agenda-festival-innovation-returns-malvern/

More views from the day, including (bottom) Jane Waterfall on the IASME Consortium stand. (AB)

Top: David and Margaret Cross test the IoP's Van de Graaf generator and, middle, the team of IoP volunteers including Dr Alan Smith on the left who has helped me organise the Malvern Science in the Park that you'll read about later. Bottom: Other STEM Ambassadors from the University of Worcester. (RM)

6.

For the second year of the festival in 2013, I decided it would be good to extend the event by a day to conclude on Saturday, staying in the Malvern Theatres for the duration and hosting a Family Day on the Saturday morning. This would be a ticketed family show in the auditorium with two speakers as a double-bill with intermission, and a free hands-on exhibition in the foyers for people to visit.

INNOVATIVE STUFF! THE MATERIALS REVOLUTION

I knew (now Professor) Mark Miodownik from my time at Oxford University where we both completed our PhDs (DPhils). He would often arrive cheerfully in the tearoom for morning coffee and his exuberance and enthusiasm was an early indication he would go far and that he'd probably be on telly one day helping to popularise science. Well, he has been of course, delivering the Royal Institution Christmas Lectures in 2010 and then appearing in a number of BBC science shows thereafter. When Mark came to Malvern, he had just published his first book *Stuff Matters*.

Before Mark came on stage, we had Dr Jonathan Hare, another person I had met from my days undertaking scientific research in the field of carbonaceous materials. Jonathan had worked

FAMILY DAY

alongside the Nobel Laureate Sir Harry Kroto on the chemistry of C60 Buckminsterfullerene, then becoming a freelance science communicator as well as co-presenting the television shows *Rough Science* and *Hollywood Science*.

Our first family show had set the bar high with Jonathan talking about the fascinating element carbon with his range of molecular models and Mark using his digital microscope to view an assortment of materials live on stage. Outside in the upper and lower foyers we had a number of exhibitors, many who stayed on from the previous days. These included a number of learned membership institutes with a remit to promote STEM subjects to the general public; the IoP, IMechE, The IET, RSC and the RMS. Alongside were local companies and other organisations like GeoVation, the open innovation initiative from Ordnance Survey. This was a fantastic opportunity for children and their parents to interact with a broad range of exhibitors and it all seemed to work well as a public event in the Malvern Theatres venue.

CREATIVE MINDS. INNOVATION & REPUTATION!

Organising the family show is great fun, because it gives me the excuse to contact leading science communicators and, when possible, meet them

Once again, we had a good mix of exhibitors in the foyers, this time running on until late afternoon so that it was now a full day of family fun[35].

Clockwise from top left: Jonathan Hare chatting to the audience after his talk about the carbon revolution; the IMechE exhibiting in the foyer; a local start-up company exhibiting their new Dooup dog poo garden collector, and long-term supporter of the festival Mark Edwards chatting about his eco-light project. (AB)

Left: Mark Champkins begins his talk about being an inventor and how he's developed new things that solve problems. Dr Quentin Cooper discussing scientists and innovators. (SW)

the evening before for a meal or drink. The great challenge for this subevent lies in making sure it is well advertised and encouraging parents to bring along their children to what may seem like an unorthodox science show. Over the years, other science festivals and science shows on the television have begun to popularise science subjects, but it remains hard to fill a large auditorium. We would distribute fliers, inform all the local schools, do press releases, use social media and latterly use paid promotions on Facebook, but over the years I have always been disappointed by how few people made the most of the opportunity to hear world class science communicators on their doorstep.

This year, 2014, was no exception; we hosted the then Inventor in Residence from London's Science Museum Mark Champkins and the science broadcaster Dr Quentin Cooper (who has the great twitter handle @Qwerty). Mark showed us a number of his creative inventions as well as replaying his time on the BBC's *Dragons' Den*. Quentin then entertained us with his thoughts on geeks, freaks and eggheads, as well as referencing the term 'boffins'.

A busy Malvern Theatres foyer with plenty of interest in the exhibitors' hands-on activities, including those from the IoP (above right) and RMS (opposite). (SW)

TINY PARTICLES, BIG IMPACT!

One thing I have found over the years is that the family show audience usually has lots of very knowledgeable kids in it, to the extent that the speakers are often impressed by the questions they answer. This is partly because there are a lot of science and technology families in the town, and the parents' geekiness rubs off on their children. And when they are awe inspired by knowledgeable

35 'Science showcase at Malvern Theatres is a great success', *Worcester News*, 8th October 2014. www.worcesternews.co.uk/news/11521459.science-showcase-at-malvern-theatres-is-a-great-success/

speakers, it is good to see their interest reinforced. However, there are also plenty of kids whose parents aren't scientists or who may not have been excited by STEM subjects at school. These are the ones we really need to reach through the annual family show.

In 2015, we had Dr Kate Lancaster and Dr Sam Gregson come to Malvern. Kate was the plasma and fusion industrial officer at the York Plasma Institute and so talked about nuclear fusion and our quest to harness the power of the stars here on earth. This was followed by Sam and his able data-handling assistant Aidan Randle-Conde who provided an interactive and amusing show about particle physics and the importance of understanding statistics and bias when assessing

Top: Dr Kate Lancaster on stage talking about nuclear fusion and Dr Sam Gregson following that up with a talk about the Large Hadron Collider and experimental analysis. (AB)

experimental results. Indeed, as you'll read later, Sam returned in 2019 to take part in the comedy night and has gone on to grow his YouTube following to roughly 30k as the Bad Boy of Science. It's always satisfying when you book science communicator talent early on and have them featured before they become too popular, busy and expensive to attract!

This year we had another well-rounded exhibition including large companies HP and Mazak. Although we had the electric vehicle innovation showcase event the next day organised by ElectrAA in collaboration with the festival, the family day

marked the end of the heavy lifting for me this year, and it had been another good week[36].

Clockwise from top left: The Mazak team from above with their engineering exhibit; University of Birmingham's student formula racing team car just outside the foyer; the IET stand was busy in the upper foyer; and HP stayed on to exhibit at the family day in the main foyer. (AB)

PROGRESS, IN MANY DIMENSIONS

Dr Emily Grossman joined us in 2016 with her talk about 'Body Building in 3 Dimensions' which covered recent advances in the fields of cloning and regenerative medicine, from Dolly the sheep to 3D-printed livers, and how stem cells are now being used to re-grow human body parts. Emily was resident science expert on ITV's *The Alan Titchmarsh Show*, a member of the panel of experts for Sky1's celebrity panel-show *Duck Quacks Don't Echo*, a regular contributor to Discovery Channel's *How Do They Do It?* and a biology expert on Channel 4's *Food Unwrapped*. So, Emily was an experienced performer and a safe pair of hands for our first family show with an emphasis on the biological sciences.

36 'Malvern Festival of Innovation helps build the future', *Malvern Gazette*, 13th October 2015. www.malverngazette. co.uk/news/13843338.malvern-festival-of-innovation-helps-build-the-future/

'Festival of Innovation attracts 2,500 visitors', *Malvern Observer*, 15th October 2015. malvernobserver.co.uk/news/festival-of-innovation-attracts-2500-visitors-10198/

The second half was an extravaganza of amplified rock guitar in 11 dimensions. Dr Mark Lewney, a member of staff at the Intellectual Property Office by day, and the Rock Doctor by night, used his electric guitar to explain waves, acoustics and superstring theory, and could play pretty much any requested rock guitar solo on demand. One person emailed me later to say "Just to let you know my husband and daughter attended the lectures on Saturday morning and thought they were great, particularly the second one with the guitar solos!"

Top: Dr Emily Grossman starts her talk on the human body, before Dr Mark Lewney took to the stage with his electric guitar and amp to journey through the physics of acoustics and superstring theory. (AB)

This year, the free exhibition had a good mix of organisations. Alongside our regular learned scientific membership organisations, we were also joined by chartered surveyor David Prosser with his drone equipment for aerial inspection and surveillance, and Ross Robotics that demonstrated their modular robotic platform that could be modified for particular tasks: youtu.be/36M2zbn4fbg. The University of Worcester also filled a table-top with a variety of drones used in their research on applications for agriculture, business, security and mapping.

This extra drone content had partly come about because we had been trying to get a drone racing display set-up in Priory Park as part of the event. I had been in dialogue with the Chairman of the British First Person View (FPV) Racing Association about the health, safety and technical requirements for such a spectacle, and one of their team happened to live fairly nearby. In the end, it hadn't worked out, a major event in their calendar clashed with ours.

We also featured drones because private drone flying had started to become popular and the Malvern Hills Conservators (now Malvern Hills Trust) had announced they were banning drones flying above their land. This had started to become a divisive issue in the town, and so we took the opportunity to ensure the innovation and technology angle of drones and their future potential was not side-lined, and thus invited the organisation to attend and find out more from users; generating some extra publicity[37].

The day rounded off another successful and generally well-attended week with some fantastic speakers, exhibits and activities[38].

CONNECTED PLANET TO EXTENDED UNIVERSE

The BBC's *Robot Wars* was a popular TV show and electronics-maker Dr Lucy Rogers was one of the programme's judges. Her set involved lots of Raspberry Pi computers, Internet of Things devices, and nerves of steel in hoping everything would work as planned at the time it was asked to! Having built and demonstrated temperamental electronic

[37] 'Conservators accept Drones experience invite despite banning stance', *Malvern Observer*, 19th August 2016 https://malvernobserver.co.uk/news/conservators-accept-drones-experience-invite-despite-banning-stance/

'Malvern Hills Conservators accept invitation to find out more about drones at festival of innovation, despite push for a ban', *Malvern Gazette*, 20th August 2016 www.malverngazette.co.uk/news/14695267.malvern-hills-conservators-accept-invitation-to-find-out-more-about-drones-at-festival-of-innovation-despite-push-for-a-ban/

[38] 'Thousands glimpse the future at Malvern Festival of Innovation', *Malvern Gazette*, 21st October 2016. www.malverngazette.co.uk/news/14816641.thousands-glimpse-the-future-at-malvern-festival-of-innovation/

'More than 2,000 visitors attend Festival of Innovation', *Malvern Observer*, 27th October 2016. malvernobserver.co.uk/news/more-than-2000-visitors-attend-festival-of-innovation/

devices over the years, I found it hard to relax during the entertainment. But Lucy was an adept presenter who knew her props inside out and delivered a fantastic interactive show of connected widgets.

The second half featured astrophysicist Dr Megan Argo who gave an enthralling tour of our solar system and outer space as she explained the birth and eventual death of the universe and the celestial bodies within it. Her talk was particularly

Top left: The expo from above, with the University of Worcester's table of drones in the centre. The foyers were generally busy again this year and RSC (left) were also sponsors and had a well-attended stand. (AB)

good at putting everything into a size perspective; the extent of the solar system with its various planets spaced out beyond the sun, and then on further to the neighbouring galaxies[39].

The expo was also well attended again this year, with GE Aviation joining us as a newcomer to the event. Revathi Timms also brought along her pink 3D-printer that printed and tempered chocolate. Her 3D-printing exhibits had been well received at the schools' day exhibitions in the past, so it was great that she could come along to the

family day this year too. As you'll read later, she shared her engineering journey at TEDxMalvern, which you can still watch if you are interested to learn how she came about developing this bit of kit.

Left: Dr Lucy Rogers on stage with her 'Internet of Tat' as she referred to it, followed by Dr Megan Argo as she set off on her journey around the universe before lunch. (AB)

Clockwise from top left: The morning sun brightens up the Malvern Theatres main foyer, with GE Aviation in attendance; regulars Mazak returned with their engaging stand, as did the RMS; Adam Clay and Debbie Hunt are pictured here helping a young microscopist view some specimens. Bottom: The Avatar 3D-printer and University of Birmingham's award-winning Student Formula Racing car were also on show.

39 'Festival family day includes a chance to tour the universe at Malvern Theatres', *Worcester News*, 2nd October 2017. www.worcesternews.co.uk/news/15571274. festival-family-day-includes-a-chance-to-tour-the-universe-at-malvern-theatres/

'Tour the universe at festival family day at Malvern Theatres', *Malvern Observer*, 5th October 2017. malvernobserver.co.uk/news/tour-the-universe-at-festival-family-day-at-malvern-theatres/

INSPIRATION, EXPLORATION & ADVENTURE

Our double bill in 2018 comprised Sophie Kain and Huw James. Sophie used to work as a quantum physicist but joined us as an enthusiastic science and business presenter who inspired the audience to solve real world problems and explore what is required to turn an innovation into a commercial reality. Sophie had appeared on BBC's *The Apprentice* back in 2007, where she was proudly 'fired' for sticking to her principles!

Sophie had actually contacted me about presenting at the festival, and so it was refreshing to be approached rather than having to scratch my head and think who to invite. It was evidence that the festival was becoming more widely known and I hoped an indication that one day it would be easier to put a good quality programme together.

Huw was (and probably still is) an adventurer and astronomer who was a Fellow of both the Royal Geographical Society and the Royal Astronomical Society. Like Megan last year, he took us on a journey to explore where in space we'll go next and he explained how we are already sending probes beyond our solar system to learn exciting new things about our galaxy. Huw had a table full of illustrative experiments and props, and I actually got into a bit of trouble with the venue for not having ensured we received the risk assessment beforehand for them to carefully review. But Huw was well practised and nothing burnt down nor exploded (more than it should have).

The 2018 festival was thankfully deemed a success[40].

Top left: Sophie Kain on stage talking about having good ideas and turning them into a commercial reality for all the budding business-minded kids in the audience. This was followed by a table packed full of experiments as Huw James rattled through his repertoire. (AB)

Clockwise from top left: The busy upper foyer with STEM Ambassadors doing a range of engaging experiments this year from their stand. GE Aviation were back with a bigger flight simulator, and the Steve Dawes from the Malvern Hills Pi Jam club had an eye-catching table of Raspberry Pi kit and brightly coloured LED displays. (AB)

THE SMALL AND THE WOBBLY

This somewhat odd title for 2019 came about because the line-up this year was to be Dr Marty Jopson with his real time light microscopy show followed by Dr Kate Oliver aka Dr Scary Boots and her talk about 3D-printed body parts and other soft materials. However, just a couple of days before the

show, Kate had a bereavement in her family and had to drop out.

In her place, I managed to persuade Dr Martin Khechara to stand in at very short notice. He, as you will soon learn, was booked to appear the evening before at the comedy night, and so he was able to bring along some extra kit and do his show all about bacteria, biology and excrement which as you can image was generally well received by the young audience. I have to say, as it was not as advertised, a few did leave when Martin illustrated

---

40 'Malvern Festival of Innovation is a success once again', *Malvern Gazette*, 18th October 2018. www.malverngazette.co.uk/news/16990985.malvern-festival-innovation-success/

the length of tapeworms across the auditorium and then wheeled out Shamus the Anus to illustrate the science of pooing.

Marty, however, had been on stage beforehand and already given the audience their money's worth. I had met Marty previously at an RMS event, but had to leave to catch a train before his talk, so was looking forward to watching the show as much

> A FEW DID LEAVE WHEN MARTIN ILLUSTRATED THE LENGTH OF TAPEWORMS ACROSS THE AUDITORIUM AND THEN WHEELED OUT SHAMUS THE ANUS TO ILLUSTRATE THE SCIENCE OF POOING.

as everyone else. He had a full-to-the-brim stage set up of different microscopes and cameras, and showed a variety of organisms in glorious high magnification. It was also interesting chatting to him afterwards; he lived in a small rural town called Otley, not unlike Malvern, and he had started the Otley Science Festival and was also busy running the Otley MakerSpace. I had been putting together plans for a Malvern MakerSpace but had so far not got it off the drawing board, something you can read more about towards the end of this book.

This year, we had a special guest at The IET stand. A local resident Elin had won a national competition with the IET and *Beano*. Their Life on Mars competition asked six to sixteen-year-olds to redesign something they couldn't live without should they ever move to another planet, and ten-year-old Elin reworked her clarinet to operate in space so she could play it with her astronaut helmet on! Part of her prize was that she was featured with her instrument in a published *Beano* cartoon story that she had on display.

We also had a bumper table exhibit from the University of Birmingham and University of Nottingham; partly because one of the researchers at Birmingham had encouraged her partner to come along from Nottingham too. This was great, because neuroscience, food science and psychology were covered as a result; helping to balance the physics and engineering which always tended to be well catered for.

The festival ended for another year after a week of well attended, insightful events[41].

IN THE MIND'S EYE

This was the subject for our virtual, Covid-restricted family show in 2020. On this occasion I hosted two speakers over Zoom from the relative

Clockwise from top left: Dr Marty Jopson imaging live specimens on stage with his suite of light microscopes. This was followed by Dr Martin Khechara demonstrating the length of tapeworms to a squirming audience, and yes, those are bare buttocks sitting on his table of props. (AB)

41 'Malvern Festival of Innovation is a big success', *Worcester News*, 14th October 2019. www.worcesternews.co.uk/news/17968196.malvern-festival-innovation-big-success/

comfort of the Wyche Innovation Centre, and although the morning was far easier to organise, it wasn't quite as rewarding as meeting the speakers in person and introducing them to an auditorium of avid listeners.

But the quality was as high as previous years. We opened with Professor Gina Rippon, the Emeritus Professor of Cognitive Neuroimaging at the Aston Brain Centre from Aston University and she gave a fascinating talk about the brain and whether there is such a thing as a male and female brain. She also talked about the complex subject of neuroscience in a very accessible way, and because it was part of our virtual year, you can still watch it on YouTube: youtu.be/1DWNkUI8dLk.

Clockwise from top left: The University of Birmingham's Sensory Motor Neuroscience (SyMoN) lab from the School of Psychology, along with the Hearing Sciences section of the School of Medicine from the University of Nottingham all doing hands (and ears) on experiments. The IoP stand was busy most of the day, and Elin exhibited her prize-winning re-engineered clarinet on the IET stand. (AB)

Then we were joined by Andrew Hanson MBE from the National Physical Laboratory. We'd been liaising for a few years about the festival, but clashes with other events had meant that the stars had not aligned. This year we'd fixed the date far enough in advance that it was in Andrew's diary only to be thwarted by the pandemic preventing him from joining us in person. But, the science of colour was well suited to a digital virtual talk by screen, and Andrew gave a very thorough and interesting walk through the world of colour and how we measure and perceive it. Once again, the silver lining of the pandemic is that we have it all on video for you to enjoy: youtu.be/p2tiDegW6H8.

With no exhibition this year, it was all wrapped up and I was home before 2pm.

BACK FOR ANOTHER FAMILY AFFAIR

In 2021 we were back live in the Malvern Theatres with another double bill. I did have a tentative themed title for this year of 'Creativity: Making & Sensing', but as you may recall from earlier, Dr Anna Ploszajski's appearance was rejigged from the family show to the schools' day and so in the end I just went with two titles rather than one overarching one!

The punk biologist Lucy Eckersley gave a talk aptly titled 'A walk on the wild side' about animals, protecting wildlife and nature conservation. She had been performing the evening before at the comedy night, and had apparently continued drinking and socialising into the small hours, so she admitted to having a bit of headache that morning. However, she quickly buried any signs of a hangover and delivered a great talk on a subject we'd not explored before. Her friend and wildlife conservationist Emily Madsen, who was also featured in the film she showed from the Maasai Mara, had studied at Malvern College and returned to support Lucy.

The second talk 'Come to your senses!' was by Alina Ivan who explored live on stage the numerous senses we have and how our brain works to interpret the world around us. Alina was part of the Brainstastic! science communicator team led by

Ginny Smith. I'd actually been in touch with Ginny a couple of years previously to see if she might be available to give a talk about neuroscience, but like many potential speakers I contact, she was travelling at the proposed time. And on this occasion, she was now based in Singapore (with somewhat restricted travel because of the pandemic), but fortunately she'd built a team of capable presenters closer to home.

Clockwise from top left: Lucy Eckersley, the Punk Biologist, speaking about nature conversation (AB) and Alina Ivan talking about human senses. A member of the audience wears some confusing earphones as Alina demonstrates how the brain works out where sounds originate from (Bc)

This year's attendance had been a bit disappointing; once again the local schools and families had failed to capitalise on a first-rate pair of speakers (who also happened to be fantastic female role models for science) visiting their neighbourhood.

The exhibition was a little smaller this year, as a few regulars like Mazak and MRATHS were not able to attend this time round. Instead, we just occupied the main foyer and some of the long-term supporters like the IoP and IET filled their table tops with hands-on experiments and exhibits. Steve Dawes returned with an array of Raspberry Pi and Arduino devices, and GE Aviation came with a group of graduate engineers to enthuse kids with their flight simulator. Discover Materials also brought along a wide selection of materials and fluid-based exhibits to demonstrate surface properties and bulk structures. As IMechE had to pull out on the day, I set up my digital microscope once I had hosted the show, and we had a look at a few specimens at high magnification; always a crowd pleaser especially the insects! o

Using a digital microscope to investigate specimens. (AB)

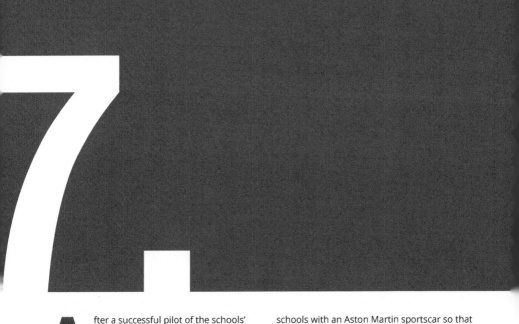

7.

After a successful pilot of the schools' day at Malvern College, you'll recall that we located the Next Generation Innovators event to the much larger venue at the Three Counties Showground. When I explained the move to Darren Stokes, the then Head of Design & Technology at Malvern College, I had a new plan up my sleeve.

I had made contact with Aston Martin at the suggestion of Steve Dowling, the regional chair of the IMechE, and their STEM Ambassador outreach lead Dr Bal Choda got in touch to offer support. They have this great scheme where they visit schools with an Aston Martin sportscar so that students can take a look at the vehicle and they give an hour audio-video presentation about what it is like to design, develop, build and test a high-performance motor vehicle. The talk, delivered by Bal and usually one of his apprentice or graduate colleagues, is a great introduction to a glamorous world of the E in STEM.

As you can imagine, an initiative like this is popular with schools and Bal basically volunteers one Friday afternoon every other week to visit a school (I think he enjoys driving the Aston Martin around the countryside!). So, securing a booking,

CREATIVE CAREERS

never mind one that coincides with the festival, is not easy, but we managed for 2014 on the Friday of festival week.

ASTON MARTIN COMES TO MALVERN, 2014

Rather than Aston Martin just visiting and presenting to one school, Malvern College were happy to host the session and have other schools invited along too. And so, we laid on an afternoon in which older school students from years 10, 11 (GCSEs) and 12–13 (sixth form / A-levels) were invited to attend.

The added complication was that I was tied up with the Business of Innovating themed symposium at the Malvern Theatres, so Darren had to welcome Bal and get him all set up, and then Emma went over to thank him afterwards. The IMechE also organised to bring along the University of Birmingham's student formula racing car to put on show alongside the Aston Martin. And the STEM Ambassadors network and WCC also had tables in the foyer to engage with students and teachers about their initiatives.

Later I saw the photos and heard reports that it had all gone well and that the attendees had enjoyed the experience and learnt a lot from it. Just over 200 students and their teachers had registered to attend, including the local schools of The Chase, Dyson Perrins, Hanley Castle, Malvern College and John Masefield.

ASTON MARTIN RETURNS TO MALVERN, 2015

Apparently, on arrival in 2014, there had been a problem with Bal's laptop presentation such that he had to get it urgently transferred over from HQ with the help of the college IT team. This minor hiccup had apparently embarrassed Bal, so he kindly offered to return again in 2015; an opportunity we gratefully snapped up.

The format was similar, we filled the Gryphon Room at Malvern College pretty much to capacity with another 200 or so registrations from eight schools. We heard that one school bus broke down on route, but otherwise the event went to plan with the UBRacing car once again on display courtesy of IMechE's assistance. Bal and

Above: The Aston Martin sportscar on show in the grounds of Malvern College and (left) the packed Gryphon Room of students who had come from ten schools around the region to listen to Dr Bal Choda. (SW)

RGSW Careers
@RGSWCareers

@RGSWorcester **pupils at careers STEM event with** @astonmartin **What an experience & so informative** @festivalofinnov

4:51 PM · Oct 9, 2015 · Twitter for iPad

From top left: A full seminar room of students at Malvern College ahead of the talk from Aston Martin's Bal Choda. Outside the UBRacing car with their student representatives alongside the Aston Martin. Below: Malcolm Salisbury 007 from MHDC. (ZS). Above: A tweet from the Royal Grammar School in Worcester summarises the afternoon nicely.

his colleague Tom arrived in a convertible Aston Martin this year and then delivered the usual high quality audio-visual feast about sports car design and engineering.

CREATIVE CAREERS AFTERNOON

Up until this point, the afternoon session at Malvern College was themed around Aston Martin's STEM

Dr Jamie Mackrill from Imperial College London starts his talk on linking design thinking and engineering. (AB)

outreach programme, but in 2016 Aston Martin were already booked to be elsewhere during our festival week so we adopted the Creative Careers

THEY WATCHED A NEATLY SPLICED TALK CONSISTING OF OFFICIAL JLR VIDEOS AND PERSONAL DESCRIPTIONS OF THE EXCITEMENT OF WORKING IN THE MODERN AUTOMOTIVE INDUSTRY.

title and mixed it up a little by inviting two different speakers to join us.

Darren from Malvern College invited Dr Jamie Mackrill a Lecturer and the Outreach Officer at the Dyson School of Design Engineering at Imperial College London to speak, and I invited Dionne Oliver a Principal Innovation Consultant from QinetiQ to speak about her career in electronic engineering and the defence industry.

MORE AUTOMOTIVE FEATURES

Bal returned again in 2017 with another Aston Martin and delivered his well-received presentation to about 100 students and their teachers.

In 2018, I was struggling to fill the Creative Careers slot as Bal had to pull out and so I called on David Bott for help. Through his work at WMG at the University of Warwick he was well-connected to Jaguar Land Rover and so asked if he might be able

to find a "relatively young and inspiring person at JLR who might be able to do something at short notice".

In the end, they pulled out all the stops and a team of them arrived in the new electric iPace. I could not have put it better than David in his thank you note to JLR: "A big thank you from me and Adrian (copied) for sending Azam, Matthew

Clockwise from top left: The full hall for the talks from entrepreneur Pete Hill and the JLR team (DB). Outside the static EV display attracted crowds of students (DB), with both David's Tesla Model S and JLR's iPace looking stunning (AB).

CREATIVE CAREERS

and Myles to Malvern today. They were awesome. There were 150 school kids from Malvern College and local schools. They watched a neatly spliced talk consisting of official JLR videos and personal descriptions of the excitement of working in the modern automotive industry. They then spent over an hour answering questions as most of the kids swarmed around the iPace."

Ahead of JLR's presentation, we had the charismatic serial inventor Pete Hill speak to the students about being motivated to succeed. He explained his invention Pedaldish to automatically feed pets and how he pitched it on BBC's *Dragons' Den* before securing investment from Deborah Meaden. He also talked about the product design process, being entrepreneurial, and taking measured risks to advance his career.

Outside, students could view the iPace electric car and David Bott's Model S Tesla that he kindly added to the static display (not so static as David also demonstrated the remote control of the Tesla from his iPhone app).

As an additional bonus this year, with a bit of coordination with Malvern Town Council, we managed to accommodate a group of students that happened to be visiting from Malvern's twin town Bagnères-de-Bigorre.

ASTON MARTIN RETURNS ONCE MORE

Bal returned again with an Aston Martin sportscar and associated audio-visual presentation in 2019. It has been great that he has found it worthwhile to return to the festival on several occasions, as his STEM outreach is often over-subscribed so he likes to maximise exposure to as many students as possible when he makes a visit.

Malvern College's enthusiasm to host the event for us has also helped, especially on this occasion when I was still tied up with the tail end of the Environment and Sustainability symposium in a different venue across town, and so couldn't get

down to the event to see it in action. But, we had over 170 attendees in the end which was slightly more than I expected as Malvern College managed to get another couple of classes to go along and fill the hall.

We didn't hold a Creative Careers event in 2020 because of the pandemic, and with schools still recovering and trying to cope in 2021, we missed repeating it then too. Interestingly electric vehicles (EVs) are now becoming more sought after and I suspect any future creative careers event that showcases the automotive industry will only feature EVs and highlight their design process. Not surprisingly, Aston Martin are busy on their new all electric EVs too, so hopefully Bal will return to Malvern one day in the future to talk all about how this went from drawing board to racetrack. O

Another full house inside as Bal talks about engineering at Aston Martin. Outside, Bal is pictured alongside the Birmingham Student Formula Racing team and their project car. (DS)

8.

After a few years, I felt it would be good to have a subevent that marked the beginning of the festival, especially as it was now beginning to fill a week with various activities.

PRELUDES 2016–2017

During 2016, MHDC started a series of outdoor cinema nights in Priory Park in collaboration with the Malvern Town Council and the Malvern Theatres. They suggested to me that they could schedule the last one of the season on the Sunday 2nd October just before the festival to round off the summer series and to help market the festival. It would be a bit chilly in the park by then, but just about feasible weatherwise.

They also thought it would be an opportunity to screen a science fiction / innovation-related movie. We had originally considered showing *Blade Runner*, but there was a licensing issue because the new *Blade Runner 2049* was due out the following year making it problematic to screen the original film. In the end, we went with the 1999 film *The Matrix*, which is still an innovative thought-provoking movie to this day, particularly as it may well turn out we are actually living in a simulation! But there was

PRELUDE & EMBARKATION

also a local connection, as the soundtrack features a sample of Elgar's *Enigma Variations*. And, later that week, our principal business symposium was cyber security and artificial intelligence.

In 2017, the open-air film nights were held again, and this time just before the festival, MHDC screened the 1977 original and ground breaking *Star Wars Episode IV, A New Hope* which also coincided with the start of that year's World Space Week. The film nights were well attended and provided an opportunity for the opening video sequence to be shown at the start to advertise the week of innovation ahead.

EMBARKATION WITH MARCUS DU SAUTOY

Since 2013 I had been in contact with Professor Marcus du Sautoy OBE, the Charles Simonyi Professor for the Public Understanding of Science at the University of Oxford. He had written an interesting piece in the alumni magazine *Oxford Today* about one of this era's greatest challenges being the multi-disciplinary nature of research and discovery. But, as you might imagine, he was a busy man and he was trying to write a new book, so had been unable to appear at the festival.

However, in 2016, his book *What we Cannot Know* was published, and he kindly agreed to speak about it at what was to be the fifth festival in a new special opening evening slot that I called Embarkation. As I suspected, he was a popular choice and we filled St Edmund's Hall on the edge of Malvern College with an attentive audience. Marcus delivered a fascinating talk about things we can determine and those that we cannot, introducing chaos theory, fractals and more. He then signed copies of his new book over networking and refreshments, and as you'll have read earlier, he stayed the night in Great Malvern so that he could talk further to students at the Next Generation Innovators schools' day.

Marcus du Sautoy speaking about the subject of his new book What We Cannot Know. *(AB)*

Left: Brian Clegg speaking about 'Science and technology – the goal-driven golem'. (AB)
Right: Dr Edmund Hunt beginning his talk in the Lewis Lecture Theatre in Malvern College. (AB)

University of Bristol to see if she would be able to speak at the festival. Sabine was unable to come along, but suggested that her post-doctoral researcher Dr Edmund Hunt present instead. He gave a great opening talk about swarm robotics and how a variety of automated devices like drones could operate in unison drawing on inspiration from nature around us, like for example in the world of insects and sea life.

INNOVATION SHORTS

In 2019, I decided to revisit the Prelude concept to encapsulate a series of short presentations ahead of the main evening launch event. For a while I had wanted to use the tiny Theatre of Small Convenience, a converted Victorian gentleman's toilet near the centre of Great Malvern that had been acknowledged in the *Guinness Book of World Records* as the world's smallest commercial theatre. Equipped with a very tiny stage and about a dozen seats, it was a quirky venue with people walking past to visit the shops and poking their head in to see what was going on.

I also joked that this could be the venue of choice for the future, as you could pretty much guarantee a full house and not have to worry about on-going marketing and selling enough tickets.

For the line up, I approached Worcestershire's technology accelerator BetaDen located on MHSP to see if they would encourage their start-ups to make some short presentations. Jack Wratten from Bloom.Space was advising the BetaDen cohort at the time, and he enthusiastically generated

BRIAN CLEGG

Sticking with the theme of kicking off the festival with the thoughts of a science writer, in 2017 we welcomed Brian Clegg. He is a prolific author focusing mainly on the subject of physics, cosmology and the history of science, making complex ideas like relativity, quantum physics, and infinity accessible to the layman. He opened the festival with a fascinating talk about the real danger of trying to direct scientific study purely with practical applications in mind as all the evidence was that the best breakthroughs come when scientists are allowed to explore freely.

This time we had a good turnout in Malvern College's modern Lewis Lecture Theatre and Brian signed and sold a range of his books in the foyer afterwards.

EDMUND HUNT

During 2018 I had been in contact with Dr Sabine Hauert, a lecturer in robotics research at the interest. I then cast my net amongst a few other entrepreneurs to complete the line-up, stepping in myself to fill the last slot for good measure.

I also asked Dan Barker who had not long set up his photography business to film the talks, meaning that we have the presentations available on YouTube for you to peruse at your leisure.

To kick off the morning, Nick Tudor opened with his talk about making sure software does what it is supposed to: youtu. be/40JivYYnufc. Nick has been mentioned on numerous occasions in the book, not least as one of the early protagonists, so now you can watch to find out what he has been doing in his day job over the course of the decade.

> I ALSO JOKED THAT THIS COULD BE THE VENUE OF CHOICE FOR THE FUTURE, AS YOU COULD PRETTY MUCH GUARANTEE A FULL HOUSE AND NOT HAVE TO WORRY ABOUT ON-GOING MARKETING AND SELLING ENOUGH TICKETS.

Then another good friend and entrepreneur Paddy Fawcett talked about design. You'll remember reading that he had helped with the Raspberry Pi activity at the schools' day pilot. After hot desking at the Wyche Innovation Centre he moved to larger premises at MHSP, and since his talk he has been in cohort four of BetaDen: youtu.be/6zxKelVXw4k.

The next speaker was Dr David Lowe from a company called Syndial, also a participant of the BetaDen programme. He is an expert on data analysis and machine learning in de-centralised systems, but he maintains a very light digital footprint. So, at his request, we removed his presentation from our channel after a few months.

Imogen Mornement, who started Penny and a Pearl and had recently won the WINN Make it Happen challenge gave the next talk about her business to bring sewing and craft creativity in to the home: youtu.be/SiOUfG0bdBc.

Then my BlockMark Technologies co-founder Tom Alcott gave a presentation about blockchain and certificate management: youtu.be/aVhng8SrwCU. Jon Wills from Worcester Scientific followed, the second BetaDen alum to be featured, talking about novel nanotechnology-based sensors: youtu.be/drWMyE8xyN4.

Nikki Hollier, who had also won a WINN award for innovation, explained how she conceived, marketed and improved her horticultural 'border in a box' product, including how celebrity gardener Alan Titchmarsh helped in the journey to her success: youtu.be/85V4mdoFEFo.

Dr Clive Summerfield, another entrepreneur who had benefited from the BetaDen programme, gave the penultimate talk about voice-based security. He is an eloquent speaker, and on this occasion won the prize for the most flamboyant shirt as well: youtu.be/uMmE5w5iNBw.

And as mentioned, I then brought up the rear with my talk about LiveWorkGo, an event aggregation platform I had conceived a couple of years earlier and had some coders working on behind the scenes. As I write, the web application is still not quite ready as there were no events during the pandemic which meant we focused on other projects, and now it has been revisited, the software platform it was built on needs a major update. So,

Clive Horrobin in *The Archers*) led to the discovery that he knew Marcus Chown, a well-known science writer, journalist and broadcaster. Al was sure that Marcus would be keen to speak at the festival and he thought he would give a great talk on something physics-related based on one of his past books.

So, I contacted Marcus and he was available to speak. His latest talk was titled 'Bonkers Things About the Universe', in which he explored thought-provoking and profound science, providing a new perspective on life and the Universe in which we live. This was just the thing to kickstart the week's proceedings[42], and Al was in the audience to see first-hand that his recommendation came to fruition.

Dennis Neale, retired puppeteer who created the Theatre of Small Convenience back in 1997 and performed regularly in the venue, came by to see our show. (SS)

Marcus Chown presenting in the science lecture theatre in Malvern College at the opening evening in 2019. (AB)

The speakers who can all claim to have performed in the world's smallest commercial theatre; top row, L–R: Nick Tudor and Paddy Fawcett; second row, L–R: David Lowe and Imogen Mornement; third row, L–R: Tom Alcott and Jon Wills; and fourth row, L–R: Nikki Hollier (all AB) Clive Summerfield (NH), and, bottom, me! (NH)

A VIRTUAL LAUNCH

In 2020, we launched the virtual Malvern Festival of Innovation with an opening talk from Andy Stanford-Clark, the CTO of IBM UK and Ireland[43]. I'd tried to get Andy over to give a talk during an earlier edition of the festival, but his schedule was too busy

it remains to be seen if it will ever go mainstream! youtu.be/-HEJTrFboKM

MARCUS CHOWN

A chat down the local pub with friend Alex Jones (a celebrated playwright who also plays the villain

42 'Scientist and writer Marcus Chown headlines Malvern Festival of Innovation', *Malvern Gazette*, 3rd September 2019. www.malverngazette.co.uk/news/17877699.scientist-writer-marcus-chown-headlines-malvern-festival-innovation/

43 'Popular Malvern science event returns (with a difference)', *Worcester News*, 3rd October 2020. www.worcesternews.co.uk/news/18767639.popular-malvern-science-event-returns-difference/

at the time. However, on this occasion it worked out as he could join us over Zoom from his home without the need to travel.

His talk was about the *Mayflower Autonomous Ship*, and how artificial intelligence would hopefully navigate it across the Atlantic. At the time, it had just been successfully launched and was undergoing sea trials ahead of its challenging journey. The talk is still available to watch here: youtu.be/Xid6JEVcxvs and as I write the last few bits of this book in late May 2022, the ship is actually mid-Atlantic on its voyage!

On stage with Rory Cellan-Jones at the Coach House Theatre. (PF)

Left: In the Wyche Innovation Centre studio ahead of the virtual festival in 2019 (EP). Above: Andy Stanford-Clark speaking over Zoom and broadcast on Facebook Live. (AB)

IN-CONVERSATION WITH RORY CELLAN-JONES

In February 2020, just ahead of the pandemic, I sat and watched the BBC's Technology Correspondent Rory Cellan-Jones interview Thuan Pham the CTO of Uber live in the Fox Theatre in the heart of Silicon Valley at the Startup Grind conference. It occurred to me that Rory had interviewed many fascinating technologists and founders over the years and that it would be fantastic if I could somehow persuade him to come to Malvern.

Well, as luck would have it, Rory had his new book *Always On, Hope and Fear in the Social Smartphone Era* published in 2021, and this gave me the opportunity to make contact and suggest he come to talk about it and sign some books. He

kindly agreed, and we opted for a fireside chat format which Rory said he much preferred[44].

Mindful that Rory would have participated in numerous interviews and chats about his book by the time he reached us, I watched a few on line and thought it would be refreshing for Rory, and a bit different for us, if I created a slide show of video and photo excerpts from Rory's career of reporting technology over the years to refer to and steer the conversation. The format worked; Rory later tweeting "Great audience at @festivalofinnov in Malvern and @apburden had assembled an amazing "This Is Your Life" collection of video clips".

We all retired next door to Bloom.Space for light refreshments and an opportunity for people to buy a signed copy of Rory's book. We collaborated with the Malvern Book Cooperative again who had organised a bulk order of books and managed to estimate demand to perfection as the last one sold to the final person in the queue! ○

---

44 'Rory Cellan-Jones to open 10th Malvern Festival of Innovation next month', *Malvern Gazette*, 17th September 2021. www.malverngazette.co.uk/news/19584970. rory-cellan-jones-open-10th-malvern-festival-innovation-next-month/

'BBC's Tech Correspondent Rory Cellan-Jones to open tenth Malvern Festival of Innovation', *Business & Innovation Magazine*, 30th September 2021. www.businessinnovationmag.co.uk/bbcs-tech-correspondent-rory-cellan-jones-to-open-the-tenth-malvern-festival-of-innovation/

9.

Sometimes, ideas just come together with very little effort or angst. I'd become aware of a genre of comedy featuring scientists on the stand-up stage, and as luck would have it, the Public Engagement and Research (PER) team at the University of Birmingham included something on this topic at their annual meeting in April 2019. I attended the day and ended up in a workshop about using comedy for engagement hosted by Jon Wood and Dr Martin Khechara (from the University of Wolverhampton).

By the end of it, I had decided the festival could usefully have a Science and Technology Comedy night. A few months later, having watched James Veitch deliver his somewhat nerdy TED talk on replying to spam, and having seen a selection YouTube videos of engineer-turned-stand-up comedian Don McMillan wax lyrical about Venn diagrams and PowerPoint slides, I was ready to curate our new evening of entertainment.

THE 2019 EXPERIMENT

Fortunately, a new venue was about to open in Great Malvern. The original Malvern Hills Conservative Club located below the Post Office Sorting Office, that for some time had been

LAUGH OUT LOUD

referred to as the Re-Con, was being painstakingly refurbished by Chris Winstanley. It was to have a fresh coat of paint, a stage, sound and lighting, a licensed bar and lounge area. In short, perfect for a comedy club, even though the new venue's initial name Malvern Radio might have confused some.

And so, I penned an introduction to a new event page on the festival's website:

"Abstract: We outline an innovative experiment to lighten the mood. Apparatus: Some science eggheads, computer nerds and engineering geeks (together referred to as boffins [1]), a stage, a microphone, some props, a digital projector, some drink and an adult audience. Method: Allow the boffins to speak consecutively into the microphone from the stage using the digital projector and their props to amuse the audience. Results: Laughter out loud and consumption of drink. Conclusion: Science and technology comedy is not an oxymoron. References: [1] *The Times*, 15 Sept. 1945 referring to a band of scientific men who performed their wartime wonders at Malvern. Tickets £10.00 per person. Strictly 18+ because of the licensing rules, ID may be requested. Bring your lab book and safety goggles."

Already I felt it was taking shape, despite not having a line-up.

But that came together remarkably quickly, and the capacity of one hundred seats sold out through Eventbrite and Facebook marketing before the evening began. Chris had kept true to his word and finished the decorating, and we ended up having a fun, very different evening of high-brow science and technology amusement[45].

Dr Ria Lina was our over-qualified host; having obtained a BSc in Experimental Pathology, an MSc in Forensic Science, and a PhD in viral bioinformatics, and then she worked as an IT Forensic Investigator for the Serious Fraud Office. All before becoming a comic. And she was a true professional taking it upon herself to find out from me how the evening should run and then chatting with the acts in the green room to understand their background and their routine.

Ria Lina introduces Sam Gregson on the stage of the Science and Technology Comedy Night. (AB)

Dr Sam Gregson, whom you'll remember had joined us as a family show presenter back in 2015, returned to Malvern as The Bad Boy of Science. He was the founder and project manager of LHComedy, CERN's first comedy show, so well suited to the requirements of the evening. He had

people up and out of their seats as he explored bias in how humans think.

After the toilet break began the toilet humour. Dr Martin Khechara whom I'd met at that aforementioned PER workshop, brought along that also aforementioned Shamus the Anus and soon

Martin Khechara and his model posterior. (AB)

the audience was subjected to fake faeces and a graphic discussion of bacteria and viruses.

We finished the evening off with a fantastic nerdy double-act from Foxdog Studios, featuring computer programmers Lloyd Henning and Peter Sutton. True to form, they had been doing last minute repairs, testing and soldering in the green room, trying to get their spaghetti wired tech to work after transportation. And then they captivated us with their interactive games and DIY gadgets, by which time my phone battery was flat and I was exhausted with just the Family Day to go next morning.

LOL:-) 2021

During the pandemic, we didn't attempt a virtual comedy night, as although this might have worked surprisingly well, it was not something we thought worth testing. Instead, we waited until 2021 and planned another evening in what was now rebranded The Old Con Club. This also coincided

45 'Why science is a laughing matter', *Malvern Gazette*, 28th September 2019. www.worcesternews.co.uk/news/17934070.science-laughing-matter/

Above: *Lloyd Henning and Peter Sutton from Foxdog Studios connecting us all to Wi-Fi. (AB)* *Left:* *Full house in the then Malvern Radio venue. (CW)*

Malvern Hills Comedy Festival poster.

which was set to run for about a month, and our evening was the first event in the programme.

My main concern was that one or more of the line-up would succumb to Covid ahead of the event and need to cancel so as to self-isolate, especially as they were likely to be starting back out performing in the clubs and pubs where the virus seemed to readily transmit.

In the end, however, it was the trains that let us down, not the virus. The last train back to London was cancelled forcing our compere Dr Steve Cross to dash off before the final act because he had to be back home very early Saturday morning at the latest for family reasons. Fortunately, he'd been keeping an eye on the situation, as I'd been warning him back stage before the event that there was a high chance the late-night train service would be disrupted.

But Steve had done a good job up until then kicking off the evening with his own segment and then introducing the acts that followed. Steve had actually worked with a couple of the performers

Dr Steve Cross compering the Science & Technology Comedy Night. (AB)

already through his Science Showoff business, so the chemistry at this science comedy night (did you see what I did there?) was great.

This year's line-up worked out well. Dr Hannah Little, a senior lecturer in science communication at

with the new Malvern Hills Comedy Festival convened by the Malvern Hills District Council,

UWE Bristol, performed a quintessential stand-up routine mixing science with observational comedy. This was followed by Jon Matthews who brought Venn diagrams and politics together in a hilarious segment. Jon had managed to play a few gigs over the summer, but for many this was the first time back out on the road with a live audience because of the Covid restrictions.

Lucy Eckersley, the punk biologist, performed after the break with her amusingly risqué piece bringing together amongst other things personal relationships and biology. Hannah then had to step back on stage as the impromptu compere to introduce the final act whilst Steve raced to catch the last train home.

This year's finale was fantastic, with John Hinton performing his science-based songs with gusto. Clearly a trained actor and musician, he rattled through his complex raps and modified covers (like Suzanne Vega's tweaked *Luka* to feature LUCA, the last universal common ancestor) without missing a beat.

Unfortunately, I was too exhausted to join them all afterwards for what turned out to be, from the reports I heard next day, a long night of drinking and camaraderie. I had a family event to set up

Dr Hannah Little (above left) and Jon Matthews on stage. (SC)

Top: Lucy Eckersley performing (SC) and, left, alongside her stunt double (AB).
Above: John Hinton and his musical segment. (AB)

STEVE HAD ACTUALLY WORKED WITH A COUPLE OF THE PERFORMERS ALREADY THROUGH HIS SCIENCE SHOWOFF BUSINESS, SO THE CHEMISTRY AT THIS SCIENCE COMEDY NIGHT (DID YOU SEE WHAT I DID THERE?) WAS GREAT.

the next day remember. But pulling together and meeting a series of acts for a comedy night is really great fun and rewarding. By their very nature the performers exude positivity, and given they are normally on the road before and after late night shows with very little compensation, they are pretty easy to please by organising and covering the cost of a decent hotel room so that they can enjoy the rest of the evening too.

This year, it was the first time any of the five had visited Malvern, and so suddenly the town with its stunning hills and quirky population of artists and scientists that made up the audience was on their map. They'd add their visit to their websites as examples of past engagements, and word would continue to spread about the festival and its events as they travelled to other gigs and met other fellow performers. The science communicator / science comedy world is actually quite small and well connected, and when people are well looked after and enjoy their visit, they are much more likely to remember the trip and to speak positively about it to others. ○

10.

As the family day was drawing to a close in 2016, Dr Alan Smith from the IoP sidled up to me and suggested it would be good to do an outside version of the day's event.

He mooted a 'science in the park' in which exhibitors could capitalise on open space to demonstrate scientific principles. We both thought Priory Park, just outside the Malvern Theatres in which we were then standing, might be the ideal setting earlier in the summer when there was a chance for fine weather.

And so, the idea of a smaller sister event to the festival was born; a kind of warm-up for the main event. It turned out there wasn't much already out there that was similar either; Nottingham claimed

Malvern Science in the Park

First-cut logo derived from the Malvern Festival of Innovation's branding, appeared on some of our early promotional material until Zoe Smith came up with something much better.

MALVERN SCIENCE IN THE PARK

an indoor "Science in the Park" in late winter which from what I could gather was more like our indoor family day at the festival.

As the idea developed, it became clear that organisations could 'exhibit' with hands-on demonstrations and interactive activities at stalls dispersed around the park, giving it a summer fete vibe.

The Priory Park venue in the centre of Great Malvern is an ideal location, with vehicular access for setting up, a café in the Malvern Theatres for those wanting refreshments, and a short walk to carparks and the railway station. There's also a public toilet nearby which meant we didn't have to worry about porta-loos either.

The park, originally known as the Winter Gardens, also has plenty of shade, plenty of grass on which to set up the stands, and best of all, a bandstand which provides a focal point and seemed to be ideal for some scheduled short-talks.

And that led to the idea of a concurrent programme of science busking. Scientists would speak for about ten minutes in quarter-of-an-hour slots on a science subject of their choosing, using props not PowerPoint. This was borne out of necessity as there wasn't sufficient power to have computers and digital projectors, and no one wants to sit and listen to slideshow when all around are other hands-on experiments and activities.

The final element (no pun intended) was to introduce some science-themed trails in which people could walk around the park and find out more about a scientific subject. Once again, the environment lent itself perfectly to this activity, as trail artefacts and information boards could be set-out in different areas to encourage people to spread out around the venue and make the most of the space.

MHDC were as supportive as ever, with their graphic designer Zoe Smith coming up with the logo, flyer and a great photograph of her daughter in the park that we used in the marketing material. The council were also invaluable in facilitating the use of the park and helping us to review the risk assessments and fine tune the event logistics.

Amy Smith kindly humoured her mother and agreed to be part of the marketing collateral. This photograph appeared in the Worcester News *article ahead of the event on 22nd June 2017[46]. (ZS)*

The logo we adopted after Zoe Smith's marketing flyer incorporated this design element.

ALFRESCO 2017

And so, on 1st July 2017 we staged our first Malvern Science in the Park event, opened by Councillor Jeremy Thomas from the Malvern Town Council who were also supporting the event with a special grant.

We had fifteen exhibitors, five science buskers and four trails along with fine sunny weather and what we estimated to be about nine hundred visitors during the day.

As with the festival, we had the mainstay learned societies who provided both financial backing and enthusiastic support. The IoP stepped up to lead from the front, largely because Alan was the main protagonist for the event, and they hosted a vibrant corner of the park with gigantic bubble blowing to demonstrate surface tension and optical refraction, ropes slung between trees to illustrate waves, and balloon helicopters to explain thrust

The Malvern Theatres were also a great help, as backing on to the venue, they allowed us to use their outside water tap for some of the activities and of course benefited from footfall in their foyer and café.

46 'Hunting dinosaurs and sunspots in Malvern's Priory Park', *Worcester News*, 22nd June 2017. www.worcesternews.co.uk/news/15363858.hunting-dinosaurs-and-sunspots-in-malverns-priory-park/

'Experiment with Malvern Science in the Park this weekend', *Malvern Observer*, 26th June 2017. https://malvernobserver.co.uk/news/experiment-with-malvern-science-in-the-park-this-weekend/

and lift. They also had slinkies travelling down the Theatres' steps and bouncing balls to illustrate Newton's Laws of physics.

The IMechE had bridge building and an activity to control a hydraulic robotic arm. The IET had visitors assembling a Mediaeval siege engine before trying it out to see how well the finished design worked. The Chartered Institute for IT (what was once called the British Computing Society or BCS) also supported the event.

The challenge of putting on an engaging exhibit without the luxury of power at the stand was ably met by Gordon Coppock who brought along two pedal power bike generators that gave people a feet-on activity to illustrate how power stations provide electricity to the National Grid and then power household items like light bulbs and kettles. Gordon had been involved in the BBC programme *Bang Goes the Theory* which had a barn full of cyclists trying to generate enough power for a family of four as they got up one morning and went about their daily routine.

Another science that was well represented at our inaugural event was geology. The Earth Heritage Trust and local amateur palaeontologist Dr Mark O'Dell had a fine display or rocks, minerals and fossils, as well as a large wooden model dinosaur called Vernon. Mark also slotted into our science busking programme with a talk about fossil hunting before cracking open some nodules live on-stage to reveal ammonites that hadn't seen the light of day for millions of years.

Applying science and engineering in the commercial world is also an important activity to highlight, and gives the opportunity for local industry to get involved. QinetiQ, a long-standing employer of scientists and technologists in the town, came with their branded gazebo and a very popular activity to mix liquids of different colours and densities.

Komatsu, a mining equipment engineering company from nearby Worcester, also attended.

They brought along some table-top trebuchets so that participants could have a go at understanding the science of projectiles.

Another organisation that made full use of the open air was the Worcester Astronomical Society. They set up some telescopes and capitalised on the sunny weather of the daytime event not to look for stars and planets, but to image sunspots. They needed an unobstructed view of the sky and we had to site them away from the IoP's bubbles so that the soap solution didn't land on their lenses!

One of the key challenges with an event like this is securing enough funding, and putting it to good use whilst remaining within budget. There are a number of science communicators and science workshop organisers that make a living from their participation, and so charge a fee. But they also bring along experience and enthusiasm. In our first year, still unsure how things would work out, it was reassuring to have some professionals booked as well! FizzPop Science were one such organisation that were used to coping with young children at birthday parties, and so came along with a range of exciting chemical solutions and laboratory experiments.

Another interesting activity was that provided by Flux Dance, a fusion of physics-inspired dance and exercise, making use of large colourful parachutes and other props. This enabled groups to

Flux Dance also provided some much sort after shade as part of their physics-inspired dance and motion activities. (AB)

work off excess energy, think about motion physics, and certainly appealed to the less technically-minded visitors.

Another potentially rich seam to tap for engaging outreach are the armed forces, as they have a remit to keep the public posted about their work and to encourage the younger generation to think about a career in defence. Moreover, much of their activity is underpinned by STEM subjects, so very relevant to an event of this nature. Over

> ## DON SOUTHEY CAME AS SIR ISAAC NEWTON AND DROPPED APPLES FROM THE BANDSTAND TO ILLUSTRATE HIS EUREKA MOMENT!

the years we've often clashed with Armed Forces Day, ironically making it more difficult to get these organisations along, as they are usually involved in their affiliated events. However, back in 2017, we had the Royal Air Force join us with a Meccano challenge and technical assault course.

The science busking also worked surprisingly well, and credit has to go to Ian Dunne "The Professor", and experienced science communicator, who took it upon himself to rally the crowds and pull in the audience whilst people were still acquainting themselves to the workings of the whole event!

Dr Rowena Fletcher-Wood was another able science communicator who joined us, dividing her time at both the bandstand and under a gazebo with mini workshops using jigsaws and storytelling to explore pollination, crystallography, and a short history of natural medicines.

I too decided I'd better show willing and busk at the bandstand, using the audience to build a human microscope with large lenses and coloured string to create a ray diagram that in turn showed why objects were magnified. It kind of worked!

We also had our first scientist dressed in costume; the then Chair of the local IET Don Southey came as Sir Isaac Newton and dropped apples from the bandstand to illustrate his Eureka moment!

Looking back, it was the gazebos and feather flags that gelled the event. They provided a splash of colour in the sun and gave coherence to the eclectic mix of activities spread out across the park.

Another inspired feature, though I say so myself, was the inclusion of a few trails. They provided an excuse for some independent exploration and helped to disperse the attendees around the park.

We started out with four trails that have proved popular in ensuing years. Our first, and most ambitious, was the Planetary Trail in which we had inflated beachball-like celestial bodies; the sun, eight planets, moon and the dwarf planet Pluto. These were attached to poles and spaced out in a long line to scale with their relative distances if they were indeed all in such a conjunction! This meant that one metre in the park was equivalent to some forty million km in space.

I included the relative positions of the Asteroid belt, a few man-made probes (the Rosetta probe / Philae lander that had explored comet 67P/ Churyumov–Gerasimenko and the New Horizons probe that had not long previously flown past Pluto), and Halley's Comet that at the time was also in the outer reaches of the Solar System. We asked the question of where in the town the Voyager probes would be at this scale; it turned out to be nearly half a mile away at the Malvern library!

Another trail that captured the imagination of the younger participants featured inflatable dinosaurs that accompanied a 'prehistoric' quiz. We quipped that it was no longer Priory Park but rather Jurassic Park!

As a Fellow of the Institute of Materials, Minerals and Mining (IoM3), I felt it was important to include some materials science content. The materials trail was adapted from an IoM3 "Can you make it?" activity pack in which we located different examples of household materials around the park with information panels; metal drinks can, plastic bottle, ceramic mug, glass lightbulb, composite crisp packet, wood-based cardboard, and a ball of wool to illustrate yarns and fibres.

And, as a Fellow of the Royal Microscopical Society (RMS), I complemented my bandstand talk on microscopy with a microscopy trail. The RMS kindly sent through a pack of give-away Fresnel magnifying hand lenses and I created a worksheet encouraging people to find and draw specimens from around the park. Equipped with clipboard and coloured pencils, we had plenty of takers who came back with micrographs of insects, worms, concrete surfaces, and park fauna.

REPRISE, 2018

After the successful first year, which Alan had also written up in an IoP blog, it was felt the event merited a repeat the following year[47]. All the previous sponsors and supporters chipped in again, along with Worcester City Council who were keen to encourage people from their community to visit and learn something about science[48]. This time the

Two young, intrepid explorers braving the triceratops. (AB)

event was opened by our local MP, Harriet Baldwin; a regular supporter of our events and giving her an opportunity to meet some of the participating organisations and hear about their work. We also provided branded sun caps for all the exhibitors to wear, protecting them from another hot day of glorious sunshine.

Harriet Baldwin MP visits the Cancer Research UK stand. (RM)

A few new organisations joined the party this year, including Cancer Research UK from the University of Birmingham who did a great nerf gun activity to simulate targeted cancer tumour treatments. On a similar subject, the Department of Oncology from the University of Oxford also came along, with one challenge being identifying various fruit from their Magnetic Resonance Imaging (MRI) scans. They wrote about their attendance in a blog[49], saying "At the end of a long and tiring day I

---

47 'Malvern's Science in the Park set to become annual event after huge turnout', *Malvern Observer*, 20th July 2017. malvernobserver.co.uk/news/malverns-science-in-the-park-set-to-become-annual-event-after-huge-turnout/

'Science event set to return to Malvern after this year's success', *Worcester News*, 21st July 2017. www.worcesternews.co.uk/news/15423954.science-event-set-to-return-to-malvern-after-this-years-success/

48 'Budding scientists can enjoy fun-filled day of alfresco experiments', *Malvern Gazette*, 11th June 2018. www.malverngazette.co.uk/news/16282637.budding-scientists-can-enjoy-fun-filled-day-of-alfresco-experiments/

'Final line-up is revealed for Malvern's Science in the Park', *Worcester News*, 25th June 2018. www.worcesternews.co.uk/news/16311969.final-line-up-revealed-malverns-science-park/

---

49 'Science in the park – a day out at Malvern Park', Department of Oncology blog, University of Oxford, 6th July, 2018. www.oncology.ox.ac.uk/blog/science-in-the-park-2013-a-day-out-at-malvern-park

felt very grateful, especially when children told us they wanted to become scientists and adults expressed their thanks for our work (I think it is not a personal gratitude, but a general acknowledgement to all researchers). It is these people who tend to encourage you to continue with your work. Participating in these events is rewarding as they are full of positive energy and inspiration, which helps to face better your hardest moments in this profession."

We also boosted our prehistoric science content with Aimee-Jane Hacker's Schoolasaurus activities, and added meteorology to the sciences covered with the presence of the Met Office and a Raspberry Pi solar powered weather station exhibit from Steve Dawes, one of the active members of the Raspberry Pi Computer Jams we held regularly in Malvern.

The alfresco stands below the coloured gazebos, including Vernon the Velociraptor at the Earth Heritage Trust. (RM)

Hands-on experiments around the park, including, top left, acoustics at the IoP, top right, slime at Fizz Pop Science, and bottom, rocket launching with John Bibby. (RM)

Another good outcome was to have some of the organisations that had taken part in the festival come along this year to be in the park. MRATHS, the Malvern Radar and Technology History Society, attended with a Doppler radar ('speed camera') to measure how fast children could run, and the ever-enthusiastic Dave Watson from the Cheltenham Science Group came along with some hands-on exhibits from their headquarters.

The Transition Worcester group erected a demonstration wind turbine to illustrate the promise of wind energy, and Dr Chris Hamlett travelled down from Nottingham Trent University to represent the RSC with a hands-on series of experiments to explore wetting of materials and surface tension of liquids.

Finally, where as last year STEM Ambassadors had helped out at various organisations' stands, this year the regional STEM Learning Hub came with their own set of activities.

The busking programme was also busier this year. We did have astronomer and television celebrity Dr Chris Lintott booked, but as he had warned us might happen, he was called away at the last minute to be on duty at the BBC's *The Sky at Night* programme.

However, we had a fantastic line up never-the-less. Dr Mark O'Dell returned with more fresh nodules to crack open, Dr Chris Hamlett somehow managed to get away from his busy stand to show the surface wetting properties of a giant lotus leaf, and Sarah Cosgriff was new to the event with both a hands-on workshop on making balloon rockets, and a talk about rockets from the bandstand. Dr Sean Elvidge and Matt Ward both joined us from the University of Birmingham to talk respectively about space weather and radiotherapy. Nicky Thomas

provided a spectacle with dry ice and Richard Henson put on a costume and stepped out from a cardboard Tardis as George Boole. I dug up some facts about carbon from my scientific research days and showed off a few molecular models of diamond, graphite, C60-fullerene, and carbon nanotubes.

Having seen some cuddly soft-toy microbes at a recent microscopy conference, I added to the trails this year by suspending about ten furry but generally nasty microbes around an area of the park for children to find and draw. Each toy came with a description of the virus or bacteria, so it made for fascinating reading. And all before the pandemic too!

I also decided it would be fun to have the *Big Bang Theory* cast of scientists available for a photo call. Of course, getting Jim Parsons et al over to Malvern was a big ask, but luckily life-sized cardboard cut-outs were available. I only wanted the scientists (sorry Penny), but that turned out to be harder than I imagined; Sheldon, Leonard, Raj and Howard could all be sourced easily in the UK, but I actually had to get Amy and Bernadette shipped over from Canada! What does that say about STEM-equality in the UK I wonder?

We also had a "MadLab" zone as another photo opportunity; an Einstein wig, safety goggles, lab coat and a selection of laboratory bench equipment so that people could dress up, stand in front of a periodic table shower curtain, and post to Instagram or Twitter. I don't think we had many takers!

We estimated about 1,500 visitors came during the day this year, and we were up on last year with over twenty exhibitors and eight science buskers[50].

Clockwise from top left: At the bandstand. The sublimation of dry ice with Nicky Thomas, George Boole courtesy of Richard Henson, science communicator Sarah Cosgriff, chemist-extraordinaire Chris Hamlett, and me demonstrating the allotropes of carbon. (RM)

50 'Experiments enthral youngsters at Science in the Park', *Malvern Gazette*, 3rd July 2018. www.malverngazette.co.uk/news/16330655.experiments-enthral-youngsters-science-park/

'Malvern's brilliant brains gather at Science in the Park to inspire next generation', *Malvern Observer*, 12th July 2018. malvernobserver.co.uk/news/malverns-brilliant-brains-gather-at-science-in-the-park-to-inspire-next-generation/

THIRD TIME STILL LUCKY, 2019

This was coincidently the UNESCO International Year of the Periodic Table (#IYPT), marking the 150th anniversary of the Mendeleev periodic table, so we couldn't avoid staging another Malvern Science in the Park[51]. By now, the event was easier to organise as we had a couple of years of experience to systemise the processes and a growing list of contacts to encourage back.

And so, on 29th June 2019 Paul Walker MBE, the recently retired Managing Director of Malvern Panalytical, kindly opened the event as our guest VIP from the bandstand and took a tour with me of the park.

Clockwise from top left: Hands-on in the park again with IoP's bubbles, IMechE's robots, particle size analysis with Malvern Panalytical, and digging for fossils with the Earth Heritage Trust. (CM)

Paul Walker MBE offers some opening remarks from the bandstand. (CM)

We had the usual suspects throw themselves back in and a solid line-up of exhibitors. In addition, Girl Guiding joined us to encourage their members to complete their science badges, and Worcestershire County Council's Libraries and Learning Services promoted their summer reading challenge that had a science theme called Space Chase. We also had one of the Usborne franchisees join us with both science books to sell and a paper aeroplane challenge to engage the visitors.

These additions to the programme provided more educational content and created a link with the visitors that could extend beyond the day itself.

Two more local organisations also exhibited this year; Malvern Panalytical demonstrated the measurement of particle size in a suspension by filling up a fish tank and shining a laser pointer through it, and the University of Worcester's Institute of Science and the Environment set-up an eye-catching stand of microscopes and samples.

Christine Swan joined Richard Henson at the bandstand for a double act, dressed as Ada Lovelace and Charles Babbage respectively. Off stage, they wilted in the heat, but on it they explored the story of early computing, coding and logic.

Revathi Timms, past supporter of the festival and also a TEDxMalvern speaker, kindly appeared at the bandstand to talk about 3D-printing and showed some samples.

We also boosted our portfolio of science trails with a new one called "Elementary, my dear Watson!". This was a treasure hunt to find the elements of the periodic table dotted around the park and then work out the name of the scientist they spelt. The answer was Co P Er Ni Cu S. We used

51 'Malvern park event brings science to life', *Worcester News*, 26th June 2019. https://www.worcesternews.co.uk/news/17730212.malvern-park-event-brings-science-life/

some of the RSC's #IYPT materials for this, as they were slowly rolling out new posters about each element during the year. I was in touch with their Public Engagement Officer, and it turned out they had all but Er available in time for the event, with the Er poster being scheduled for publishing later that year. So, in the end I created our own Er poster to complete the set!

Over the course of planning Malvern Science in the Park, I sometimes come across experiments or potential exhibits that would be great for the venue. Once such example is the use of two large parabolic radio dishes across a long distance so that when someone whispers in one, the sound is directed efficiently to the recipient and they can hear them. I'd seen such an arrangement at the Discovery Centre in Singapore, and had been trying to encourage a local amateur radio club to take up the mantle for this one. In the end, I bought two dishes used for listening to wildlife, two tripods, and Alan humoured me by taking it under his wing and featuring at least one of the dishes on the IoP stand

Amplifying the sound across the park with Dr Alan Smith at the controls. (CM)

so that visitors could rotate it around and listen to distant sounds clearly. These kinds of props also look the part in situ!

A special mention must also go to Dave Pedlar and his two kids Tamsin and Alex who, on my cheeky request, created several fantastic models of probes using cereal boxes, tin foil, straws and more to augment our Interplanetary Trail. This meant we could also put Voyager 1 and Voyager 2 probes inside the children's book section of the library this year (even though the two probes are not in reality travelling through space together), promoting both the event and the Space Chase reading challenge.

We had another great day. The sun was almost too hot, though we should never complain about such good weather, as rain and wind would be very problematic for an event of this nature. We estimated 1,400 visitors attended this year, and had 23 exhibitors alongside 7 science buskers and 6 science trails[52].

This was also the year that business mix were the Platinum Sponsors of the festival, which meant they were also highlighted at this event too. Their CEO David Page and COO Vicky Young trekked over from London for the day to see what it was all about, and they managed to speak to numerous exhibitors and start to make the all-important connections in the community for their own business development.

VIRTUAL 2020

In March 2020, as we were gearing up for the fourth edition, the country went into lockdown as the Covid pandemic spread. It quite quickly became clear that an in-person event was not going to be possible this year. But I was keen not to lose the momentum of previous years and just concede defeat to the virus.

52 'Photos: Families enjoy scientific fun day in Malvern', *Worcester News*, 2nd July 2019. www.worcesternews.co.uk/news/17742378.photos-families-enjoy-scientific-fun-day-malvern/

And so, as our press release headlined, we decided to 'knock it out of the park this year'[53] and create a virtual event.

This had the advantage that there was an opportunity to reach a wider audience beyond Malvern, and to involve speakers from further afield too. The event would of course be less expensive to stage, and also somewhat easier to organise in terms of the usual need to corral the participants to send me all their risk assessments, insurance documents, stand requirements, etc.

But there was still the technical challenge of delivering a reasonably professional and captivating event. We decided to use Zoom as the webinar platform combined with a live stream on Facebook, although to be honest we were still working out the finer details at the eleventh hour.

One thing I couldn't fault was the enthusiasm of our long-term supporters to work with the new format, and the equal enthusiasm of other contacts I'd approached to see if they would get involved.

We decided to have a full day of live talks and pre-recorded videos, with me as the host. It was just how I imagine being a Radio DJ for the day might be, and it was surprisingly exhausting and stressful making sure the tech worked, the programme stayed to time, and remaining focused on being the host. With hindsight, I over did it a bit with the number of participants and the length of time we were 'on air', but then again it was a fun day and fantastic to connect with so many science communicators around the country from our makeshift studio in the boardroom of the Wyche Innovation Centre.

Alongside the live show, we had a few things going on. The IET had put together a quiz for those

living in Malvern to go out and about looking for clues. And for the show we had created a Science Bingo sheet so that the audience could listen out for scientific terms and cross them off.

After a couple of technical rehearsals in which we discovered the crucial settings to allow PowerPoint slides and embedded videos to be streamed with audible sound through Zoom, and in which I worked out the pre-flight check list to ensure that the right screens were visible whilst streaming to Facebook Live, we made a start.

The temporary studio at the Wyche Innovation Centre, with a parabolic dish for good measure. (AB)

Professor Malcolm Macleod, the Chief Scientist, Research and Innovation & Dean of Fellows at QinetiQ, and Visiting Professor at the University of Strathclyde joined us from his home on Zoom to officially open the event. I had posted the speakers our usual Malvern Science in the Park sun caps, so Malcolm sported his with pride as he explained the importance of science to our world and in fact its role in enabling us to stage the virtual event in progress.

One advantage of the event format was that we could record all the content and make it available afterwards. So, you can visit our YouTube Channel and watch all of the segments I'm reporting here: youtube.com/playlist?list= PLrJ2usPi65Vb9U3tWsUOIFl8tnSBp9yvV.

To make things easier, I had created a master slide show with all the title slides, video links and speakers' slides in sequence. This turned out to be a wise move, as it enabled me to simply advance through the PowerPoint deck as we progressed through the day. In the 'studio', we also had help from the IoP; Nicky Thomas keeping an eye on the social media and posting to the Zoom chat and Facebook timeline. We also had someone

53 'Knocking science out of the park', *Business & Innovation Magazine*, 12th June 2020. www.businessinnovationmag. co.uk/knocking-science-out-of-the-park-in-malvern/

'Malvern Science in the Park to go ahead as virtual event due to coronavirus', *Malvern Gazette*, 19th June 2020. www.malverngazette.co.uk/news/18528133.malvern-science-park-go-ahead-virtual-event-due-coronavirus/

throughout the day communicating with the speakers as they logged into Zoom and waited in the wings before their slot. And I had an iPad with the website's programme on enabling me to welcome the next speaker without a hitch.

The first two segments after the opening address were pre-recorded videos. These took the pressure off a little, because they could be cued up and played, and I knew how long they ran for in advance. Margaret Cross and her two granddaughters had recorded a piece in their garden about floating and sinking, and I had helped John Bibby record a segment of him launching his water-pressure powered rockets in a field near my home.

Our first live demonstration was provided by Steve Dawes from his garden shed a few miles away in Gloucestershire, in which he showcased his Raspberry Pi controlled weather station. We soon moved to another part of the country, Swindon, to link up with Sarah Cosgriff who explained and demonstrated why astronauts need a space suit.

The STEM Response Team at the University of Wolverhampton also provided pre-recorded videos, including a great piece debuting Dr Martin Khechara's two sons investigating bouncing eggs with the usual 'egg' puns to amuse the audience.

Dr Mark O'Dell, another regular supporter of the event in the park, joined us from south

Worcestershire to talk about fossils from the Malverns and the Cotswolds, before we were back to Gloucestershire with STEMWorks as they explained how to build a water clock. Then we moved across to Birmingham to join Dr Chris Hamlett in his living room use microscopy to show the surfaces of different samples. He returned, after another segment from Sarah and an engineering video from Caroline Alliston, with his daughter all kitted out in lab coat and sun cap to show their pièce-de-resistance; elephant's toothpaste.

Clockwise from top left:
Sarah Cosgriff on astronauts,
Chris Hamlett with his able
apprentice, Ionna and Vass
doing a taste test, and Mark
O'Dell revealing an ammonite inside a nodule. (AB)

HE RETURNED ... WITH HIS DAUGHTER ALL KITTED OUT IN LAB COAT AND SUN CAP TO SHOW THEIR PIÈCE-DE-RESISTANCE; ELEPHANT'S TOOTHPASTE.

Then we had a double act from the home of Dr Ionna Zefeiri and Dr Vassilis Pelekanos on food science and neuroscience respectively. The ever-popular giant bubbles that usually adorn the park were demonstrated in another video courtesy of the IoP before Dr Andrew Holding beamed in from near York with his talk about scurvy and nutrition. We then had a battery quiz from Dr Azar Shirazi at the University of Birmingham, before a number of pre-recorded videos about numbers from The IET, a new competition from the Big Ideas initiative, insects from the Worcestershire Wildlife Trust, and software defined radio from Derek Cunningham. This enabled me to gobble up my lunch before introducing Graedon Crouch from QinetiQ who, in true *Blue Peter* style, made Möbius strips for all to try.

Another newcomer to the event was Syd Femtinos who did a fantastic live segment with Zoom-filled backdrop and camera pointing down at her table-top worksheet that she drew as she spoke. Mark then came back with a fossil show-and-tell, before I had a chat with Dr Ilija Rašović about carbon whilst referring to my molecular models that were conveniently on hand.

Later in the programme, we went live to Portsmouth to speak with my son's housemate Evie Snedker about microbes (the cuddly ones had been sent on down to her so she could refer to them as she spoke), and then my son Sam did a live segment making and testing different types of paper aeroplane. We also had a talk about geology and the rock cycle from Hilary Edgeley, a fantastic live demonstration of cola 'fireworks' triggered electronically by a Raspberry Pi and mentos sweets in Steve's back garden, and a chat about the history of computing from Mike Church. Sibghat Ullah was our most distant speaker, joining us live from the Netherlands to talk about artificial intelligence. In fact, in the end we had rather more videos than we

could show, but Jon Wood rounded off the day with his pre-recorded video about oxygen and breathing.

Phew! I was well and truly exhausted after all of that, but what made it all worthwhile was the feedback, including "I wanted to express our gratitude for the time and organisation that you put into creating the [virtual] Malvern Science in the Park event and all of the speakers who made it a great success in our household. My twelve year old daughter was instantly consumed with the fascinating topics, engaging speakers and stayed focused on the event for its duration."

So, in summary we had nineteen live acts joining live on the day and we showed fifteen pre-recorded videos. We had a hundred registered as Zoom attendees and about 50% attendance rate on Zoom on the day. We collected attendee postcode data via Zoom, and of those that joined most were from Worcestershire, but we also had people from: Tunbridge Wells, Brent, Herefordshire, Chester, Bristol, Bath, Gloucestershire, Chelmsford, Birmingham, Belfast, Swindon, Kingston Upon Thames, Nottingham, Dudley, and overseas: Boston (USA) and I think Singapore. On Facebook, we had over 2,000 views of the live stream. 95% were in England, just over 3% in Wales, just under 1% Scotland, and then a few overseas.

And, as we have all the material available as legacy videos, we can see at the time of writing that the Facebook video has now reached over 7,000 people, although very few will have watched all seven hours! And the segments on YouTube have also had multiple views since they were published after the event.

Clockwise from top left: Evie Snedker and a furry microbe, Sam Burden and his paper aeroplane, Syd Femtinos and the Big Bang, and the fizzy coke launch with Steve Dawes. (AB)

ENCORE, 2021

It was touch and go, but we actually managed to stage the event live and in-person once again[54]. It

54 'Science is once again a walk in the park in Malvern this summer', *Business & Innovation Magazine*, 15th June 2021. www.businessinnovationmag.co.uk/science-is-once-again-a-walk-in-the-park-in-malvern-this-summer/

wasn't straight forward, as Covid was still ravaging the nation and the gradual release of lockdown was facing some hurdles.

On the 14th June, less than a fortnight before our event, the Prime Minister Boris Johnson was set to announce that lockdown restrictions would ease into their final phase of no significant restrictions (step four). But, for a number of weeks this looked unlikely, and so I had been liaising with MHDC and the Worcestershire Regulatory Authority about contingencies should things stay the same and limits on crowds remain in place.

As such, I'd filled my Amazon basket with plastic barrier fencing, stakes, signage boards and

Left: The Laboratory Notebook (programme booklet) cover and, below, plan of the park with all the Covid-secure zones.

more ready to press 'buy' once it was confirmed that restrictions were neither improving nor getting tighter. And so, I scrambled to finalise the details for a Covid-secure in-person event on Saturday 26th June 2021. In our favour was the fact that this was an outside event; had we usually been indoors it would simply not have been possible to stage it.

Fortunately, we also had a new sponsor this year; the West Midlands Trains Your Community Your Fund[55] was supporting both the festival and the park event, which meant we could afford all the extra expenditure incurred by the pandemic.

These considerations included ensuring all the exhibitors had undertaken a Covid risk assessment in their plans, that we had a robust plan, and that the district council was happy too. I had divided the park up into six zones that would be fenced using stakes and as many in situ features as possible (like trees, bushes, benches, bins, walls, etc). Each zone would need a marshal throughout the day and we'd need to limit numbers to 30 at any one time in a zone. Some mathematics revealed that we could expect people to circulate through a zone in about half an hour, and that the capacity for the day would be about 2000 people 'slots' (as some people would visit more than one zone of course). It was decided that the way we would control the crowds would be to issue free tickets for every half hour that people wanted to be there, and these 'sold out' on Eventbrite by the Friday evening before with just some modest Facebook and local media marketing.

This year's brainwave was to contract our local handyman Martin Reeves into using his van to transport all the paraphernalia early in the morning to the park and for him to then help erect all the fencing whilst other volunteers erected the gazebos and feather flags.

55 www.westmidlandsrailway.co.uk/about-us/your-community-your-fund/what-weve-done-so-far

For many, this was the first public fete-like event since lockdown some fifteen months earlier[56], and so it was satisfying to see so many people enjoying themselves whilst also being patient with our crowd-control system. Not everyone with tickets turned up of course, and plenty arrived on spec without a ticket, but we managed to get them all through the exhibits with minimal queuing and whilst maintaining the required social distancing.

Above: Katy Gibson from the IoP Midlands opened the fifth Malvern Science in the Park (AS) and, right, one of our fine volunteer marshals and good friend, Paul Snelling. (RM)

The exhibitors and buskers were all fantastic. They embraced the challenge of creating safe yet engaging exhibits and activities. They had also all been enthusiastic for the event from the start; keen to return to in-person events with the general public. Something I had worried may not have been the case at the outset.

Once again, we had our key stakeholders back in the saddle like the IoP, the IET, IMechE (who unfortunately had to drop out right at the last minute because of a transportation problem), Malvern Panalytical, Earth Heritage Trust, STEM Ambassadors Hub, Steve Dawes and his Raspberry Pis, Dr Mark O'Dell and his fossils, John Bibby with his rockets, MRATHS and the University of Worcester.

The Army STEM team came along this year with some explosive zip-wire rockets, and Discover

Materials (led by long-term supporter Dr Chris Hamlett) showcased materials science. QinetiQ came back into the fold, and both Legrand and the Regional Organised Crime Unit (ROCU) who had been to the main festival tried out exhibiting in the park too. We also welcomed IASME Consortium with their packet-sorting firewall activity (coloured balls and buckets) and the STEM Response Team in person from the University of Wolverhampton who had helped out with videos last year.

The Worcester Astronomical Society was facing some issues, but Chris Livingstone returned with his telescopes to image sunspots. And, another franchise holder for Usborne Science Books was able to join us at the last minute with some paper plane activities. The University of Birmingham's School of Mathematics came along this year; Dr Azar Shirazi who had helped out online before and then moved department encouraged their attendance. This relocation happens quite a bit in academia as post

Clockwise from top left: Hands-on science activities back in Priory Park, with the Heather Angell pictured from the STEM Response Team at the University of Wolverhampton, electrical measurements courtesy of MRATHS, astronomy with Chris Livingstone, and loud zip-wire rockets with the Army. (RM)

docs move between research groups in their quest to secure a longer term contract, making staying in touch with prospective participants that much harder.

Similarly, the science busking at the bandstand went well too. Dr Martin Khechara came along with his

56 'Which summer events are returning to Malvern this year?', *Malvern Gazette*, 17th June 2021. www.malverngazette.co.uk/news/villages/19376840. summer-events-returning-malvern-year/

now famous Shamus the Anus, ably helped by his two sons whom we had met last year in their *eggstremely* good video. We also welcomed Coco Sato, an award-winning Japanese origami artist who was a guest on the mathematics stand, and Ebrima Sallah, one of the Discover Materials ambassadors who demonstrated some exciting thermal shock experiments.

And we had some old favourites like Dr Mark O'Dell and his fossils, Christine Swan and Richard Henson in their Ada Lovelace and Charles Babbage costumes, Nicky Thomas with her fun physics, Dr Chris Hamlett with his giant lotus leaf, and I was back with my carbon molecules.

So, in many ways, it really was just like old times[57]. And the feedback was good too: "Thank you for an amazing Science in the Park. We ended up staying for 6 hours! The boys really enjoyed it and learned so much – we discovered T who is 6 loves micro biology and was good on the Periodic table whereas his 8 year old brother has always liked Geology and rocks and the cyber security challenges.", "We all had a fantastic time, had to drag E away after 5hrs, she loved it and so did her friends. Thank you", and "My son, who told me science was his least favourite subject, had a great time, thank you."

The new addition to the first aiders' family and one of the youngest visitors to Malvern Science in the Park! (RM)

Clockwise from top left: Charles Babbage (Richard Henson) and Ada Lovelace (Christine Swan), Dr K with his two sons on standby, and Ebrima Sallah with his heat experiments. (RM)

We rolled out the science trails too; inflatable dinosaurs, inflatable planets, materials, microbes and microscopy. And the cardboard cast from the *The Big Bang Theory* were also aired again.

We should also mention our first aiders, Severn Valley Training and Medical. Liz and her team came to our rescue back in 2017 when we were still trying to find first aid cover as the event drew worryingly close. They have been with us since at all the park events and also provided cover at the Next Generation Innovators schools' day at the festival. Her son Harry has enjoyed attending too and is now into science, and this year they brought along their newest recruit.

As we had marshals and registration data, it was easier to estimate the overall attendance this year. We had about 200 unique bookings with an average party size of 3.75 people, selling out all 2000 slots ahead of the event. This meant 750 different people had pre-booked tickets for some time during the day, planning to spend on average 1–1.5 hours at the event. Analysing the marshals' records we see that we processed just over 2000 people through the zones, averaging 335 people per zone (29 per zone per half an hour on average) which was very much as we planned it. And given that there were people outside the zones at any given time as well as walking the trails, transiting between zones, buying ice cream, talking to us at the information desk, we estimate about 1040 different visitors attended the event. And on top of that, we had just over 100 people participating as exhibitors/buskers/helpers (22 different exhibitors and 9 science buskers). ○

57 'Family fun as Malvern Science in the Park returns after Covid', *Malvern Gazette*, 8th July 2021. www.malverngazette.co.uk/news/19426190.family-fun-malvern-science-park-returns-covid/

In many ways TED is the gold standard for engaging presentations about innovation. The short talks on technology, entertainment and design (hence TED) have become a worldwide phenomenon because of the way the annual TED conference has been curated with world-class speakers and a passion to inspire.

Back in 2009 the TED movement, under the relatively new leadership of Chris Anderson, spawned TEDx. This was a means for local organisers to embrace the globally recognised brand and curate local events in towns and cities around the world.

I had not really clocked TEDx until Amanda Lloyd at the MHDC suggested back in 2016 that I look into it and see if it could be part of the Malvern Festival of Innovation. Some research showed that a TEDx event in Malvern would be a real possibility, but it would have to be stand alone and distinct from the festival. Moreover, it had to be organised by an individual (and associated team) rather than through a corporate entity like Innovate Malvern.

PREPARATIONS

So, in a personal capacity, I applied to TED to be the first license holder of TEDxMalvern with a view

TEDxMALVERN

to staging a small evening event commensurate with small-town Malvern in the spring so as to be diametrically opposite the usual festival dates.

I was successful in my application, and before long had to start arranging this new event for the community. Of course, all the experience with the festival helped immensely. Firstly, we were limited by the rules to one hundred attendees, so the Coach House Theatre was the perfectly-sized venue. Secondly, any sponsorship was to just cover costs and not make any money unless it was used for a future TEDx edition. To be honest, this was not a problem as usually sponsorship barely covers the cost and the actual challenge is not to lose money.

The TEDx brand is very strong, and also carefully policed. But having our own TEDxMalvern did look cool.

Anyone who has watched a TED or TEDx talk will know that speakers often stand on a circular red disk on stage and speak for about twenty minutes without notes; often well-rehearsed and flawlessly. Indeed, the rules are that a speaker should talk for a maximum of eighteen minutes, and it has to be videoed in front of the live audience so that it can be made available for people around the world to see

The TEDxMalvern banner ready for the marketing.

later. This is part of the winning TED / TEDx formula, as the talks are all available in a vast and growing video library for people to watch at their leisure.

In our case we needed a circular red carpet, some stage branding and most importantly a competent video engineer to record and edit the proceedings against the tight TEDx specification. Luckily, MHDC were happy to pay for the video recording and Carl Walker at Wild Edric Media was very familiar with the Coach House Theatre and happy to rise to the challenge.

The other stipulation for the format at that time was that live speakers had to be complemented with some other existing TED video showings from their library. Actually this requirement worked well, as it meant fewer live acts were needed for a full programme and by carefully choosing the video segments, it was possible to augment the chosen theme with additional insights from around the world.

TAKE 1

Our first TEDxMalvern was set for the evening of the 26th April 2017. Once a license is approved, TED provide a webpage template on which to promote the event, and it gets added to the TEDx map of events so that people can find upcoming editions in their area.

Having by this time organised five festivals and witnessed how hard it was to attract a sell-out audience, I was surprised just how well the TED brand worked. Within days of putting the tickets up

for 'sale' (I decided it was actually easier to make the tickets free and make sure the costs were covered by sponsorship), the event was sold out and the waiting list was starting to fill. This was even before I had announced who was going to speak, so it really was the reputation and reach of the brand that was pulling in the crowds.

The theme for the inaugural TEDxMalvern[58] was *Creativity without Borders* and was kindly sponsored by Hewett Recruitment, MHSP, WINN, and of course MHDC, with their economic development manager Simon Smith also helping me organise the event in his personal capacity.

We opened with the mandatory TEDx introductory video before showing the TED film with Sangeeta Bhatia titled *This tiny particle could roam your body to find tumours*. This set the scene for our first (ever) live TEDxMalvern speaker Stephen Ward-Smith from Malvern Instruments to give his talk *Size really matters*. And, of course,

 you can still watch his performance on YouTube as one of the TEDx collection: youtu.be/GOzc-pnjFWA].

This was followed by the TED film *The magic ingredient that brings Pixar movies to life* by Danielle Feinberg and the animated short TED film *The playful wonderland behind great inventions* by Steven Johnson. We then welcomed local composer Paul Farrer, whom you may recall spoke at the first

 edition of the festival, to elaborate on *Composing creatively on the run*: youtu.be/ F3ysXPMdjlk. At the time of writing this video has now been viewed over 1,200 times.

We then screened Sonaar Luthra's TED talk *Meet the water canary* as a segue into Katie Alcott's live talk *From contracting dysentery to delivering clean water* describing her motivation to start her clean water charity FRANK Water. Katie, who lives locally near Colwall and is the wife of my blockchain start-up

58 Online page for TEDxMalvern 2017:
www.ted.com/tedx/events/22485

Clockwise from top left: TEDxMalvern speakers Stephen Ward-Smith, Paul Farrer and Katie Alcott (CWa). The relieved group of inaugural TEDxMalvern speakers pictured with me after the event. (ZS)

company co-founder Tom, went on to receive a much-deserved MBE for services to international development in the Queen's New Year Honours list of 2019. youtu.be/TafGbof_uEI

We rounded the evening off with some networking and refreshments in the foyer. The event had been a success and generated a buzz of discussion with the legacy of the video recordings to share with the world. It is worth noting that as with all these kinds of events, it is not over for the organisers at the end of the night: Carl edited the videos and Simon and I had to watch them, suggest amendments and approve the final cut. Then I had to upload them to TEDx with all the right metadata.

Another interesting part of TEDx is that they circulate a simple survey to all the attendees asking them to rate the event out of ten and provide any feedback. We received 26 responses with 21 being positive about the evening. Some of

the comments were: "Great event, well managed with interesting speakers and great have it within my own community!", "The whole evening was interesting, varied, informative and entertaining", "Interesting speakers with local interest, combined with TED films was a good combination. Networking opportunities as well.", "It was amazing to have a TEDx event on our doorstep and the array of speakers and films complemented one another perfectly. I left inspired and uplifted by the creativity of the individuals we'd heard from and the application of science and technology". The one detractor wrote "It was ok but my expectations were high and only one of the live presentations was v good." There's always one!

TEDX REVISITED

Buoyed by the positive feedback and having my license renewed for a further year, I set about organising a second TEDxMalvern[59] which we held on the 25th April 2018. It was a similar story

---

59 Online page for TEDxMalvern 2018:
www.ted.com/tedx/events/27861

That's me welcoming the audience to the second TEDxMalvern at the Coach House Theatre in 2018. As the host and license holder, this was the closest I could get to being a TEDx speaker. But I wore a red dress shirt never-the-less! (CWa)

Left to right: Speakers Rhea Freeman and Ross Renton. (CWa)

Revathi Timms in her stunning red sari, pictured next to the 3D-printer her company designed and prototyped. (CWa)

of fast-selling tickets and plenty of interest in the programme which this year had the theme *Thoughts for the Future*. Our sponsors this year were once again MHSP, MHDC and WINN, and Carl from Wild Edric Media returned to film the proceedings.

This time we opened with the TED film from Lucianne Walkowicz title *Let's not use Mars as a backup planet* before Revathi Timms spoke live

 about *My extraordinary career falling in love with engineering*: youtu.be/ qhK0FjdgwfM. I have mentioned Revathi earlier as a repeat participant of the schools' day, family day and also a science-busker at Malvern Science in the Park.

We followed this up with Jennifer Golbeck's TED film *Your social media "likes" expose more than you think*. This has kind of become common knowledge now, but when she delivered this lecture, the underbelly of social media was not well known. But it also provided a good balance for Rhea Freeman's

 live talk *Supporting rural communities with social media, and why it's a force for good*: youtu.be/fFyT9FA1WE4. At the time, Rhea was building her social media audience around her equestrian interest and professional marketing offer for rural businesses, so the TEDxMalvern

The 2018 TEDxMalvern line-up, *from left to right*, Ross Renton, Revathi Timms, me as host, and Rhea Freeman. (SS)

Damien Mark Smyth and Cathy Garner. (RB)

exposure helped her grow in popularity. She also spoke at TEDxTelford the following year!

We squeezed in another animated short TED Film from Adam Savage called *How simple ideas lead to scientific discoveries* before Ross Renton, who was the Pro Vice Chancellor Students at the University of Worcester, spoke about *What students of the future will expect from their university education*: youtu.be/qfZ3YYsM87c. I had briefly met Ross at a university event in the previous year, and he struck me instantly as a very capable public speaker. This was borne out with his succinct and well-paced TEDxMalvern talk; to date it has been our most watched one by a long way chalking up over 12,000 views!

This year we had 18 survey responses of which 16 were positive. Comments included "As well as hearing and sharing great ideas, it's an amazing opportunity to network with likeminded people. I had a fabulous time – thank you!", "Very well organised. Well-chosen, thought-provoking short films and engaging speakers. Followed by networking with inspiring people. Excellent all-round.", and "I thought it was a superb event. Well organised, really interesting, diverse and friendly too". The one detractor didn't leave any comment, just scored us zero!

THIRD AND FINAL FOR ME

Looking back, I'm not sure how I managed to organise the TEDxMalvern events with everything else that was going on. I'd usually ensure the license and date were in-hand before Christmas and then start to sort out the finer details in the new year. This year I felt that it was time to organise the third and then see if someone else would take the baton.

So, I turned the handle again and we staged the third TEDxMalvern[60] on 24th April 2019 back in

60 Online page for TEDxMalvern 2019:
www.ted.com/tedx/events/32934

The speakers Damien Mark Smyth, Cliff Jones and Cathy Garner, with me centre and my co-organiser Simon Smith from MHDC on the right. (RB)

Introducing Professor Cliff Jones ahead of his talk on display technology, and Cliff recounting some of Malvern's tech history. (RB)

the Coach House Theatre with another full auditorium. The theme was *Positive Progress and Optimism*, opening with a TED film from TED2012 in which Tali Sharot talked about *The optimism bias*.

This was followed by Damian Mark Smyth, an accomplished public speaker, author of *Do Nothing!* and, actually, a past TEDxSquareMile speaker. So, he knew the drill and delivered a great first live talk on

 Understanding your mind to solve problems, overcome depression and be more entrepreneurial: youtu.be/LvcpUUXJDJs. His video has now had more than 1,400 views.

After Jonathan Tepperman's TED film on *The risky politics of progress* we had the ebullient Cathy Garner deliver a very animated talk on *The science of relationships* whilst her husband was in the front

 row of the audience entrusted with advancing her slides: youtu.be/bP-bnmNFKwA. If you haven't seen it, watch her now and advance the already impressive 3,200 views at the time I write.

We followed this with a really interesting short film from TEDWomen 2018 in which Shohini Ghose explained quantum computing in just ten minutes. I had learnt that changing subject like this within the bounds of the TEDx theme kept the audience engaged and interested. And with such a large range of films to choose from within the growing TED library, it was very unlikely anyone from the audience would already have watched it.

Our final speaker was Professor Cliff Jones, a scientist and entrepreneur who had spoken at our first Malvern Festival of Innovation, and had co-founded ZBD Displays (later DisplayData) at the MHSP. I had actually got to know him many years before when I too worked in the electronic displays industry, well before moving to Malvern. In fact, he had been at the same display conference in Singapore a few days before I stayed on for a job interview there, and I remember him saying to me that if it didn't work out, he could offer me a job in Malvern. I think that had planted the seed in my head that Malvern might one day be an interesting place to live.

So, after Cliff's fascinating talk on *How display technology impacts all our lives*: youtu.be/KJMLAvOMVLM, we were once again networking with refreshments and Friday Beer in the foyer.

And I'm sure you are curious about this year's survey feedback too: 33 responses with 25 promoters and 2 detractors. One detractor left a comment "Interesting content, but there should have been breaks in between to discuss what we had heard. Leaving it to the end is too late for that many ideas to think about." Some of the positive feedback was: "It was well curated, well organised in a lovely convivial venue that generated an openness and appreciation.", "Very interesting talks on a diverse range of subjects, interspersed with thought-provoking film clips. And always a lively discussion afterwards with nibbles and drinks", "It was well organised, a great venue, great speakers and we had a very warm welcome. We would have happily paid to go, but as an added and unbelievable bonus, the tickets were free."

PASSING THE BATON

I had already mentioned to Stuart Wilkes, a fan of TED and TEDx, that I was looking for someone to takeover, and as luck would have it, he introduced me to Elaine Watt and Steve Birch during the evening of the event. They were both active members of the Worcester Speakers and Malvern Speakers (Toastmasters), and so very well placed to organise TEDxMalvern with good quality talks in the future.

> **WE FOLLOWED THIS WITH A REALLY INTERESTING SHORT FILM FROM TEDWOMEN 2018 IN WHICH SHOHINI GHOSE EXPLAINED QUANTUM COMPUTING IN JUST TEN MINUTES.**

We successfully moved the license across to Steve, as he lives in Malvern and would take the role of lead organiser. After a few meetings explaining how I'd done things, and passing over the graphics files, poster boards and of course the red circular floor mat, they were ready to proceed.

Scheduled for April 2020, all seemed to be going well as I watched a new programme being advertised, only for the coronavirus pandemic to strike and the UK to enter lockdown a few weeks before their planned date. They tried to reschedule a few times, but finally went ahead with an ambitious line up of six live speakers at the end of September 2021. TEDxMalvern hopefully lives on. ○

12.

I nearly title this book *In case you missed it* (*#ICYMI*) because over the last ten years I kept meeting people in and around Malvern who didn't know about the Malvern Festival of Innovation. Just the other day I was chatting to an entrepreneur based towards Hereford who has a keen interest in high tech business and STEM education, and he too had never heard of it! But this has not been for want of trying.

SOCIAL NETWORKS

The obvious approach to spreading the word, other than press releases and articles in newspapers and magazines is to make use of social media. In the case of the festival, we've made use of Twitter, Facebook, LinkedIn, YouTube and Instagram. We've even dabbled with Pinterest and written a number of blogs (which you can read in Appendix B).

We've tweeted regularly on Monday evenings at #WorcestershireHour, and taken part in #MalvernHillsHour and even participated in a few other local hours (#WestMidsHour, #Bromsgrovehour, #MalvernHour, #MidlandsHour, #cybersecurityhour, #EveshamHour, #KiddyHour, #covhour, and #TewksburyHour), but as you can imagine, this activity could take up all the hours

GOING VIRAL

in your day! We adopted #InnovateMalvern and #ScienceInPark as our hashtags for Twitter.

One year, MHDC helped by engaging one of the PR agencies they worked with to do some tweeting for us in the three-month lead up to the event. I used the opportunity to look at how many referrals we got to our website from Facebook (unpaid posts I was doing) and Twitter (mainly paid posts by the PR agency). It was interesting that Twitter was about twice as effective in terms of total referrals, and accounted for over 35% of referrals, but still only a little over 10% of the traffic. We could also calculate that the Twitter campaign cost an average of about £2.40 per referral which seemed rather high given that not every referral will have resulted in a ticket being 'sold' and that most tickets were in fact free anyway. We did, however, double our followers with just over a thousand new ones as a result of the campaign. But all this goes to show that social media can be a time-consuming and relatively costly way of marketing, even if 'done properly' with the help of a professional agency.

More recently I discovered that paid promotions on Facebook do seem to be good value. With a budget of approximately £50 to boost a post about a speaker, event or activity, this can be allocated across the month or so before the event and usually leads to many thousands of views and hundreds of clicks to the ticketing site. The post can also be targeted to a particular geographic location (such as 30 miles around Great Malvern) and to specific demographics (such as parents with school-aged children).

LinkedIn is another useful platform for the business events, but personal posts seem to get the most engagement and posts in LinkedIn Groups often go unnoticed. I haven't tried paid promotions in LinkedIn; when I investigated this one year I found the interface to be a bit clunky and confusing, and just focused on Facebook instead.

FOLLOW THE FOOTSTEPS

In the first year we actually put some coloured footprints down on the pavements between Great Malvern station and the Malvern Theatres, through Priory Park. These were done with permission from MHDC and used non-permanent chalk-based spray paint which would easily wash off in the rain. Emma had fun applying them a few days before the event using a stencil.

People did ask what they related to, including the tourist information office who it appeared had not got the memo from the council. So, it kind of worked in that it generated curiosity. And I remember watching a toddler enjoying them in Priory Park on the first morning as I walked back to the venue having off-loaded and parked my car.

One problem was that one particular colour, green I recall, was a bit more persistent than the other colours and didn't wash off so readily despite being the same brand. So, remnants remained for quite a few months and I heard rumours that the MHDC street scene manager was not best pleased.

But, by the following year, all traces had gone and we were permitted to do some white footprints this year using a more conventional chalk-based spray. These were brighter, but the weather was not great, so I think they went down in drizzle and were all washed away very soon after.

Samples of the 2012 coloured and 2013 white footprints sprayed on the pavements. (EP)

THE INNOVATION EXPRESS

This made me particularly happy. Inspired by seeing the *Entrepreneurs Express* at the MADE Festival in Sheffield back in 2012, I contacted what was then First Great Western to see if they could do something similar on the direct train out of London Paddington to Great Malvern that would arrive in time for the event. At first, they thought I wanted to formally name the train, which apparently takes some time, but when they realised I just wanted the service named temporarily for the few days over the festival, they said they'd see what they could do.

And, then out of the blue I had some inspired artwork to approve where they had designed a window sticker making use of our logo. Back in 2013, the trains were the old diesel HS125s that had window stickers added near the doors of each carriage for each journey, listing the stations that would be called at on route. First Great Western kindly agreed that they could indeed add a second sticker as part of the process and thus we had our *Innovation Express*[61]. In 2015, the rail franchise First Great Western became GWR and so the window stickers were rebranded to match their new livery. And In 2017, a number of people boarded the *Innovation Express*, including our keynote speaker Emma Jones MBE, and tweeted about it!

In 2018, GWR updated many of their trains on the London route with the Hitachi Class 800 Intercity Express Trains. These are equipped with digital information screens within the carriages and

61 'Special train to celebrate Malvern Festival of Innovation', 6th November 2013. news.gwr.com/news/special-train-to-celebrate-malvern-festival-of-innovation

so stickers were no longer applied to the windows. As such, they were not able to continue with our *Innovation Express* labels either.

In 2019, having seen the special GWR train celebrating Pride, I approached them about adding a graphic wrap to the front and rear units of the train. To their credit, their team did respond, but explained that though possible, it was pretty expensive and complicated; needing to take the trains out of service to have the decals professionally applied and to adhere to safety legislation in terms of the materials used and where they could be applied on the train. As far as I know,

Top: The original artwork for First Great Western's Innovation Express label in 2013, and then three different tweets in 2017 as people remarked on GWR's Innovation Express service.

they did continue to refer to the service as the *Innovation Express* on station information boards and in manual train and platform announcements.

THE INNOVATION SHUTTLES

Malvern is actually served by two rail franchises, and back in 2015 it was London Midland that ran

services between Birmingham and Hereford. They were keen to be supportive as well, so ran what we termed the Innovation Shuttles during the week. Their trains did not have labels attached to the carriages, but they added information to the customer information systems so that Innovation Shuttles were referenced on the platform and in-train displays.

Left: The London Midland's Innovation Shuttles graphic to highlight the regular services running between Birmingham New Street and Hereford throughout the day and enabling visitors to travel to the festival and alight at Great Malvern. Right: The revised graphic in 2018 after West Midlands Railway had taken over the franchise.

THE INNOVATION STATION

In 2018 I was discussing the Innovation Shuttles with the West Midlands Railways team in Birmingham, and they felt that the Innovation Shuttles were on their own a bit underwhelming and possibly confusing for the passengers.

So, we brainstormed a few ideas to raise the profile of their rail service and provide more visibility for the festival and their support. Interestingly, they were also the franchise responsible for Great Malvern station, and so they suggested that they could rebrand it as The Innovation Station during the festival week. I must admit I was surprised that this might be possible, especially as it was September already and only about a month to go until the event.

A few weeks later I was amazed to receive the artwork to approve that they would apply as wraps to the platform signage, and low and behold, on the weekend before the festival, Great Malvern station was transformed in to The

Innovation Station[62]. And as quickly as it went up, so too it was returned to normal on the Sunday after the festival.

Top: Me standing on The Innovation Station in Great Malvern courtesy of West Midlands Railway (ZS) and, bottom, one of the signs outside the waiting room. (AB)

THE INNOVATION GET-AROUND

Keeping with the train theme, in 2016 I thought it would be good to tie in our relationship with both GWR and London Midland, and revisit the footsteps that we had applied to pavements in the first two years.

This time, Simon Smith and I talked to a local company called Fleet Line Markers who specialised in paint for surface markings in places like playing fields and sports grounds. We wondered if they might have some washable paint that could be applied quickly to the paths, and possibly different coloured lines could be traced around the town.

My tentative idea was to create a series of walking routes between the station and venues similar in style to the London Underground map. For this we would need coloured markers on the pavement corresponding to the various lines.

We met up with Carl Haffield who had suggested using some new aluminium stickers designed to adhere outside to concrete and comprised a special roughened anti-slip surface for added safety. This proposal came about because they had some experimental quantities in stock and their coloured paint products would need to be jet-washed to clean up afterwards which sounded more troublesome than the original chalk-based paints we'd tried previously.

After a demonstration we agreed that this approach would be good, and I worked out the routes that would need marking. The stickers were designed to be 30cm x 30cm squares with the cloud logo and coloured arrows on. It was necessary to have stickers spaced sufficiently close to each other so that you could see the next one from the one you were at and therefore follow a route by foot. Also, just as with the London Underground, certain routes overlapped (like the Circle Line and the District Line), and so some stickers needed both colours present. We also wanted stickers at the designated stops, which included venues and some of the hotels, to be named and indicate the colour lines they were on.

In the end Simon, Amanda Lloyd also from MHDC, and I walked my various routes, and I

62 'Great Malvern to become the home of innovation during annual technology festival', West Midlands Railway, 3rd October 2018. news.wmtrains.co.uk/pressreleases/great-malvern-to-become-the-home-of-innovation-during-annual-technology-festival-2702873

'Great Malvern railway station to become 'The Innovation Station' for popular festival', *Malvern Observer*, 5th October 2018. malvernobserver.co.uk/news/great-malvern-railway-station-to-become-the-innovation-station-for-popular-festival/

discussed and refined them, creating a detailed spreadsheet of all the combinations needed and finally ordered over 130 stickers of varying colours as well as named location stickers. It was the somewhat circuitous route that connected the station and town to the two Malvern College venues that proved the most difficult because the walk required quite a few stickers and the road layout needed a spur.

Of course, it was one thing ordering all the stickers, but they also had to be adhered along the route when the ground was dry, and not so far in advance that they would be damaged before people could use them at the festival. Very kindly, Amanda and her colleague at MHDC chose a fine day and went round the town and stuck them all down[63].

I, in the meantime, had created the 'Innovation Get-Around' map which was available to download via the QR codes on the stickers. It comprised six lines designated by the different colours in the festival logo; Charles Darwin Line, Wilson-Gulley Line, Jenny Lind Line, Lewis-Tolkien Line, Dummer-Woodward Spur, and the Elgar Line. All of the lines are named after people with innovative, entrepreneurial, or creative connections to Malvern. We didn't attempt to place stickers from the station to the Three Counties Showground, hence the dotted line on the map, as this was not a readily walkable distance!

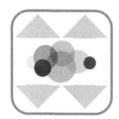

Examples of the floor sticker artwork: a single line indicator with QR code for more information, a dual (overlapping line) indicator, and two location stickers; one for Great Malvern station and one for the Malvern Theatres. The latter two photos show the actual stickers on the ground having been subject to muddy footfall in the streets!

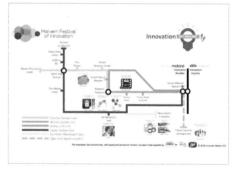

The first Innovation Get-Around map in 2016 linking the venues and a few hospitality stops with the Great Malvern Station and the mainline Innovation Express and Innovation Shuttles.

I did actually update the Innovation Get-Around map in later years too, with versions created for 2017, 2018 and 2019. In these later years we didn't have the resources to print and affix the street markers everywhere again, but I did print some

63 'Screening of 'The Matrix' kicks off 2016 Festival of Innovation', *Malvern Gazette*, 30th September 2016. malvernobserver.co.uk/news/screening-matrix-kicks-2016-festival-innovation/

welcome stickers based on the same material which we placed outside the venues.

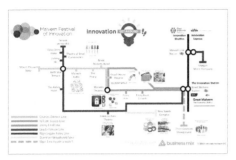

The 2019 Innovation Get-Around map included more venues and of course the Innovation Station. It also had a Nightingale Foley line as a legacy from 2017 when we held the Automotive Advances session at the Morgan Motor Company which is nearer to Malvern Link station.

The 2019 welcome stickers highlighting our Platinum Sponsor business mix, on the platform of Great Malvern Station[64] and at the entrance to the Mount Pleasant Hotel.

OPENING VIDEO SEQUENCE

As you will recall, in 2012 we heard Paul Farrer speaking about his creative work composing theme tunes and musical scores for television, film and video gaming. He followed this up with his TEDxMalvern talk in 2017.

However, in 2013 I asked Paul if he might please compose a signature tune for the festival that inspires and excites. I even suggested I could give him a ridiculously tight deadline so that he could innovate the whole composition whilst the clock ticks! Within a day, and without having to set any kind of deadline, he was back to me with a two-minute piece that became the longstanding opening theme music for the festival.

We then launched a competition for people to create an opening video sequence to accompany the music that we could use to open the various events. We felt this would be a good advert for anyone who wanted to showcase their capability and we'd get a range of entries both to choose from and to feature across the event.

Not everyone agreed, one company I contacted to let them know about it responded, "We don't provide our professional video production services for free as it's how we make our living. Sorry, but the remote possibility of gaining a bit of PR is not a viable substitute. Furthermore, we don't believe that securing professional services without paying for them is healthy to our industry or any other industry for that matter. Wrapping it up in the disguise of a competition also devalues those that have trained to develop their professional skills. If they are good enough to produce a professional production, then it's disrespectful to expect them to work for nothing. Competitions are okay for armatures [sic]."

Anyway, despite this view, we had some interest and the winner for 2013 was Artwork Creative, the company that had kindly provided us with our logo the year before: youtu.be/SwYvCYgleSM. This was a nice little animated story that demonstrated they understood the brief and which was used to open the themed symposia and the family show. The music really does build excitement and anticipation in the audience and when it is played loudly in the auditorium, it always sounds impressive and commanding. We're very fortunate to have a piece like this from a world renowned yet local composer!

64 'West Midlands Railway partners with Malvern Festival of Innovation', My News Desk, 7th October 2019. www.mynewsdesk.com/uk/westmidlandstrains/ pressreleases/west-midlands-railway-partners-with-malvern-festival-of-innovation-2928567

A screen shot from Artwork Creative's opening video sequence in 2013 when we opened a competition to provide animation over Paul Farrer's signature tune composition.

opening night to showcase the good effort: youtu.be/rlThHc8wEtg.

For the ensuing years I have used stock video to create new opening sequences along a similar theme. You can fill your boots here: 2017 youtu.be/HeoiqugPR34,

2018 youtu.be/ev3vgtwGPWI, 2019 youtu.be/TT86ExYGAiQ, 2020 youtu.be/BEvswLguOgs (which features a pandemic face-masked avatar and virus animations), and 2021: youtu.be/YHGMpPjf9cg.

In 2014 we had some interest but didn't receive any entries, so I used a number of photos and videos from the previous festivals, some general photos I had of Malvern, and some video excerpts from our various sponsors to compile an opening sequence using iMovie on my MacBook. Unfortunately, we didn't have the funds to engage a production company to do something properly: youtu.be/h5xXBe17DNg.

In 2015, we were entry less again, despite letting some of the local schools, art colleges, etc know about the opportunity and sending out the audio file to some interested entrants. So, this year with just a few days to go, I used PowerPoint and iMovie to create a sequence featuring mainly components of the logo! youtu.be/rE0VBajKxvQ.

By now I was getting used to the fact that I would be the one that had to create the opening sequence, and started to pull it together whilst I had a bit more time on my hands. In 2016 I made use of some free stock videos and animated shorts, and it made for a more professional looking composition: youtu.be/mio3PwBnYyg. That year we did, however, have an entry from a local school student who had been involved in the local Raspberry Pi jams we hosted, but it was only a 30 second excerpt of the music, so I also aired it on the

ADVERTISING SHORTS

Sometimes, organisations are just kind and helpful. In 2021, I had a chat with Ian Woodley from the local StiloTouch Design & Branding Agency and he said he'd be delighted for his team to put together a couple of 30 second video shorts to help us advertise the festival on social media. I sent him over some logo files and weblinks and before you knew it, he'd sent back some video files of various sizes and resolutions for us to use.

They were really rather effective, as we started to use them on LinkedIn, Facebook and Twitter, and other organisations who were participating also requested the video files so they could utilise them in their posts. You can see the two animations here: youtu.be/5bnYiNfYrEg and youtu.be/4-qjHv8zIos.

IMITATION IS THE SINCEREST FORM OF FLATTERY

Back in September 2012 I wrote the following on our new website "Today we need to innovate more than ever: the way we do business, the way we use resources; the way we live. We need new ideas to stay competitive, new technologies to improve lives, and new insights to lead the way. Join us to discover what's coming next, to learn how others are innovating, and to showcase your own research and development." It's the same wording used to welcome people to the homepage as I finish writing this chapter in 2022.

As mentioned in my book *Start to Exit*, in 2015 I stumbled upon the Wales Festival of Innovation website using some very similar wording to our website in their vision statement: "Innovation is changing the way we live. We need new ideas to stay competitive, new technologies to improve lives, and new insights to lead the way."

The same phraseology also appeared on a Business Wales infographic about innovation, and in a press release the co-chair of a new Innovation Advisory Council for Wales was quoted as saying, "We need new ideas to stay competitive, new technologies to improve lives, and new insights to lead the way. The festival showcases what's coming next, and highlights how Wales is already leading the way."

Well, even though I was born in Wales and have plenty of affinity for the country that is visible from the Malvern Hills, I thought it was ironic that their festival of innovation was copying us rather than being innovative themselves. I wrote to their media contact and suggested that they either remove the statement from their website and literature to avoid confusion with our festival, or reference its source with our web address. I didn't hear back, but the wording on their site did change soon after!

Festival flags flying along Belle Vue Terrace and Church Street in Great Malvern, kindly put up by the Malvern Town Council. (AB)

FLAGS

Great Malvern occasionally sports flags on the town centre buildings along Belle Vue Terrace and down Church Street. In 2013 I enquired about who was responsible for them and was soon in conversation with the Malvern Town Council. They were receptive about putting some up for the festival and so I asked our sign producer to create some flags using the same material as we'd been using for the pull-up posters.

> ## TODAY WE NEED TO INNOVATE MORE THAN EVER: THE WAY WE DO BUSINESS, THE WAY WE USE RESOURCES; THE WAY WE LIVE.

They looked okay in that they hung down, but they didn't really flutter like a flag is supposed to and stormy weather caused them to tear and break. It was a good experiment, but we could do better!

In 2014 I ordered some proper fabric flags; a number of them in plain colours reflective of the colours on our logo, or as I liked to refer to them "festival colours", and then a few white ones printed with our logo. These looked great and have been used each year since to add a splash of colour to the high street. You can see one fluttering in the wind here: youtu.be/LbAWazO4bdc.

ACCEPTING BITCOIN

In 2016 we made it possible for dinner guests to buy their tickets with bitcoin. This was a bit risky because the cryptocurrency was pretty volatile (as it is now) and so the amount paid may or not cover the cost of the dinner once converted to pound sterling, as of course we had to still pay for the dinner in fiat currency. Of course, this was really just a calculated publicity stunt to demonstrate we were embracing the future and being innovative. In fact, we were ahead of the curve and unfortunately no one paid for their dinner in this way.

Had somebody paid for the 2016 dinner in bitcoin in late September, the £66.00 ticket price including VAT would have been 0.14 bitcoin. If we had then kept the payment in bitcoin and sat on it until the end of 2021, that would have been worth just over £5,000!

In later years, we displayed QR codes on our website to facilitate cryptocurrency donations to help support the festival. These have included accepting bitcoin and Ethereum, but alas, these options have also not been exercised. By all means send some over now!

Bitcoin (bc1qv3jdzln0v5j47l5rcvy8fjhr53hm0mu2s0kcnk) and Ethereum (0x603f60942400328FE243e90429171Efc9dcc39C8) public addresses which were set up to receive cryptocurrency donations.

#PIJACKET

Inspired by Matthew Bellamy's jacket worn on the Muse live tour, I thought it would be cool to create a visual gimmick for both advertising the festival and wearing something eye catching during the event.

We had a work experience student Theo Osborn join us in the summer to program a Raspberry Pi to control some flexible Neopixel LED panels. I then sourced a heavy 'gothic style' jacket which had plenty of pockets so that I could secrete the Pi, two heavy duty lithium-ion batteries and

plenty of wires within the lining. A friend's partner who was a seamstress helped to affix some Velcro patches and large rivet-like holes to facilitate connecting the panels to the wiring loom.

I rushed to get a version working for a WINN Innovation evening where I was going to say a few words about the festival, and frantically soldered things together in preparation. Theo had worked out how to get text and graphics files to scroll on the LED panels, but the complication was running the python program in such a way

Assembling and testing the #PiJacket. (AB)

that the jacket display could be switched on at the right time. I ended up setting the code running in the lobby with a screen and keyboard, then carefully putting on the jacket, and using a wireless presenter stick in my hand to advance the program to set the display running. The whole thing was very fragile and could easily become disconnected or crash the Pi.

Fortunately, it worked for WINN and some valuable lessons were learnt. At the 2019 festival I improved the wiring and the software, and it generally worked when needed. I had a few frantic minutes before the formal dinner trying to coax it

Left to right: The #PiJacket on stage at the WINN event (RH), and opening the Cyber Security symposium at the festival.

to operate so that I could walk in with it on showing our Platinum Sponsor business mix's logo.

APRIL FOOLS

I've always liked the idea of using April Fools jokes as a means of subliminal advertising and so, when inspiration and time allowed, I penned one as a press release to raise awareness of the festival's planned appearance later in the year.

The first was back in 2016 when I thought it would be interesting to base something around the Malvern Hills, as anything relating to changes in their condition or upkeep tends to stir the local population. As I was mentioning the then Malvern Hills Conservators (now the Malvern Hills Trust), I did give them warning that the piece might run in the local press and cause their switchboard to light up. The *Malvern Observer* ran the story, but at the time of writing it is no longer on their website, so the press release is reproduced below.

Malvern Hills to provide a beacon of colour during Malvern Festival of Innovation

1st April 2016, Malvern UK. Volunteers have been busy on the Malvern Hills over the Easter weekend sowing genetically modified grass seeds that will yield vividly coloured blades in the early autumn of this year.

Planned to create a spectacle that will coincide with this year's Malvern Festival of Innovation, the grass seed has been planted such that each of the peaks will be adorned in a hue not unlike the festival's logo on or around the first week of October.

Dr Adrian Burden, founder of the festival explained "We want the fifth year of the Malvern Festival of Innovation to be bigger and bolder than ever, and what better way than having a coloured backdrop to Great Malvern that embodies the Festival colours and logo using the natural landscape that has inspired so many innovators to the town."

The Malvern Hills Conservators were rightly cautious that genetically modified seeds could impact the environment. However, the suppliers of the grasses have provided assurance that the risks are minimal and that the grasses, being infertile, will not cross-pollinate nor grow back in future years.

Dr Burden continued "soil condition, altitude and weather can each influence the growth and colour of the grasses, so although tests in inconspicuous regions last year worked well, there is still a chance that the colour palette will not be an exact match with the logo, or the grasses may be at their brightest before or after the festival. However, nothing like this has been attempted before, so this really is pushing the envelope as far as landscape advertising is concerned."

The image below provides an artist's impression of how the Malvern Hills may look during the festival week that will run from 3rd–8th October 2016.

In 2021, after a year of the Covid pandemic and at a time when the UK's vaccination programme was making great strides, I ran another spoof press release about the Malvern Festival of Inoculation. This time the *Business & Innovation Magazine* kindly ran with it[65].

Malvern Festival of Inoculation

1st April 2021, Malvern UK. This year the annual Malvern Festival of Innovation will be rebranded the Malvern Festival of Inoculation, and is being planned

---

65 'Malvern Festival of Innovation rebrands as …', *Business and Innovation Magazine*, 1st April 2021. www.businessinnovationmag.co.uk/malvern-festival-of-innovation-rebrands-as/

as a live, in-person event from Monday 4th October to Saturday 9th October 2021.

It is anticipated that the Festival will be a celebration of the emergence from the COVID-19 pandemic in which innovation and creativity in science, technology and business have all helped society cope with this far-reaching global issue.

Dr Adrian Burden, the managing director of Innovate Malvern, the social enterprise behind the Festival that in turn is soon to be renamed Inoculate Malvern, states "The rapid development, testing and deployment of vaccines to counter the virus is a clear demonstration of the scientific ingenuity of mankind. We hope that by October the virus that has caused so much anguish and suffering will have been suppressed enough to allow the Festival to go ahead. This will enable students to once again be enthused by our STEM content, business professionals to be meet and network with their peers, and members of the public to be inspired by our speakers and exhibitors."

The Malvern Festival of Inoculation will include an opening lecture on the Monday evening, followed by the Next Generation Inoculators schools' day on the Tuesday. It is also hoped that a number of business and entrepreneurship focused symposia will run mid-week, along with a Formal Dinner on the Thursday evening, the Science Comedy Night on the Friday evening and the popular Family Day on the Saturday.

MORE COLLATERAL AND CLUTTER

Over the years we've tried various other things to address the marketing. In the first year, we did have some toroidal shaped coloured balloons for inside and outside the venue, but it is not a good use of helium so we didn't repeat this in later years.

We often prepared and printed A5 fliers about the overall festival and the Family Show. These could be put in racks at the Malvern Library, Tourist Information Office, Malvern Theatres, MHDC offices and circulated to the schools. In the early years, primary schools would put the leaflets in the children's school bags, but this became harder as newsletters became digital. To cover the schools, MDHC kindly toured the local ones and dropped of batches of fliers at their front desk.

Some local businesses and organisations also got on board and created their own email signature or social media posts to promote their involvement. This was really helpful, as it spread the word wider and gave credence to the event.

Another advertising medium was the festival bags which delegates received on arrival. These

Top: The MHDC email signature in 2015 and BloomSpace advertising their involvement in hosting Rory Cellan-Jones for his book signing after the fireside chat.

were primarily designed to hold information and giveaways from sponsors, as well as the programme. When applicable, we also had the logo of the headline sponsor on the bags too. In the first two years, we had jute cloth bags with QinetiQ and TSB logos on, printed in just two colours (black and the QinetiQ logo colour) to keep costs reasonable. In the third year when Lockheed Martin was the platinum sponsor, we went with dark blue cotton bags and white writing.

In 2015, we reduced the cost with brightly coloured plastic bags printed with Cisco, IDS Indata and QinetiQ logos. This was partly because we needed many more bags as we also had STEM leaflets and booklets for the school students to collect on their day as well.

In later years we had plain coloured plastic bags without the any lead sponsors logos (partly because none were 'lead' enough to benefit from this perk). The advantage was lower cost and the fact that the bags could be used the following year as well (as they didn't have sponsors or dates on), but the disadvantage was that they were just bags without even the festival logo printed on, so although they looked colourful at the event, they didn't advertise the festival when used elsewhere.

In 2019, business mix's headline sponsorship warranted logos on bags again, but we were also mindful of the environment as plastic was of course frowned upon, even though one year we had used biodegradable plastic. I used the opportunity to do a bit of research; cotton bags are re-usable but actually not great for the environment because they use a lot of resources, water and energy to manufacture. And if they don't get re-used many times, they are particularly poor candidates. Plastic bags are of course the bad guys because they end up in landfill and in oceans, but actually if they are reused multiple times and disposed of responsibly, they are actually not so bad. This is because they don't use so much energy per bag and they can also be recycled. The biodegradable versions are

better for landfill and oceans, but they can't be reused as much, they sometimes take ages to degrade depending on the conditions they are left in, and if they get mixed into recycling streams, they can cause problems for the things made out of the recycled material. And, then there are paper bags; they are actually quite resource intensive to manufacture, often can't be used very many times before they fail (or get wet and fall apart), but they are quick to degrade and can be recycled.

In the end, we went with paper bags with rolled paper handles and full colour logos. The larger ones were for the optional delegate bags and the smaller ones were used for the schools' day volunteer packed lunches that we also supplied via the Café H_2O at the Wyche Innovation Centre. We'd used brown paper bags with thank you postcards for the volunteer lunches in the past, so this was a step up to highlight the support of business mix.

The festival's bags over the years, including the Business & Innovation Magazines *that we used to include from our Media Partner. (AB)*

By 2021 I was fed up with bags! Packing them each year was not a lot of fun, and early on we used to pack different things in different bags for different days. Then we had to cart all the bags (hundreds at a time) for each day and more often than not we had stacks left over that needed emptying, sorting and storing or somehow using (rather than throwing away).

WINDOW DRESSING

Finally, it is worth noting that there was actually a fair amount of stuff designed and wheeled out each year to decorate the event and make it look a bit more attractive and professional. In the first year, the expo looked a bit like a jumble sale because the

> THE DOWNSIDE WAS THAT IT WAS ME EACH YEAR WHO TOOK THEM HOME AND WASHED THEM; FORTUNATELY THEY DRIED QUICKLY AND RARELY NEEDED IRONING!

tables lacked tablecloths and not every exhibitor thought to bring one.

So, I ordered a large collection of coloured tablecloths in colours as closely matching our logo as possible and in sizes that were compatible with the Malvern Theatres' trestle tables and round tables. They stood us in good stead, being reused in successive years particularly at the Next Generation Innovators event and the business exhibitions. The downside was that it was me each year who took them home and washed

them; fortunately they dried quickly and rarely needed ironing!

Seeing the difference that a splash of colour made, we also added bright feather flags and gazebos to the prop selection, as you will have seen in the various photos throughout this book. Hanging banners, a podium logo and free-standing stage logos were used as further decoration as the years went by. One issue was that the podium sign (the coloured circles from our logo) could often be affixed upside down and go unnoticed until the event was started, at which point it was suddenly obvious (to me at least!).

We also used pull-up banners for quickly deployable signage about the registration desk, auditorium, seminar rooms and exhibition areas. We used to include sponsors on these at first, but soon realised this rendered them useless the next year when the list of sponsors changed, so I took to having separate sponsor-thanks notices at the registration desk and catering areas. I also made use of a Raspberry Pi digital sign some years, which had dynamic programme information and a live Twitter feed. But I usually found myself trying to troubleshoot it the evening before when there were many other things to do, so this was not a long-lived feature. A more reliable substitute was a series of PowerPoint slides running on an iMac giving programme and sponsor information.

Finally, for those waiting for the proceedings to begin in the auditorium, a similar slide show was prepared for the main screen. This needed editing at the end of each day to show what had been before and what was still to come.

And another bit of window dressing was to have the small team of helpers wear branded polo shirts. These looked good, but they weren't cheap and we needed different sizes and in some cases a few each as the festival lasts days and it wouldn't be good to wear one for the entire week when there was so much lugging of stuff to and from cars at the start and end of each day! O

13.

During the course of running the Malvern Festival of Innovation and the Malvern Science in the Park events, there have been a number of other events and initiatives that have fed into them, come out of them, or just generally been synergistic.

BEYOND THE RAINBOW 2014

In September 2014 I helped the IoP organise a STEM event about the electromagnetic spectrum in the Malvern Library[66]. It was interesting to participate on the organising committee (the

advantage of spreading the load and distributing the tasks was finely balanced against the sheer number of meetings that were convened for a relatively small one day event!). But it was also good to see how well attended the event was by virtue of the high footfall of the venue on a Saturday morning, and I also used the event to advertise the festival that was to follow during the next month[67].

SCIENCE AT THE HIVE

The Worcester library (the Hive) has also hosted science events over the years, sometimes clashing

---

66 'Science show highlights the invisible waves that rule our lives', *Malvern Gazette*, 16th September 2014. www.malverngazette.co.uk/news/11477135.science-show-highlights-the-invisible-waves-that-rule-our-lives/

67 'Science show at Malvern Library is a smash hit, with over a thousand visitors', *Malvern Gazette*, 29th September 2014. www.malverngazette.co.uk/news/11503265. science-show-at-malvern-library-is-a-smash-hit-with-over-a-thousand-visitors/

OTHER EXCURSIONS

with our family day largely because of World Space Week being over that weekend. However, the Hive also organised science nights in the spring to

coincide with British Science Week, and this was another opportunity to advertise the upcoming festival or Science in the Park events.

Given how well the digital microscope was received at the Malvern Library event, I often used this as the means of engagement at these events too[68]. Steve Dawes also joined me with various Raspberry Pi demonstrations, and this turned out to be a useful event for him to test hardware and levels of engagement for things that would appear later at our events.

The festival stand featuring a digital microscope activity and RMS information at the IoP event all about the electromagnetic spectrum. (AB)

---

68 'Microscopy outreach in and around Malvern', *RMS Infocus* magazine, issue 52, 8th December 2018. www.rms.org.uk/library/infocus-magazine/infocus-listing/microscopy-outreach-in-and-around-malvern.html

THE BIG BANG FAIR

As a Fellow of the IET, I have volunteered to help on their stand at the Big Bang Fair in Birmingham NEC on a number of occasions. This has been an excellent opportunity to see a range of national organisations exhibiting on a bigger scale at a major STEM event, and thus gain new ideas, make new contacts and better understand what engages school children.

The Big Bang Fair is a larger event over several days with full scale exhibits that would cost quite a bit to stage. The exhibitors pay to be there and the schools and families that visit also pay an entrance fee, so it is a very different model to our Next Generation Innovators event where sponsorship just about funds it on a much smaller scale and exhibitors and schools get to participate for free.

EVENTS HERE AND THERE

Over the years I've also made a point of attending various events about technology, innovation and entrepreneurship. This is to stay abreast with what's new and on topic, but also to make new connections and find people or organisations that might want to exhibit, participate or speak.

Some have been on a local or small scale, such as the Malvern Small Business Forum, WINN Wednesday events, WCC & MHDC events[69], the new Malvern Technology Network, and so forth. Birmingham has also been fertile ground for making connections; such as the University of Birmingham's Collaboration and Knowledge Exchange (CAKE) meetings, the Silicon Canal network and of course my time there on secondment as a Royal Society Entrepreneur in Residence[70].

69 'Encouraging the next generation of business leaders', *Worcester News*, 8th July 2015. www.worcesternews.co.uk/news/business/13377462.encouraging-the-next-generation-of-business-leaders/

70 'Royal Society announces recipients of first Entrepreneurs in Residence scheme', The Royal Society, 20th March 2018. royalsociety.org/news/2018/03/first-entrepreneurs-in-residence-scheme-recipients-announced/

Previous page top left: Innovisions 2013 and, top right, the group attending the Digital Agenda event in Birmingham in 2017 (Digital Agenda), then, second row, coming second place in the category of Best Example of Innovation in a STEM Programme at Innovisions 2014. (NEF Org.). Third row: The Fox Theatre as the main auditorium for Startup Grind, with, bottom row, the co-founder of LinkedIn Reid Hoffman on stage, (AB)

Institute, CogX, and Startup Grind in Silicon Valley. These tended to have bigger budgets and did things on a grander scale, but provided plenty of inspiration and expanded my network of contacts to entice to Malvern.

RASPBERRY PI JAMS & PIONEERS

Other events have been bigger like the MADE Entrepreneurs Festival, Venturefest, the Business Show, Innovisions organised by NEF: The Innovation

As a direct result of Clive Beale attending the festival in 2013 and bringing along some hundred Raspberry Pi computers for school children to take

Raspberry Pi workshops at the Wyche Innovation Centre were well attended. Bob Bilsland, third row, helped out as a STEM Ambassador, and Paddy Fawcett, fourth row, helped me get them running by leading on many of the activities during the early days. A young Jake Walker, above, has since become a cyber security apprentice at QinetiQ in Malvern. (AB)

away with them, we started a Raspberry Pi club with Paddy Fawcett (and his Little Pi Shop venture) at the Wyche Innovation Centre[71]. In fact, we held one each month directly after school and then one a bit later in the evening for adults and older students. We used the Code Club material (Code Club later merged with Raspberry Pi) and encouraged kids to program in Scratch and python.

Some of the early members like Joe Charrot, Will Scargill and Jake Walker continued with their IT interest during senior school at The Chase and entered the Pioneers programme competition to devise an interesting use for a Raspberry Pi device.

71 'New class attracts Malvern's young computer whizzkids', *Malvern Gazette*, 21st February 2014. www.malverngazette.co.uk/news/11027985.new-class-attracts-malverns-young-computer-whizzkids/

The Chase team at the Google HQ in London as Pioneer winners. The accompanying adults also had a chance to play, and you can see how me and my companion for the day were ecstatic at getting the code working! (AB, latter Raspberry Pi Foundation).

Camp[73]. The team, the Pi Chasers, actually went on to win another competition the following year too[74].

STEM INSPIRATION AWARDS

We didn't win, but Innovate Malvern CIC did come runner up in the national STEM Learning STEM Inspiration Awards 2018 for STEM Employer, Small and Medium Enterprise Award[75]. ○

Above: The IET volunteers including Clive Harding, Mandy Harding and Alison Hodge, preparing for the Raspberry Pi workshop for the Next Generation Innovators schools' day. (AB)
Below: Pictured on the Terrace of the House of Lords at the STEM Inspiration Awards in November 2018.

I popped along to their classroom occasionally to mentor the project and see how they were progressing. Their submission was one of the winners[72], which meant I was able to join them and their parents on a trip to Google HQ in London for a day of Raspberry Pi hacking at their Summer

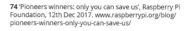

73 'Pioneers Summer Camp 2017', Raspberry Pi Foundation 11th Sep 2017. https://www.raspberrypi.org/blog/pioneers-summer-camp-2017/

74 'Pioneers winners: only you can save us', Raspberry Pi Foundation, 12th Dec 2017. www.raspberrypi.org/blog/pioneers-winners-only-you-can-save-us/

72 'Chase computer science students win Raspberry Pi competition, invited to Google HQ in London', *Malvern Gazette*, 25th July 2017. www.malverngazette.co.uk/news/15432658.chase-computer-science-students-win-raspberry-pi-competition-invited-to-google-hq-in-london/

75 'Top award for tech enterprise Innovate Malvern CIC', *Malvern Gazette*, 5th November 2018. www.malverngazette.co.uk/news/17202247.top-award-tech-enterprise-innovate-malvern-cic/

14.

JUST HOW MUCH WORK?

Not wanting to put a potential organiser off, I thought I'd try to quantify the work required to stage the events. The table shows the number of sub-events each year for the festival, and also the fact that Malvern Science in the Park and TEDxMalvern are single events that required effort.

The organisation files refer to the approximate number of files (emails, documents, etc) in the year's directory. It is not an accurate measure of effort, because not all emails are kept and back-and-forth correspondence may just be retained as one email file. Also, the marketing emails and event collateral were filed in different directories rather than on a yearly basis. So, the column is an underestimate of organisation activity, but captures the amount of work to coordinate venues, speakers, exhibitors, and attendees.

The cost of the events is also interesting and was largely determined by venue hire costs and speaker travel and subsistence (hence the low cost of the virtual events). But also, TEDxMalvern required filming costs to be included. However, the cash cost does not include overheads such as insurance, accounting, bookkeeping, equipment storage, phone, etc that is spread across the year.

THAT'S A WRAP

The cash cost also does not include my time. If a half-time event manager was employed on the National Living Wage (just under £10/hr), then the annual costs would increase by about £10,000 to cover salary, holiday pay, auto-enrolment pension and National Insurance.

During recent years I have kept a record of time spent on different activities, so looking back over these records I have been able to quantify the hours I have spent organising the events. Again, this doesn't cover some of the overhead activity like company administration, accounting and compliance. The table also shows the approx. cost if these were considered as volunteer hours which are currently recognised as being approximately £15 per hour for benchmarking. In reality, my charge out rate for consultancy during this period has been over £175 per hour, so this is more like my opportunity cost (when I could have been undertaking paid consultancy work rather than organising these events!). I haven't tabulated the latter as it is unnerving.

The overall attendance data is estimated based on the subevent data collected at the time. Note that some people attended multiple subevents at the festival, so this is not unique visitors. Also, on

EVENT	NO. OF SUB-EVENTS	ORGANISATION FILES	CASH COST	AB HOURS (AT £15/HR)	TOTAL ATTENDANCE
MFoI 2012	3 (+fringe)	1,000	£12,800	No data	470
MFoI 2013	5	1,600	£17,900	No data	650
MFoI 2014	7	2,000	£22,300	No data	2,600
MFoI 2015	7	2,400	£16,800	No data	2,700
MFoI 2016	8	2,100	£17,500	No data	2,400
MFoI 2017	9	1,900	£14,100	No data	2,300
MFoI 2018	9	1,500	£12,100	340 (£5.1k)	1,500
MFoI 2019	11	2,000	£21,500	500 (£7.5k)	2,200
MFoI 2020 (virtual)	5	400	£300	140 (£2.1k)	2,900
MFoI 2021	8	1,545	£17,800	400 (£6k)	900
MFoI total	72	14,700	£153,100	Est 3500	18,600
MFoI mean	7	1,500	£15,300	350 (£5.2k)	1,900
					£11/person
MSitP 2017	1	900	£3,100	No data	900
MSitP 2018	1	800	£3,700	100 (£1.5k)	1,500
MSitP 2019	1	900	£2,700	75 (£1.1k)	1,400
MSitP 2020 (virtual)	1	600	£700	110 (£1.7k)	2,000
MSitP 2021	1	1100	£2,000	110 (£1.7k)	1,000
MSitP total	1	4300	£12,200	Est 500	6,800
MSitP mean	1	860	£2,400	100 (£1.5k)	1,400
					£3/person
TEDxMalvern 2017	1	300	£1,800	No data	90
TEDxMalvern 2018	1	300	£1,300	34 (£0.5k)	90
TEDxMalvern 2019	1	300	£1,400	32 (£0.5k)	90
TEDxMalvern total	1	900	£4,500	Est 100	90
TEDxMalvern mean	1	300	£1,500	33 (£0.5k)	90
					£22/person

Some metrics for the Malvern Festival of Innovation, Malvern Science in the Park, and TEDxMalvern over the years that I have been organising them.

some Family Days, the Theatres had other events on that drew in crowds that interacted with the exhibition beforehand or during the intermission. Also, the virtual events had a relatively high number of views on line through the Facebook live broadcast, but some of these may only have been short interactions. But equally, these figures don't capture the legacy of video recordings made at the virtual event and at TEDxMalvern in which significant numbers of viewers have followed since (and these continue to rise).

Although there is a lot of analysis that could be done with these numbers, one interesting metric is the organisational cost per person which is the average cash cost plus my volunteer cost divided by the average attendance. The Malvern Science in the Park comes out as best value in that it is the lowest organisational cost per person engaged. This is partly because the programme leverages on the existing contacts of the festival, but also because the venue is high capacity and low cost. TEDxMalvern was relatively expensive because attendance was capped at 100 and there were always a few no-shows, but also because the filming was costly. However, at the time of writing, the on-line engagement of the nine videos have garnered over 20,000 views. So, this actually works out as 10p per person engaged!

BEHIND THE SCENES

Unfortunately, organising an event brings with it some mundane tasks such as writing and collating risk assessments. In the case of the festival, we created general risk assessments and fire risk assessments for the main venues (Malvern Theatres, Coach House Theatres and Three Counties Showground). These had to cover setting up, hosting the event, and the 'tear down' afterwards. We also had to consider risks specific to what was being displayed on exhibition stands, and so requested risk assessments from each exhibitor to cover any hands-on activities beyond our template. This also included risks associated with the presentations (such as at the family show). We also needed public liability insurance to cover the events that were acceptable to venues we were hiring.

When we added the Malvern Science in the Park event, we had an extra set of risk assessments to consider, and more complex activities to review as organisations brought larger exhibits and hosted participatory experiments. This too increased our insurance bill. And holding events soon after Covid required extensive risk mitigation as well, with extra considerations around social distancing and sanitation.

Book keeping also needed to be done to ensure the finances were both recorded but also carefully monitored. We registered Innovate Malvern CIC for VAT which made venue hire less expensive in that we could reclaim the VAT component, but meant we had to charge VAT on event tickets and to sponsors, adding another layer of administration. Of course, beyond quarterly VAT filings, annual accounts and tax submissions also needed to be made.

Running a business entity brings with it a lot of unseen overheads; there is a need to be compliant with privacy and data protection laws, to run a payroll even if pay and expenses are irregular, and then to maintain websites, social media, banking facilities, general insurance and so forth. It is for this reason that it is often beneficial to broaden the activities of the organisation so that these costs and efforts are shared more widely. For example, the festival and the science in the park events combined make more efficient use of the fact that accounts, insurance, compliance and so on are needed anyway for just one.

IN MY SIGHTS

Over the years I have contacted numerous speakers to try to entice them to Malvern to speak at the festival. And with these efforts have come some highly sought-after speakers, including Luke Johnson, Mark Miodownik, Lee Stratford, Sebastian Conran, David Wood, Marcus Du Sautoy, Nick Holzherr, Emily Grossman, Emma Jones, Rashik Parmar, Lucy Rogers, Jeff Lynn, Hilary Sutcliffe, Marcus Chown, Melissa Snover, Ria Lina, Rory

Cellan-Jones, Anna Ploszajski, David Rowan, and Beatrice Freeman.

There are some of course who I've not yet managed to secure. I have tried on several occasions to schedule Jim Al-Kahlili, but despite his gracious replies, we've not yet managed to align the stars. He's usually busy filming, writing his next book, or tied up with university matters at the start of the term in October.

I did meet briefly with Brian Cox at an event and passed him a business card explaining I was determined to find a way for him to visit Malvern during a future festival, but to date this has not been achieved.

I once chatted with Alice Roberts, after she had mentioned the involvement of Birmingham University outreach teams in Malvern during an event she was hosting, and she was receptive to present but I needed to go through her agent who scheduled these things and at the time Covid led to uncertainty about committing to a show.

Alice Roberts at a University of Birmingham event on science outreach and public engagement in which she cited the Malvern Science in the Park as an event the University had participated in.

Helen Czerski, whom attended the same college as me in Cambridge, also kindly replied to my invitation, but was unfortunately too busy to add Malvern to her itinerary in 2016.

I've also hoped to have Lucie Green speak at the Family Show, and indeed suggested that she and her husband Matt Parker both come over with the idea that Matt could perform or host the comedy night so that they could make a weekend of it in Malvern. It was worth a try!

There have been numerous entrepreneurs and business leaders that I have approached too, including Stephen Fitzpatrick from Ovo, Chris

Sheldrick from What3Words, Giles English from Bremont, Samantha Payne from OpenBionics, Ilana Wisby from Oxford Quantum Circuits, Sarah Murray from Buddi, and Martha Lane-Fox to name but a few. All of these would have provided fantastic insights into their business experiences and complemented the programme in the year in mind. Looking at my computer files, I have what I call a 'pool' of prospective speakers that I have contacted or identified over the years running to a few hundred individuals.

There are two challenges with securing audience-attracting speakers. One is their availability in an increasingly hectic world, and the other is the cost. One way to reduce the appearance fee and have a better chance of scheduling them in is to identify those who have just published a relevant book. They will usually have set aside time to promote and tour with the book, will often have a talk ready to accompany it, and with the prospect of selling and signing copies, will generally have a lower appearance fee.

It took me a while to appreciate this strategy, but also as the festival has become better known, so publishers and literary agents have been in touch with me to explore if their author could be included in a future programme which has been a welcome change.

In essence, there is no shortage of great speakers out there. For a festival with as broad a subject area as innovation, there are thought leaders, policy makers, business leaders, entrepreneurs, scientists, broadcasters and more that could fit the bill.

The bigger question is whether the residents of the region really appreciate the effort in bringing them to Malvern enough to support the events by coming to listen to what they have to say. After ten years, my feeling is that there is indeed a core few who really value hearing from these people to enhance their own business, career, knowledge or life. And there are plenty who feel they have little to learn and can't be bothered to find out themselves, never mind encourage their work colleagues, their students or their children to do so.

OTHER EVENTS

One of the challenges with the festival is that it is a spike of activity in the late summer with a concentrated week of events in the autumn. Malvern Science in the Park added some activity in the spring for one day in early summer. As such, there isn't any justification or resource to support one or more members of staff during the year to be employed which then makes growth and sustainability a challenge going forward.

I did have some informal chats with the organisers of what was Malvern Science and Faith Weekend (which became the Malvern Festival of Ideas) to see if some kind of merger or shared resource arrangement might work. Their event, which I believe also started in 2012, is a long weekend in the spring, so complements our activities later in the year. Moreover, they have attracted some high-profile speakers too, including some we have approached. Despite some overlap with scientists, they tend to focus on philosophy and policy whereas we include more on design, business and entrepreneurship. Therefore, pooling effort could help both events, particularly as they too face the challenge of event costs and the stress of organising a multi-day event. So far, the two events continue independently.

MYTOWN FESTIVAL OF INNOVATION

It occurred to me that other towns could benefit from hosting a festival of innovation. This could also help fund the work by providing a critical mass of events during the year; for example the Hay Festival organises literary festivals in other countries. The model I initially went with was that we could do much of the leg work and thus better control the outcome of the event. I wrote on our website:

"Having organised quite a few editions of the Malvern Festival of Innovation, we can see the value that a celebration of creativity brings to a community. Both in terms of energising people and boosting the visitor economy.

We can bring a similar Festival to your own town or district* almost anywhere in the world, leveraging any local heritage, highlighting any local success stories, and helping to bring along world-class science communicators, entrepreneurs and business leaders.

We can tailor the content to fit local existing industry sectors or those ones that you aspire to being part of. You can pick-and-mix business symposia, schools outreach events, family events and gala events using Malvern's previous programmes as a guide. You can choose an event-in-a-day or several events over a longer timeframe. We'll use our experience to guide you and shape the programme to suit your local or regional audience.

And then we'll help market the event with your local stakeholders and through a website at mytown.festival-innovation.com #InnovateMyTown

*We won't do big cities because we just feel they get all the attention and have plenty of resources to stage, large impersonal events. We're here with this initiative to help smaller towns and communities celebrate their heritage and invigorate their future through innovation and entrepreneurship."

We had one informal suggestion to organise the schools' day at an independent school in Effingham, a phone enquiry to organise a festival in a town in Austria, and another website enquiry about hosting an event in Charters Towers, Queensland, Australia.

Another model would be to licence out or franchise the brand, rather like TEDx and Startup Grind which both have independently organised events and chapters around the world.

To date, we haven't embarked on any festivals as to be honest once a year in our home town has been enough!

MyTown Festival
of Innovation

The MyTown Festival of Innovation 'logo'.

MALVERN MAKERSPACE

One on-going idea I have is to try to anchor 'innovation' in the Malvern community all year round with a facility hosting activities in the form of a makerspace, hackspace or Fablab. Malvern is conspicuous in its absence of such an offering, although recently aspects of some of what I had in mind have come about with a local Men's Shed.

A makerspace for those unfamiliar with the concept is a premises equipped with design and fabrication tools built around a community of members and users keen to help, experiment and make stuff. Generally, the kit on hand would include woodworking tools, metal working tools, general workshop tools like a lathe and bench drill, some electronics equipment like soldering iron and oscilloscope, some textile equipment like a sewing machine, more modern fabrication tools like a laser cutter and 3D Printer, and then potentially some computer aided design (CAD) software, etc.

At its most basic, the facility would be open to members a bit like a gym. Subscribers would pay a monthly access fee, be trained on operating the equipment safely, and then pay for additional materials that might be stocked on the premises. Some users could be volunteers responsible for running sessions and helping users on specific equipment, and they may get reduced membership fees for their assistance.

Beyond this baseline, there would be scope to offer paid classes in all aspects of art, design and engineering. For example, evening classes delivered by qualified instructors or capable hobbyists could include wood working, metal working, welding, soldering, sewing, fine art, picture framing, jewellery making, electronic circuits, 3D printing, fashion, and

so forth. In a town like Malvern where the Malvern Art School was always well attended, there would be plenty of demand which in turn could be a good business model to fund the facility.

Other demographics that could be served would include school students visiting the facility to access equipment not available in their classroom, as well as families attending at the weekend to undertake activities (which could include more conventional things like pottery or arts-and-craft, but also more innovative activities like Raspberry Pi jamming, 3D-printing, microscopy, etc). Local companies wishing to prototype products or packaging could also pay an access fee, and larger companies could sponsor the facility which in turn could facilitate discounts for their employees to join.

And Malvern has a number of other groups like the Repair Café and Malvern Inventors Club that could benefit from a permanent facility of this nature.

Furthermore, depending on the size of the facility, there could also be a café, a reading space, some small offices for businesses to rent adjacent to the workshops, and even seminar and training rooms for larger classroom events, talks and exhibitions. Just like a sport centre, sessions could be run for men only (like the aforementioned Men's Shed), women only, specific classes or general access.

Emma refers to this idea of mine as a 'maker-loss', because although on paper it sounds like it ought to be well received and sustainable, in reality running premises is expensive and time consuming. There are lots of overheads (utilities, insurance, cleaning, and business rates, to name a few) and lots of headaches (repairs, maintenance, staffing issues, etc). Such a facility would ideally be open during the day to members and schools, in the evening for classes and members, and at the weekend to members and families.

Despite this, the result could be a means to sustain the festival; as any staff involved in running the maker space during the year could also stage the festival, and creative output from the maker space could also be featured at the festival as an annual showcase. And many of the clientele of the facility would also find the festival of interest which means a user base of the former (individuals, schools and businesses) would also lead to a growing participation of the latter. And the revenues and overheads of the maker space (membership fees, sponsorship, company overheads and staffing) could be shared across the festival activity.

Time will tell if this idea comes to fruition. I've pondered about it for years, getting tacit support from various stakeholders and even attempting (unsuccessfully) to secure significant grant support to get one started. My main issue is bandwidth and energy. Having run the Wyche Innovation Centre for over ten years, I know the challenges and responsibilities that operating a commercial facility brings, and I don't currently have the energy reserves left to start a new one as described here. Maybe I'll recover enough in the future to take it on, or better still, maybe someone else will seize on the opportunity and make a success out of the concept for Malvern.

WHAT'S NEXT?

As I finish writing in mid 2022, with ten Malvern Festivals of Innovations, five Malvern Science in the Parks, and three of my TEDxMalvern's completed, the hope is that these events will continue in the town but not involve much, if any, effort, from me. TEDxMalvern has been successfully handed on to new champions, and there is certainly interest in continuing the festival and science in the park events in future years. They aren't rocket science to stage, but they do require lots of work and attention to detail. Take your eye off any of the many balls and costs can spiral, events can disappoint, and stakeholders can be disgruntled.

THANK YOU AND GOODNIGHT

It has been quite a journey over the last ten years. I've met many fantastic people who have given their time and expertise to participate in the festival and related events. There is no doubt that students have been enthused, families have been entertained, entrepreneurs have been supported, and the town has benefitted.

There have been little moments of joy that have made it worthwhile and proven that ideas can be turned into reality. Seeing the festival flags flutter on Church Street, sitting on stage chatting with Rory Cellan-Jones, standing in a packed auditorium to introduce a day of cyber security, seeing Great Malvern's station rebranded as The Innovation Station, spotting people remark on the *Innovation Express* on Twitter, introducing IET Young Woman Engineers of the Year to seminar rooms full of school students, chatting to science comedians in the green room, and sitting at the front of the cinema as the family show speaker captivates a young audience are just some of my highlights that have made it all worthwhile.

And writing this all up has been cathartic for sure. It has been interesting to delve back into the archives and recall some of the stories behind the events, and to reflect on the things that worked, those that didn't, and ponder the varied feedback I've had over the years.

I have often said that the next festival will be my last, and as we neared ten, that seemed like a good number to settle on. It is not clear at the moment whether I'll be drawn back in to organise more editions, or whether I'll find a way for someone else to take the reins so I can step back and step down. It would be a shame for ten years work to stop so dramatically, but equally if there is any value in what has been achieved, it is probably time for someone else to inject their own enthusiasm into it and keep it alive for the future.

Afterall, the last thing a festival of innovation should do is stagnate and become mundane. It should either re-invent itself spectacularly or recognise its natural lifespan and blink out of existence. And there is a lot to be said for quitting whilst ahead. ○

APPENDIX A – TIMELINE

2012

Date	Event
Thursday 8th November 2012	Opening plenary
	Cyber Security symposium
	Digital Media symposium
	Exhibition of innovative technology & service companies, and organisations supporting innovation
	Formal dinner
Friday 9th November 2012	Opening plenaries
	Business symposium (innovation, invention and inception)
	Materials & Devices symposium
	Business symposium (pitching for finance)
	Sustainability & Environment symposium
	Business symposium (growth, export and exit)
	Exhibition of innovative technology & service companies, and organisations supporting innovation

2013

Date	Event
Thursday 7th November 2013	Opening plenary
	Cyber Security symposium
	The Business of Innovating symposium
	Engineering & Manufacturing symposium
	Exhibition of innovative technology & service companies, and organisations supporting innovation
	Formal dinner
Friday 8th November 2013	Opening plenary
	Environment & Sustainability symposium
	The Business of Innovating symposium including pitching panel
	Tech for Tourism symposium
	Exhibition of innovative technology & service companies, and organisations supporting innovation
Saturday 9th November 2013	The Family Show – Innovative stuff! The materials revolution
	Hands-on family day exhibition promoting STEM

Date	Event
Wednesday 1st October 2014	VIP networking breakfast
	Advanced Engineering & Manufacturing symposium
	Exhibition of organisations showcasing innovative products & services, and organisations supporting innovation
Thursday 2nd October 2014	VIP networking breakfast
	Cyber Security symposium
	Exhibition of organisations showcasing innovative products & services, and organisations supporting innovation
	Next Generation Innovators schools' day
	Formal dinner
Friday 3rd October 2014	VIP networking breakfast
	The Business of Innovating symposium including pitching panel
	Exhibition of organisations showcasing innovative products & services, and organisations supporting innovation
	Aston Martin comes to Malvern schools' afternoon
Saturday 4th October 2014	The Family Show – Creative minds
	Hands-on family day exhibition promoting STEM

Date	Event
Tuesday 6th October 2015	Next Generation Innovators schools' day
Wednesday 7th October 2015	Festival opening plenary
	Agri-Tech: Food & Drink for Thought symposium
	Exhibition of agritech companies, and organisations supporting innovation
Thursday 8th October 2015	The Business of Innovating symposium including pitching panel
	Formal dinner
Friday 9th October 2015	VIP networking breakfast
	Cyber Security & Big Data symposium
	Exhibition of cyber security companies, and organisations supporting innovation
	Aston Martin returns to Malvern schools' afternoon
Saturday 10th October 2015	The Family Show – Tiny particles, big impact!
	Hands-on family day exhibition promoting STEM
Sunday 11th October 2015	Electric Vehicle Innovation Showcase with Malvern Hills Electric Automobile Association (electrAA)

2016

Date	Event
Sunday 2nd October 2016	Prelude – *The Matrix* concluding the Malvern Outdoor Cinema Season
Monday 3rd October 2016	Embarkation – with Marcus du Sautoy
Tuesday 4th October 2016	Next Generation Innovators schools' day
Wednesday 5th October 2016	Startup Stories evening
Thursday 6th October 2016	VIP networking breakfast
	Cyber Security & IoT
	Exhibition of cyber security companies, and organisations supporting innovation
	Formal dinner
Friday 7th October 2016	The Business of Innovating symposium including elevator pitches
	Exhibition of organisations showcasing innovative products & services, and organisations supporting innovation
	Creative Careers schools' afternoon
Saturday 8th October 2016	The Family Show – Progress in many dimensions
	Hands-on family day exhibition promoting STEM

2017

Date	Event
Wednesday 26th April 2017	TEDxMalvern
Saturday 1st July 2017	Malvern Science in the Park
Sunday 1st October 2017	Prelude – *Star Wars* concluding the Malvern Outdoor Cinema Season
Monday 2nd October 2017	Embarkation – with Brian Clegg
Tuesday 3rd October 2017	Next Generation Innovators schools' day
Wednesday 4th October 2017	Automotive Advances symposium
	Startup Stories evening
Thursday 5th October 2017	Cyber Security & AI symposium
	Exhibition of cyber security companies, and organisations supporting innovation
	Formal dinner
Friday 6th October 2017	The Business of Innovating symposium including elevator pitches
	Exhibition of innovative technology & service companies, and organisations supporting innovation.
	Creative Careers schools' afternoon
Saturday 7th October 2017	The Family Show – Connected planet to extended universe
	Hands-on family day exhibition promoting STEM

Date	Event
Wednesday 25th April 2018	TEDxMalvern
Saturday 30th June 2018	Malvern Science in the Park
Monday 8th October 2018	Embarkation – with Edmund Hunt
Tuesday 9th October 2018	Next Generation Innovators schools' day
Wednesday 10th October 2018	Environment & Sustainability symposium
	Startup Stories evening
Thursday 11th October 2018	VIP networking breakfast
	Cyber Security & Quantum Computing symposium
	Exhibition of cyber security companies, and organisations supporting innovation
	Formal dinner
Friday 12th October 2018	Blockchains & Bitcoins symposium
	Creative Careers schools' afternoon
Saturday 13th October 2018	The Family Show – Inspiration, exploration & adventure
	Hands-on family day exhibition promoting STEM

Date	Event
Wednesday 24th April 2019	TEDxMalvern
Saturday 29th June 2019	Malvern Science in the Park
Monday 7th October 2019	Prelude – Innovation shorts
	Embarkation – with Marcus Chown
Tuesday 8th October 2019	Next Generation Innovators schools' day
Wednesday 9th October 2019	The Business of Innovating fireside chats
	Startup Stories evening
Thursday 10th October 2019	Cyber Security: Securing SMEs symposium
	Exhibition of cyber security companies, and organisations supporting innovation
	Formal dinner
Friday 11th October 2019	Environment & Sustainability symposium
	Creative Careers schools' afternoon
	LOL science comedy night
Saturday 12th October 2019	The Family Show – The small and the wobbly
	Hands-on family day exhibition promoting STEM

2020

Date	Event
Saturday 27th June 2020	Malvern Science in the Park (virtual)
Monday 5th October 2020	Embarkation – with Andy Stanford-Clark (virtual)
Tuesday 6th October 2020	Next Generation Innovators schools' symposium (virtual)
Wednesday 7th October 2020	Startup Stories evening (virtual)
Friday 9th October 2020	Environment & Sustainability symposium (virtual)
Saturday 10th October 2020	The Family Show – In the mind's eye (virtual)

2021

Date	Event
Saturday 26th June 2021	Malvern Science in the Park
Monday 4th October 2021	Embarkation – with Rory Cellan-Jones
Tuesday 5th October 2021	Next Generation Innovators schools' day
Wednesday 6th October 2021	Thriving Three Counties podcast live with Dan Barker
	Innovation Insights evening
Thursday 7th October 2021	Innovation on the Hills symposium
	Exhibition of innovative technology & service companies, and organisations supporting innovation.
	Formal dinner
Friday 8th October 2021	LOL science comedy night
Saturday 9th October 2021	The Family Show
	Hands-on family day exhibition promoting STEM

APPENDIX B – SPONSORS AND SUPPORTERS

Thanks to all the sponsors and supporters over the
years that enabled the events to be staged.

Name	Details
Artwork Creative Ltd https://artwork-creative.com/	Bronze sponsor: 2012, 2013
BAE Systems https://www.baesystems.com/	Palladium sponsor: 2017, 2018 Silver sponsor: 2015
BCS, the Chartered Institute for IT https://www.bcs.org/	Bronze sponsor: 2018, 2019 Bronze sponsor (MSitP): 2017, 2018 Supporter: 2015
BetaDen https://www.beta-den.com/	Gold sponsor: 2019 Silver sponsor: 2021
Bishop Fleming https://www.bishopfleming.co.uk/	Gold sponsor: 2013, 2014
BlockMark Technologies https://www.blockmarktech.com/	Silver sponsor: 2018, 2020
Bloom.Space https://www.bloom.space	Bronze sponsor: 2020 Venue supporter: 2021
BrandRefinery https://www.brandrefinery.co.uk/	Bronze sponsor: 2021
Business & Innovation Magazine https://www.businessinnovationmag.co.uk/	Media partner: 2017, 2018, 2019, 2020, 2021
Business mix https://business-mix.com/	Platinum sponsor: 2019 Platinum sponsor (MSitP): 2019
Cisco https://www.cisco.com/	Platinum sponsor: 2015
Coach House Theatre https://www.coachhousetheatre.co.uk/	Venue supporter: 2021
Department for International Trade (formally UK Trade & Investment) https://www.great.gov.uk/	Gold sponsor: 2014 Silver sponsor: 2013 Supporter: 2012
Fleet Line Markers https://www.fleetlinemarkers.co.uk/	Travel partner: 2016
FSB https://www.fsb.org.uk/	Networking sponsor: 2016
GD PR & Media Ltd (now Conteur Ltd) https://www.conteur.co.uk/	Supporter: 2012
GE Aviation https://www.geaviation.com/	Bronze sponsor: 2018, 2021
Global Entrepreneurship Week https://www.genglobal.org/uk	Supporter: 2012, 2013
GWR (formally First Great Western) https://www.gwr.com/	Travel partner: 2013, 2014, 2015, 2016, 2017, 2018, 2019

HCR Law (Harrison Clark Rickerbys Solicitors) https://www.hcrlaw.com/	Palladium sponsor: 2017 VIP breakfast sponsor: 2014, 2015
Hewett Recruitment https://www.hewett-recruitment.co.uk/	Silver sponsor: 2014 Sponsor (TEDxMalvern): 2017
HP https://www.hp.com/	Gold sponsor: 2014, 2015
IASME Consortium https://iasme.co.uk/	Gold sponsor: 2019
IDS INDATA https://www.idsindata.co.uk/	Platinum sponsor: 2015
Innovate Malvern https://www.innovatemalvern.com/	Organiser: 2015, 2016, 2017, 2018, 2019, 2020, 2021 Organiser (MSitP): 2017, 2018, 2019, 2020, 2021 Sponsor (TEDxMalvern): 2017, 2018, 2019
Innovate UK (formally Technology Strategy Board) https://www.gov.uk/government/organisations/innovate-uk	Lead partner: 2013 Network sponsor: 2017
InfoSec People https://www.infosecpeople.co.uk/	Networking sponsor: 2018
Institute for Advanced Motorists (now IAM RoadSmart) https://www.iamroadsmart.com/	Fringe event sponsor: 2015
Institute of Physics https://www.iop.org/	Gold sponsor (MSitP): 2017, 2018, 2019, 2020, 2021 Bronze sponsor: 2016, 2017, 2018, 2019, 2020, 2021 Supporter: 2013, 2014, 2015
Institution of Engineering and Technology https://www.theiet.org/	Silver sponsor: 2016 Bronze sponsor: 2017, 2018, 2019, 2021 Bronze sponsor (MSitP): 2017, 2018, 2019, 2020, 2021 Supporter: 2013, 2014, 2015
Institution of Mechanical Engineers https://www.imeche.org/	Silver sponsor: 2016 Silver sponsor (MSitP): 2018, 2019 Bronze sponsor: 2017, 2018, 2019, 2020, 2021 Bronze sponsor (MSitP): 2017, 2020, 2021 Supporter: 2013, 2014, 2015
IntaPeople https://www.intapeople.com/	Networking sponsor: 2016
Interlocutor Services	Bronze sponsor: 2014
JEMI UK	Supporter: 2012, 2013
Key IQ Ltd https://www.key-iq.com/	Organiser: 2012, 2013, 2014
Lockheed Martin https://www.lockheedmartin.com/	Platinum sponsor: 2014
Malvern College https://www.malverncollege.org.uk/	Bronze sponsor: 2013 Venue supporter: 2014, 2017, 2018, 2019
Malvern Cyber Security Cluster https://malvern-cybersecurity.com/	Bronze sponsor: 2014, 2015

Malvern Hills District Council https://www.malvernhills.gov.uk/	In association with: 2012, 2013, 2014, 2015, 2016, 2017, 2018, 2019, 2020, 2021 Supporter (MSitP): 2017, 2018, 2019, 2020, 2021 Sponsor (TEDxMalvern): 2017, 2018, 2019
Malvern Hills Science Park https://www.mhsp.co.uk/	Bronze sponsor: 2013, 2015, 2016, 2017, 2018 Sponsor (TEDxMalvern): 2017, 2018, 2019
Morgan Motor Company https://www.morgan-motor.com/	Venue supporter: 2017
Malvern Panalytical Ltd (formally Malvern Instruments) https://www.malvernpanalytical.com/	Silver sponsor: 2013, 2014, 2015, 2016, 2017, 2018, 2019, 2021 Bronze sponsor: 2012
Malvern Town Council https://www.malverntowncouncil.org/	Venue supporter: 2021 Supporter (MSitP): 2017, 2018
National Cyber Skills Centre	Silver sponsor: 2014
Nesta https://www.nesta.org.uk/	Supporter: 2012
Ordnance Survey GeoVation https://geovation.uk/	Silver sponsor: 2014
QinetiQ Plc https://www.qinetiq.com/	Platinum sponsor: 2012, 2013, 2014, 2015, 2016 Gold sponsor: 2017
QualitySolicitors Parkinson Wright https://www.qualitysolicitors.com/parkinsonwright	Gold sponsor: 2013
Quest for Future Solutions https://www.questforfuturesolutions.co.uk/	Supporter: 2018, 2019
Randall & Payne https://www.randall-payne.co.uk/	Networking sponsor: 2016
RIFT Technology https://www.rifttechnology.com/	Gold sponsor: 2018
Royal Microscopical Society https://www.rms.org.uk/	Bronze sponsor: 2016, 2017 Speaker sponsor: 2013 Supporter: 2014, 2015
Royal Society of Chemistry https://www.rsc.org/	Bronze sponsor: 2016
Santander Corporate & Commercial https://www.santandercb.co.uk/	Gold sponsor: 2013, 2014
SME Solicitors https://www.smesolicitors.co.uk/	VIP breakfast sponsor: 2014
STEM Learning (formally STEMNET) https://www.stem.org.uk/	Supporter: 2014
Sutcliffe & Co https://www.sutcliffeinsurance.co.uk/	Bronze sponsor: 2021
TextLocal Ltd https://www.textlocal.com/	Gold sponsor: 2012, 2013
The Elmley Foundation https://www.elmley.org.uk/	Venue supporter: 2021
The Hive https://www.thehiveworcester.org/	Supporter: 2021
The Royal Society https://royalsociety.org/	Bronze sponsor: 2020

Three Counties Showground https://www.threecounties.co.uk/	Gold sponsor: 2016, 2017 Venue supporter: 2014, 2018
UKRI Innovate Edge https://www.innovateukedge.ukri.org/	Official partner: 2021
UK Cyber Security Forum https://www.ukcybersecurityforum.com/	Silver sponsor: 2016, 2017, 2018, 2019 Bronze sponsor: 2014, 2015
West Midlands Railway (formally London Midland) https://www.westmidlandsrailway.co.uk/	Travel partner: 2015, 2016, 2017, 2018, 2019, 2021 Travel partner (MSitP): 2021
West Midlands Railway Your Community Your Fund https://www.westmidlandsrailway.co.uk/about-us/your-community-your-fund	Supporter: 2021 Supporter (MSitP): 2021
Wild Edric Media https://www.wildedricmedia.com/	Official film partner (TEDxMalvern): 2017, 2018, 2019
WINN Worcestershire https://winn-hub.com/	Bronze sponsor: 2017, 2018, 2019, 2021 Networking sponsor: 2016 Sponsor (TEDxMalvern): 2017, 2018, 2019
Winton https://www.winton.com/	Silver sponsor: 2015
Worcester City Council https://www.worcester.gov.uk/	Gold sponsor: 2019 Silver sponsor: 2017, 2018 Bronze sponsor: 2020 Bronze sponsor (MSitP): 2020 Supporter (MSitP): 2018
Worcestershire Ambassadors https://www.worcestershireambassadors.com/#!event-list	Bronze sponsor: 2017, 2018, 2019
Worcestershire County Council https://www.worcestershire.gov.uk/	Gold sponsor: 2014, 2015 Silver sponsor: 2013 Bronze sponsor: 2012
Worcestershire Local Enterprise Partnership https://www.wlep.co.uk/	Gold sponsor: 2013, 2014, 2017 Gold sponsor (MSitP): 2017 Bronze sponsor: 2012, 2016, 2018, 2019, 2020, 2021 Bronze sponsor (MSitP): 2018, 2019, 2020, 2021
Worcestershire Proof of Concept	Networking sponsor: 2014
World Class Worcestershire	Bronze sponsor: 2016
Wyche Innovation Centre https://www.wyche-innovation.com/	Silver sponsor: 2016, 2017, 2018, 2019, 2020 Bronze sponsor: 2012, 2013, 2014, 2015
Wynne Jones IP https://www.wynne-jones.com/	Platinum sponsor: 2016
Yoti https://www.yoti.com/	Palladium sponsor: 2017

APPENDIX C – ROLL CALL

A list of speakers in alphabetical order (based on their surname), along with their affiliation at the time, the date and title of their talk(s) and where available their LinkedIn profile / Wikipedia entry / personal website address.

Name	Details
anon	CESG Service Owner Industry Schemes 6-10-2016. Cyber Essentials 2020
John Abbott	Director of Business Growth and Partnerships at Yoti 5-10-2017. The future of identity management https://www.linkedin.com/in/johnjabbott/
Omolola Adeyemi	Technical Product Associate at Crossword Cybersecurity Plc 7-10-2021. Pitch about Rizikon product https://www.linkedin.com/in/lola-a-53871043/
Katie Alcott MBE	Founder of FRANK Water 26-4-2017. From contracting dysentery to delivering clean water (TEDxMalvern) https://www.linkedin.com/in/katie-alcott-mbe-034a89/
Tom Alcott	CEO of BlockMark Technologies Ltd 3-10-2017. Blockchain and bitcoin 5-10-2017. Certification on the blockchain 9-10-2018. New kids on the block 12-10-2018. Certification and NFTs on the blockchain 7-10-2019. BlockMark Registry – certificates on the blockchain 8-10-2019. New kids on the block 6-10-2020. New kids on the blockchain (virtual) 5-10-2021. New kids on the block 7-10-2021. BlockMark Technologies pitch https://www.linkedin.com/in/tomalcott/
Yasmin Ali	Chartered Engineer & Women's Engineering Society Young Woman Engineer 2013 8-10-2019. Engineering the world https://www.linkedin.com/in/yasmin-ali-a9655426/
Jamie Akhtar	CEO of CyberSmart 5-10-2017. Our startup journey & the GCHQ Accelerator (co-speaker) 10-10-2019. Defending the nation: the future of SME cyber security https://www.linkedin.com/in/jamieakhtar/
Caroline Alliston	STEM Educator and author of Technology for Fun series of books 27-6-2020. Engineering a balloon-powered buggy (pre-record) 27-6-2020. Coloured wheel spinner (pre-record) https://www.linkedin.com/in/caroline-alliston-a8897412/
Ruth Allsopp	Operations Coordinator at Worcester Foodbank and Director at Worcestershire LitFest & Fringe 6-10-2021. In conversation with Dan Barker https://www.linkedin.com/in/ruth-allsopp-6a81283b/
Neil Anderson	Managing Director and Owner of Qcom Outsourcing Ltd 7-10-2016. Panel member at pitching session https://www.linkedin.com/in/theoutsourcer/

Heather Angell	STEM Outreach and Public Engagement Intern at University of Wolverhampton 27-6-2020. Home-grown crystals (pre-record) https://www.linkedin.com/in/heatherangell/
Dr Megan Argo	Lecturer at the University of Central Lancashire 7-10-2017. Around the Universe in 60 minutes https://www.linkedin.com/in/drmeganargo/
Paul Ashcroft	Co-founder of The Ludic Group 9-10-2019. How organisations can thrive in a connected world 'fireside chat' https://www.linkedin.com/in/paul-ashcroft-ludic/
Dr Diane Aston	Training and Education Executive at Institute of Materials, Minerals and Mining 2-10-2104. Materials in action 6-10-2015. Materials in action https://www.linkedin.com/in/diane-aston-6b778478/
John Atherton	Founder & CTO, Surevine Ltd 9-10-2015. The rise of the social network: Are cyber criminals planning their attacks on Facebook? https://www.linkedin.com/in/johnpaulatherton/
Elliott Atkins	Head of Cyber Intelligence at QinetiQ 8-11-2012. Inadvertent data leakage https://www.linkedin.com/in/elliottatkins/
David Atkinson	Director at Fortitude Cyber Security 5-10-2017. Real-time cognition for cyber defence https://www.linkedin.com/in/david-atkinson-50028b156/
Andy B	CTO Economy & Society Engagement Sector, National Cyber Security Centre 5-10-2017. Protecting our digital landscape
Richard Baker	Chartered Electrical Engineer 27-6-2020. The magic of numbers (pre-record)
Harriett Baldwin MP	Member of Parliament for West Worcestershire 9-10-2015. Opening address 30-06-2019. Opening remarks at Malvern Science in the Park 11-10-2019. Opening address https://www.linkedin.com/in/harriett-baldwin-b18985194/
Mike Bandar BEM	Founding Partner at Turn Partners 4-10-2017. On Silicon Canal, with a paddle https://www.linkedin.com/in/mikebandar/
Lucy Barkas	Founder of 3WH 6-10-2021. In conversation with Dan Barker https://www.linkedin.com/in/lucybarkas/
Dan Barker	Owner of Dan Barker Studios and Host of the Thriving Three Counties Podcast 6-10-2021. Host of Thriving Three Counties Podcast Live session https://www.linkedin.com/in/danbarkerstudios/
Polly Barnfield OBE	CEO of Maybe* 6-10-2017. Innovation in retail technology 6-10-2017. Panel member at pitching session https://www.linkedin.com/in/pollybarnfield/
Andy Bates	Executive Director UK & EMEA, Global Cyber Alliance 10-10-2019. Innovation at a small scale https://www.linkedin.com/in/andy-bates-3107b41/

Dalim Basu	Chairman of the BCS North London Branch, the Chartered Institute for IT 9-10-2018. Exciting careers in computing. https://www.linkedin.com/in/dalim-basu-a66288/
Kevin Baughan OBE	Chief Development Officer at Innovate UK 7-10-2016. Innovation economies: a UK perspective 7-10-2016. Panel member at pitching session https://www.linkedin.com/in/kevinbaughan/
Peter Baynham	VP Product Engineering at GE Aviation 7-11-2013. Global research centres and GE's approach to innovation https://www.linkedin.com/in/pete-baynham/
Clive Beale	Director Educational Development at Raspberry Pi Foundation 7-11-2013. Creative coding with a Raspberry Pi
Tony Bennett	Managing Director at Coomber Electronic Equipment 7-11-2013. Final destination: how to make lifts safer (co-presenter) https://www.linkedin.com/in/tony-bennett-97492228/
Sonal Bhadane	Global Product Specialist – Clinical Applications at Elekta Ltd 9-10-2018. New innovations in medical physics and radiotherapy https://www.linkedin.com/in/sonalbhadane/
John Bibby	Managing Director at JBY Engineering & STEM Ambassador 27-6-2020. 3-2-1 blast off (pre-record) https://www.linkedin.com/in/john-bibby-9832b524/
Ian Blackburn	Head of Delivery at IntaPeople 6-10-2016. VIP Breakfast panel session on cyber skills https://www.linkedin.com/in/ianblackburnhw/
Prof. Simon Blackmore	Head of Engineering at Harper Adams University 7-10-2015. Towards robotic agriculture https://www.linkedin.com/in/simonblackmore/
Kevin Blacktop	Head of Delivery at Birmingham Centre for Rail Research & Education (BCRRE), University of Birmingham 6-10-2020. HydroFlex – the UK's first mainline hydrogen powered train (co-presenter, virtual) https://www.linkedin.com/in/kevin-blacktop-aa51b676/
Jane (Garrett) Blennerhassett	Enterprise Director at the Quantum Technology Enterprise Centre at the University of Bristol 9-10-2019. Fancy starting, scaling and listing a tech. venture? https://www.linkedin.com/in/janegarrett/
Simon Bond	Head of Enterprise & Innovation Centre at University of Bath 9-11-2012. The cleantech start-up challenge https://www.linkedin.com/in/simonbond/
Katy Boom	Director of Sustainability at University of Worcester 9-11-2012. Skilling students in sustainability – preparing the next generation https://www.linkedin.com/in/katy-boom-73355684/
Vincent Borgraeve	Co-founder of FloWide 7-10-2021. Pitch about FloWide https://www.linkedin.com/in/vincentborgraeve/

Dr David Bott	Non-Executive Chairman of Oxford Biomaterials 1-10-2014. The epidemiology of innovation 3-10-2014. Panel member at pitching session 8-10-2015. Navigating Innovate UK for R&D support 8-10-2015. Panel member at pitching session 9-10-2019. PR for the innovators – how to raise your profile and tell your brand story 'fireside chat' https://www.linkedin.com/in/david-bott-65a07729/
Chris Boulton	Independent VC / Private Equity Professional 9-11-2012. Panel member at pitching session https://www.linkedin.com/in/chris-boulton-662160/
Ben Boxall	Director of Just EVs Ltd 11-10-2015. Buy an EV for under £8,000 – an EV story
Dr David Bozward	Senior Lecturer in Entrepreneurship, University of Worcester 8-10-2015. Panel member at pitching session https://www.linkedin.com/in/bozward/
Steve Braithwaite	Managing Director at ASH Wireless Electronics 7-11-2013. Where are we heading with wireless communication? https://www.linkedin.com/in/steve-braithwaite-a7a463/
Anna Bright	Chief Executive at Sustainability West Midlands 11-10-2019. Sustainability and innovation in the West Midlands https://www.linkedin.com/in/anna-bright-09a2b941/
Andrew Brock	Manufacturing Engineering Manager at Malvern Instruments 1-10-2014. Additive manufacturing: 3D printing and building-block particles (co-presenter) https://www.linkedin.com/in/andrew-brock-b32a5b55/
Mike Brooks	Senior Lecturer at University of Gloucestershire and Head at BrooksDesigns 8-11-2013. Interpreting an ancient past as you walk the Geopark Way
Dr Mark Broomfield	Author and Air Quality Specialist Consultant at Ricardo-AEA 9-10-2020. Every breath you take: a user's guide to the atmosphere (virtual) https://www.linkedin.com/in/markbroomfield1/
Bob Brown	Partner at CMC Partners 8-11-2013. Panel member at pitching session https://www.linkedin.com/in/bob-brown-77b49213/
Dr Carla Brown	CEO of Game Doctor 8-10-2019. Creative thinking to tackle Grand Challenges workshop (co-host) 6-10-2020. From microbiology to educational computer gaming (virtual) https://www.linkedin.com/in/carlalouisebrown/
Prof John Bryson	Professor of Enterprise and Economic Geography in the Department of Strategy and International Business at the University of Birmingham 11-10-2019. End-user innovation or DIY citizen place-making and local infrastructure provision https://www.birmingham.ac.uk/staff/profiles/business/bryson-john.aspx
Lt Col Ian Buchanan	Cyber Policy and Plans at Ministry of Defence 8-11-2012. Cyber space, cyber power, cyber what? https://www.linkedin.com/in/ian-buchanan-msc-ceng-cism-crisc-miet-aciis-ccp-a429a645/

Dr Adrian Burden	Serial Technology Entrepreneur 1-7-2017. Science busking at Malvern Science in the Park on microscopy 30-6-2018. Science busking at Malvern Science in the Park on carbon 29-6-2019. Science busking at Malvern Science in the Park on carbon 7-10-2019. LiveWorkGo – the new hyperlocal event app 26-6-2021. Science busking at Malvern Science in the Park on carbon https://www.linkedin.com/in/adrianburden/
Jessica Burden	Cyber Security Analyst at The IASME Consortium 10-10-2019. Cost-effective monitoring solutions for small companies and individuals (co-speaker) https://www.linkedin.com/in/jessica-burden-74b335174/
Sam Burden	Student at University of Bath 27-6-2020. Paper aeroplanes – art or science? (virtual)
Ian Burnett	Director of JEMI UK 1-10-2014. JEMI – a model for commercial advantage through a fully integrated supply chain https://www.linkedin.com/in/ian-burnett-2749029/
Ian Butcher	Rack Scale Design Program Manager at Intel Corporation 10-10-2019. Business resilience in a data centric world https://www.linkedin.com/in/ian-butcher-82b7682/
Matthew Cartwright	Director of Business Development at Zovolt 5-10-2017. Introducing Streembit™ peer to peer networks and securing IoT https://www.linkedin.com/in/bankrolledinc/
Rory Cellan-Jones	Principal Technology Correspondent at the BBC 4-10-2021. In conversation about his book Always On, Hope and Fear in the Social Smartphone Era https://en.wikipedia.org/wiki/Rory_Cellan-Jones
Mark Champkins	Inventor in Residence at the Science Museum 4-10-2014. Creativity and new products https://www.linkedin.com/in/mark-champkins-60332b/
Dr Roger Chandler	Managing Director at Keynetix 8-11-2013. An SME's story: selling software to a global customer base https://www.linkedin.com/in/rogerchandler/
James Chappell	CTO at Digital Shadows 9-10-2015. Walk in the shadows https://www.linkedin.com/in/jameschappellds/
Dr Rebecca Charnock	Industrial Research Development Manager at AberInnovation, Aberystwyth University 9-10-2020. Circular economies and sustainable systems: an inside look at the latest biorefining and waste valorisation collaborative research at AberInnovation (virtual) https://www.linkedin.com/in/rebecca-charnock/
Dr Bal Choda	Engineer and STEM Ambassador at Aston Martin Lagonda Ltd 3-10-2014. Designing and engineering an Aston Martin sports car 9-10-2015. Designing and engineering an Aston Martin sports car 6-10-2017. Designing and engineering an Aston Martin sports car 11-10-2019. Designing and engineering an Aston Martin sports car https://www.linkedin.com/in/bal-choda-ceng-mimeche-5b83341b/
Marcus Chown	Writer & Broadcaster 7-10-2019. Bonkers things about the Universe https://en.wikipedia.org/wiki/Marcus_Chown
Mike Church	Software Engineer at QinetiQ 27-6-2020. A career in 1s and 0s (virtual) https://www.linkedin.com/in/churchmike/

Dr Caroline Clark	Director of Operations at KETS Quantum Security 11-10-2018. Building a Quantum Technology Enterprise in the South West https://www.linkedin.com/in/carolinehclark/
Dibble Clark	Chairman at 3SDL 7-11-2013. Filling the skills void https://www.linkedin.com/in/dibbleclark/
David Clarke	CTO of The Trust Bridge 10-10-2019. Data breaches and how to manage them? (workshop) https://www.linkedin.com/in/1davidclarke/
Brian Clegg	Writer 2-10-2017. Science and technology – the goal-driven golem https://en.wikipedia.org/wiki/Brian_Clegg_(writer)
Simon Clifford	Director of Technology and Digital Transformation at Northamptonshire Office of the Police and Crime Commissioner (OPCC) 11-10-2018. Police cyber alarm & cyber response portal, and their genesis through Northamptonshire Cyber Security Forum https://www.linkedin.com/in/simonclif/
Robert Cobley	Partner at Harrison Clark Rickerbys 6-10-2017. Exploiting new business ideas through commercialisation https://www.linkedin.com/in/robcobley/
Claire Cockerton	Serial entrepreneur https://www.linkedin.com/in/clairecockerton/
Neil Coker	Group Vice Principal, Curriculum at WCG 11-10-2018. Update on the National Cyber Skills Centre https://www.linkedin.com/in/neil-coker-503a852a/
Sam Collett	Co-founder of Practically.io and Lecturer at University of Worcester 5-10-2021. Educating AI on the way https://www.linkedin.com/in/collettsam/
Sebastian Conran	CEO of Sebastian Conran Associates 8-11-2015. The design paradigm https://www.linkedin.com/in/sebastian-conran-6638468/
Dr Tim Cook	Non-Executive Director and former Head of ISIS Innovation, Oxford 7-11-2013. Realising economic value from good ideas https://www.linkedin.com/in/tim-cook-28509226/
James Cooksey	Director Growth Capital at Santander Corporate & Commercial 7-11-2013. Innovative financing for the fast-growing innovative businesses https://www.linkedin.com/in/james-cooksey-b021203b/
Dr Quentin Cooper	Presenter and science consultant 4-10-2014. Geeks, freaks & eggheads: the pervasive image of scientists, inventors & innovators https://www.linkedin.com/in/quentin-cooper-7a9386/
Sarah Cosgriff	Freelance Science Communicator 30-6-2018. Science busking at Malvern Science in the Park on forces & flight 29-6-2019. Science busking at Malvern Science in the Park on forces & flight 27-6-2020. Why astronauts need a space suit (virtual, in two parts) https://www.linkedin.com/in/sarah-cosgriff/
Martin Cordey	Consultant at Catalyst Corporate Finance and Lyceum Capital 6-10-2017. Panel member at pitching session https://www.linkedin.com/in/martin-cordey-38779a7b/

Peter Cripps	Software Architect at IBM 12-10-2018. Hyperledger Fabric – a blockchain platform for business https://www.linkedin.com/in/petercripps/
Margaret Cross	Volunteer at IOP 27-6-2020. Floating and sinking, from dancing raisins to lava lamps (pre-record) 27-6-2020. Do try this at home: bubble mania (pre-record)
Dr Steve Cross	Founder of Science Showoff 8-10-2021. Host of Science Comedy Night https://www.linkedin.com/in/steve-cross-7628162/
Graedon Crouch	Cyber Security Specialist at QinetiQ 27-6-2020. Round and round the Möbius strip.
Beryl Cuckney	Founder of Malvern Business Academy 6-10-2017. Panel member at pitching session https://www.linkedin.com/in/berylcuckney/
Claire Cunningham	Director of Rockallwight PR 9-10-2019. PR for the innovators – How to raise your profile and tell your brand story 'fireside chat' https://www.linkedin.com/in/cunninghamclaire/
Derek Cunningham MBE	STEM Ambassador 27-6-2020. Software defined radio (pre-record) https://www.linkedin.com/in/derek-cunningham-mbe-83445b117/
Jonathan Davies	CTO at Pervade Software 9-10-2015. How to identify invisible cyber attacks https://www.linkedin.com/in/jonathan-davies-0147853/
Dr Nigel Davies	Principal Engineer, Secured Navigation Team at QinetiQ 7-11-2013. Secured navigation and Galileo, Europe's 21st century satellite navigation system
Steve Dawes	STEM Ambassador 27-6-2020. Raspberry Pi sensing and actuation (virtual) 27-6-2020. Mentos & Fizz (virtual)
Dr Roberto Desimone	Manager, Strategic Innovation (Disruptive Technologies) at BAE Systems Applied Intelligence 11-10-2018. Opportunities for optimising cyber threat assessment and management using quantum computing algorithms https://www.linkedin.com/in/roberto-desimone-0067789/
Azam Din	Graduate Engineer at JLR 12-10-2018. Designing and manufacturing a luxury car (co-speaker)
Professor Peter Dobson OBE	Director of Begbroke Science Park, University of Oxford 8-11-2012. Tangible products and intangible services – innovation in 2012 https://www.linkedin.com/in/peter-dobson-5702b91/
Graham Dodgson	Consultant at The Trust Bridge 9-10-2019. The business of intellectual property 'fireside chat' https://www.linkedin.com/in/grahamdodgson/
Col. (retired) John Doody	Director at Interlocutor Services 8-11-2012. State of play in cyber security and information assurance 2-10-2014. Cyber to the citizen https://www.linkedin.com/in/colonel-john-doody-fbcs-fcmi-citp-ciis-miod-9151961/
Jon Downing	Business Development Director at business mix 9-10-2019. The challenges and approach of taking a product to market 'fireside chat' https://www.linkedin.com/in/jon-downing/

Sqn Ldr James Doyle MBE	Officer Commanding 591 Signals Unit, Royal Air Force 6-10-2016. The emergent defensive cyber operations challenge
Prof. Marcus du Sautoy OBE	Simonyi Professor for the Public Understanding of Science and a Professor of Mathematics at the University of Oxford 3-10-2016. What we cannot know 4-10-2016. The number mysteries and other mathematical curiosities https://en.wikipedia.org/wiki/Marcus_du_Sautoy
Steve Dunn	Growth Accelerator programme account manager at PERA 9-11-2012. Helping your business to grow sustainably https://www.linkedin.com/in/steveadunn/
Ian B Dunne	Science Inspirer and Director at Do Science 1-7-2017. Science busking at Malvern Science in the Park https://www.linkedin.com/in/ian-b-dunne-78779a4/
Ian Dury	CEO of Prizsm Technologies 7-10-2021. Pitch about Prizsm Technologies https://www.linkedin.com/in/ianrdrury/
Lucy Eckersley	Wildlife Biologist, Science Presenter and Comedian 8-10-2021. Comedy sketch 9-10-2021. A talk on the wild side https://www.linkedin.com/in/eckersley94/
Hilary Edgeley	Retired teacher 27-6-2020. The rock cycle (virtual)
Jonathan Ellwood	Community SOC Manager at The IASME Consortium 10-10-2019. Cost-effective monitoring solutions for small companies and individuals (co-speaker) https://www.linkedin.com/in/jonathan-ellwood-98b06010b/
Dr Sean Elvidge	Postdoctoral Fellow at University of Birmingham 30-6-2018. Science busking at Malvern Science in the Park on space weather https://www.linkedin.com/in/sean-elvidge-bb743248/
Chris Ensor	Deputy Director for Cyber Skills and Growth at National Cyber Security Centre 6-10-2015. A brief on the UK's new National Cyber Security Centre. 11-20-2018. Cyber security – getting the basics right 10-10-2019. Raising the cyber security bar https://www.linkedin.com/in/chris-ensor-955791105/
Dr Ozak Esu	Electrical Engineer at Cundall, 2017 IET Young Woman Engineer of the Year 9-10-2018. Engineering in the real world https://www.linkedin.com/in/ozakesu/
Paul Farrer	TV and film music composer 8-11-2012. Creativity while the clock is ticking 26-4-2017. Composing creatively on the run (TEDxMalvern) https://en.wikipedia.org/wiki/Paul_Farrer
Paddy Fawcett	Director at Invizio Ltd 7-10-2019. Design for success 7-10-2021. Pitch about Invizio https://www.linkedin.com/in/paddyfawcett/
Syd Femtinos	Founder & Director of Inquisitive Explorers 27-6-2020. What does a plant's leaf do with sunlight? (virtual) 27-6-2020. The big bang (virtual) https://www.linkedin.com/in/syd-femtinos/
Tom Fenton	Co-founder & CEO of Veritherm 9-10-2020. Energy efficiency: measuring away the performance gap (virtual) https://www.linkedin.com/in/tom-fenton-62943ab0/

Sophie Ficek	Independent HR consultant & Associate at business mix 9-10-2019. Top 5 People Tips as you scale your business 'fireside chat' https://www.linkedin.com/in/sophie-ficek-44605417/
Giovanni Finocchio	Investment Director at Midven 9-11-2012. Panel member at pitching session https://www.linkedin.com/in/giovanni-finocchio-b7971013/
Alexander Fisher	CEO of Saturn Bioponics 7-10-2015. The rise of bioponics to economically meet food demand https://www.linkedin.com/in/alex-fisher-05290052/
Ben Fletcher	Head of Electric Vehicle Programme at Renault 8-11-2013. Progress & promise of electric vehicles (co-presenter) https://www.linkedin.com/in/ben-fletcher-8a19783a/
Dr Rowena Fletcher-Wood	Freelance Science Writer and Tutor at Science Gecko 1-7-2017. Science busking at Malvern Science in the Park https://www.linkedin.com/in/rowena-fletcher-wood-b432a35a/
Neil Fogarty	Serial entrepreneur 3-10-2014. Riding the wave 3-10-2014. Panel member at pitching session https://www.linkedin.com/in/neildfogarty/
Mo Follis	Director at STEMworks 27-6-2020. Drip drop tick tock (virtual) https://www.linkedin.com/in/mo-follis-624a3730/
Beatrice Freeman	Freelance speaker, comedian and singer 7-10-2021. After dinner speech https://www.linkedin.com/in/beatrice-freeman-34036a20/
Rhea Freeman	PR, Marketing and Social Media Consultant & Coach 25-4-2018. Supporting rural communities with social media, and why it's a force for good (TEDxMalvern) https://www.linkedin.com/in/rheafreeman/
Mike Gadd	Manager of Aircraft Certification at UK CAA 2-10-2014. Cyber – one aviation perspective https://www.linkedin.com/in/michael-gadd-75450210a/
Charles Garfit	Head of Manufacturing at Santander UK 1-10-2014. The creation and funding of innovation in the manufacturing sector https://www.linkedin.com/in/charlesgarfit/
Cathy Garner	Leadership and Relationship Coach 24-4-2019. The science of relationships (TEDxMalvern) https://www.linkedin.com/in/cathygarner-love/
Debbie Garside	CEO of GeoLang Ltd 9-10-2015. The future of information governance – Jaguar Land Rover as a case study https://www.linkedin.com/in/debbiegarside/
James Geary	Head of Corporate Tax at Randall & Payne 7-10-2016. Intellectual property: the best kept secret in business strategy (co-speaker) https://www.linkedin.com/in/jamesgearyrandallpayne/
Christopher Gell	Researcher at Extreme Robotics Laboratory, University of Birmingham 6-10-2020. Tour of the Extreme Robotics Laboratory (virtual)
Katy Gibson	Institute of Physics, Midlands 26-6-2020. Opening remarks at Malvern Science in the Park
Mike Gillespie	Managing Director of Advent IM Ltd 6-10-2016. Smart buildings and the Internet of Things require even smarter people https://www.linkedin.com/in/adventimmikegillespie/

Ian Glover	President at Bloodhound SSC 1K 7-11-2013. The Bloodhound Super Sonic Car challenges https://www.linkedin.com/in/bloodhoundssc/
Nicky Godding	Co-owner and Editor-In-Chief of *Business & Innovation Magazine* 7-10-2020. An enthusiast for the printed word (virtual) https://www.linkedin.com/in/nicky-godding-4489b710/
Dr Mike Goodfellow-Smith	Director of QUEST For Future Solutions 9-11-2012. Innovating for sustainability 10-10-2018. Symposium Chair, Environment & Sustainability 10-10-2018. Starting up without costing the earth 11-10-2019. Symposium Chair, Environment & Sustainability https://www.linkedin.com/in/mikegoodfellowsmith/
Paul Gordon	Partner at Willans LLP solicitors 7-10-2016. Intellectual property: the best kept secret in business strategy (co-speaker) https://www.linkedin.com/in/paulgordon/
Gary Green	UK Regional Sales & Business Development at AXA XL 10-10-2019. Cyber – what are the numbers? https://www.linkedin.com/in/gary-green-05389820/
Dr Sam Gregson	Bad Boy of Science & Particle Physicist at University of Cambridge 10-10-2015. Hunting the Higgs (Large Hadron Colliding) - a particle-physics comedy! 11-10-2019. Science Comedy Night act https://www.linkedin.com/in/sam-gregson-0447816b/
Dr Emily Grossman	Science broadcaster 8-10-2016. Body building in three dimensions https://en.wikipedia.org/wiki/Emily_Grossman
Graeme Hackland	IT/IS Director at Lotus F1 Team 7-11-2013. IT risk management at the Lotus F1 team https://www.linkedin.com/in/graemehackland/
Dr Chris Hamlett	Lecturer at the Nottingham Trent University, later Henry Royce National Outreach Officer, University of Birmingham 30-6-2018. Science busking at Malvern Science in the Park on surface tension 8-10-2019. Crash helmets for eggs workshop 27-6-2020. The surprising structures of surfaces (virtual) 27-6-2020. Surfactants and elephant's toothpaste (virtual) 26-6-2021. Science busking at Malvern Science in the Park on surfactants and foaming agents https://www.linkedin.com/in/chris-hamlett-2ba77012/
Mike Hankins	Growth Accelerator Access to Finance Coach 8-11-2013. Panel member at pitching session https://www.linkedin.com/in/mike-hankins-39b02010/
Andrew Hanson MBE	Senior Research Scientist, National Physical Laboratory 10-10-2020. Our colourful world, and how we measure it (virtual) https://www.linkedin.com/in/andrew-hanson-mbe-16704b8/
Dr David Hardman MBE	Chief Executive Officer at Birmingham Science Park Aston 8-11-2012. Real estate and virtual places for the entrepreneurs of the future https://www.linkedin.com/in/dahardman/
Dr Jonathan Hare	Science communicator & broadcaster 9-11-2013. The carbon revolution 6-11-2015. Wonderful molecules https://en.wikipedia.org/wiki/Jonathan_Hare
Tim Harper	Chief Executive Officer at Cientifica 8-11-2012. After dinner speaker on nanotechnology https://www.linkedin.com/in/timharper/

Prof Adam Hart	Professor of Science Communication at University of Gloucestershire 4-10-2016: A world of helpful bacteria https://en.wikipedia.org/wiki/Adam_Hart
Roland Harwood	Co-Founder & Networks Partner at 100%Open 3-10-2014. Ordnance Survey GeoVation open innovation workshop https://www.linkedin.com/in/rolandharwood/
Paul Hawes	Founding Managing Director of Smartbox Assistive Technology and Sensory Software International 9-10-2019. One big family – the Smartbox story https://www.linkedin.com/in/paul-hawes-6a1ba024/
Richard Heathcote	Director at R&J Sustainability Consulting and Director at Cool Farm Alliance 7-10-2015. Towards sustainability in food & drink upstream supply chains https://www.linkedin.com/in/richard-heathcote-9151478/
Andy Heiron	Head of Electric Vehicle Programme at Renault 8-11-2013. Progress & promise of electric vehicles (co-presenter) https://www.linkedin.com/in/andy-heiron-64243827/
Lloyd Henning	Managing Director of Fox Dog Studios Ltd 11-10-2019. Science Comedy Night act https://www.linkedin.com/in/lloyd-henning-5576b6166/
Richard Henson	Senior Lecturer at University of Worcester 30-6-2018. Science busking at Malvern Science in the Park as George Boole 29-6-2019. Science busking at Malvern Science in the Park as Charles Babbage 9-10-2018. Charles Babbage talk, alongside Ada Lovelace 8-10-2019. Charles Babbage talk, alongside Ada Lovelace 26-6-2021. Science busking at Malvern Science in the Park as Charles Babbage https://www.linkedin.com/in/richardhenson/
Pete Hill	Inventor and founder of Petvictus 12-10-2018. From garage workshop to BBC's *Dragons' Den*
Stuart Hillmansen	Lecturer at the University of Birmingham 6-10-2020. HydroFlex – the UK's first mainline hydrogen powered train (co-presenter, virtual)
John Hinton	Actor and musician 8-10-2021. Science comedy sketch https://www.facebook.com/johnny.acecraft
Dr Andrew Holding	Lecturer in Biomedical Sciences at the University of York 27-6-2020. The scourge of scurvy, and other nutritious stories (virtual) https://www.linkedin.com/in/andrewholding/
Dr Gordon Hollingworth	Director of Software Engineering at Raspberry Pi Foundation 1-10-2014. Raspberry Pi compute module and the Internet of Things https://www.linkedin.com/in/gordon-hollingworth-056a322/
Nikki Hollier	Owner and Creator of Border in a Box 7-10-2019. Border in a Box: turning an idea into a product and taking it to market https://www.linkedin.com/in/nikkihollier/
Nick Holzherr	Founder & CEO of Whisk.com 5-10-2016. From *The Apprentice* to 'Head Chef' – the unfolding story of Whisk https://www.linkedin.com/in/nickholzherr/
Richard Horne	Commercial Manager at Heber 9-11-2012. The future of real-time control https://www.linkedin.com/in/richardjwhorne/
Andrew Humphries	Dealmaker for Global Entrepreneur Programme UKTI 8-11-2012. Digital clusters in the UK and around the globe https://www.linkedin.com/in/andrew-humphries-5638003/

Matthew Humphreys	Graduate Engineer at JLR 12-10-2018. Designing and manufacturing a luxury car (co-speaker)
Dr Edmund Hunt	EPSRC Doctoral Prize Fellow at University of Bristol 8-10-2018. Swarm robotics: holding a mirror up to nature? https://www.linkedin.com/in/edmundh/
Newall Hunter	Adventurer & IT consultant 5-10-2017. After dinner speech on tech preparations extreme expeditions https://www.linkedin.com/in/newall-hunter/
Rowena Innocent	Engineering Director at Malvern Instruments 9-11-2012. Innovation is a team sport https://www.linkedin.com/in/rowena-innocent-39792514/
Paul Isherwood	Head of Technical & Quality at SHS Group Drinks Division 8-11-2013. From wild imagination to sustainable impact https://www.linkedin.com/in/paul-isherwood-ab09662/
Alina Ivan	Science Presenter at Braintastic! and Researcher at Institute of Psychiatry, Psychology and Neuroscience, Kings College London 9-10-2021. Come to your senses! https://www.linkedin.com/in/alina-ivan-638b8759/
Barry Jackson	Director of Aspire Academy 6-10-2015. Getting the job you want workshop 4-10-2016. Getting the job you want workshop 4-10-2017. If you want to change the world workshop https://www.linkedin.com/in/aspireacademy/
Huw James	Adventurer and Science Presenter 13-10-2018. Space adventures https://www.linkedin.com/in/huwmjames/
Tom Jarratt	Construction Director at UK Flood Barriers 9-11-2012. Being innovative in a conservative market https://www.linkedin.com/in/tom-jarratt-86189340/
Marie Jenkins	Founder of Advance your Wellbeing 9-10-2018. The mindset of an entrepreneur workshop 8-10-2019. The mindset of an entrepreneur workshop 6-10-2020. Innovation comes out of creativity! (virtual) 5-10-2021. The mindset of an entrepreneur workshop https://www.linkedin.com/in/mariejenkinsayw/
Simon Jenner	Serial Entrepreneur & Co-founder of Urban Coffee Company 8-10-2015. Exploring innovation through entrepreneurship 8-10-2015. Panel member at pitching session https://www.linkedin.com/in/sijenner/
Prof Paul Jennings	Professor at WMG, University of Warwick 4-10-2017. The road to autonomous, connected vehicles https://www.linkedin.com/in/paul-jennings-b9059219/
Luke Johnson	Chairman of Risk Capital Partners and StartUp Britain 9-11-2012. Innovation in business 9-11-2012. Panel member at pitching session https://en.wikipedia.org/wiki/Luke_Johnson_(businessman)
Adam Jolly	Business Journalist, and Consultant Editor at Kogan Page 7-11-2013. After dinner speaker on innovation https://www.linkedin.com/in/adam-jolly/
Prof. Cliff Jones	CTO at ZBD Displays, later Professor at School of Physics & Astronomy, University of Leeds 9-11-2012. ZBD Displays and the retail edge 24-4-2019. How display technology impacts all our lives (TEDxMalvern) https://www.linkedin.com/in/cliff-jones-b349a526/

Emma Jones MBE	Founder of Enterprise Nation & SME Representative for Crown Commercial Service 6-10-2017. Four ways to grow your business from today! https://www.linkedin.com/in/emma-jones-8063536/
Garrick Jones	Co-founder of The Ludic Group 9-10-2019. How organisations can thrive in a connected world 'fireside chat' https://www.linkedin.com/in/garrick-jones-a56398162/
Dr Marty Jopson	Writer and Presenter 12-10-2019. Invisible worlds https://www.martyjopson.co.uk/
Dr Simon Kampa	CEO of Senseye 7-10-2015. The Internet of Things meets farming https://www.linkedin.com/in/simonkampa/
Dr Sophie Kain	Science and Business Presenter, Director of Elite Learning Ltd. 13-10-2018. More inspiration, less perspiration https://www.linkedin.com/in/sophie-kain-4927492/
Zubair Khan	CEO of Tranchulas 6-10-2016. Offensive cyber security https://www.linkedin.com/in/zubairkhan/
Dr Martin Khechara	Associate Professor for Engagement in STEM at the University of Wolverhampton 11-10-2019. Science Comedy Night act 12-10-2019. Mission transmission 27-6-2020. Bouncing eggs (pre-record) 26-6-2021. Science busking at Malvern Science in the Park https://www.linkedin.com/in/martin-khechara/
Irra Ariella Khi	CEO of VChain Tech (now Zamna) 6-10-2016. Replacing trust with proof: why blockchain is the future of Individual Identity https://www.linkedin.com/in/irra-ariella-khi/
Anne Lise Kjaer	CEO of Kjaer Global 6-10-2016. A guide to the future https://www.linkedin.com/in/anne-lise-kjaer-210411/
Stuart Laidlaw	CEO of Cyberlytic 5-10-2017. Using AI for advanced cyber threat detection https://www.linkedin.com/in/stuartlaidlaw/
Dr Kate Lancaster	Plasma and Fusion Industrial Officer for the York Plasma Institute 10-10-2015. Nuclear fusion - the challenges of building a star on earth https://www.linkedin.com/in/kate-lancaster-47076146/
Brett Laniosh	Managing Partner at Catshill Design 6-10-2015. Digital leaders initiative workshop 4-10-2016. Become a digital leader workshop 3-10-2017. Build your own robot workshop https://www.linkedin.com/in/laniosh/
Jeremy Laycock	Director at Ripjar 2-10-2014. Finding valuable insights in big data https://www.linkedin.com/in/jeremy-laycock-a876614/
Claire Lyes	Executive Director at STEMworks 27-6-2020. Drip drop tick tock (virtual) https://www.linkedin.com/in/claire-lyes-212487a7/
Kate Lees	Patent Attorney at Harrison Clark Rickerbys 6-10-2017. Protecting your intellectual property for added value https://www.linkedin.com/in/kate-lees-5136522a/

Prof. Fiona Lettice	Professor at Norwich Business School 3-10-2014. The emerging innovation landscape https://www.linkedin.com/in/fiona-lettice-1275621/
Tom Levitt	Author and Consultant at Sector 4 Focus 11-10-2019. The role of business in tackling environmental and sustainability issues https://www.linkedin.com/in/tom-levitt-s4f/
Paul Lewis	CTO at Crossword Cybersecurity 9-10-2015. Bridging the valley of death – cyber style! https://www.linkedin.com/in/paulslewis/
Stuart Lewis	Head of Cyber Security at the University of South Wales 6-10-2016. VIP Breakfast panel session on cyber skills https://www.linkedin.com/in/stuart-lewis-28b9a21b/
Dr Mark Lewney	The Rock Doctor and Patent Examiner at Intellectual Property Office 8-10-2016. Rock guitar in eleven dimensions https://www.linkedin.com/in/mark-lewney-a0a31721/
Bryan Lillie	CTO Cyber Security at QinetiQ 9-10-2015. Cyber skills – a dampener on innovation? https://www.linkedin.com/in/bryan-lillie-fciis-miet-153827b/
Dr Ria Lina	Comedian, actress and writer 11-10-2019. Host of Science Comedy Night https://en.wikipedia.org/wiki/Ria_Lina
Dr Hannah Little	Senior Lecturer in Science Communication at UWE Bristol 8-10-2021. Science comedy sketch 8-10-2021. Science comedy sketch https://people.uwe.ac.uk/Person/HannahLittle
Dr John Liverton	Product Manager at Mazak 1-10-2014. Subtractive manufacturing: multitasking machine tools – what's new? https://www.linkedin.com/in/john-liverton-507225b/
Dr David Lowe	Director at Syndial Ltd 7-10-2019. The future is decentralised (but why should we care?)
Jeff Lynn	Executive Chairman and Co-Founder of Seedrs 10-10-21. Sowing small seeds and reaping big businesses https://www.linkedin.com/in/jefflynn/
Sarah Macdonell	Principal Mechanical Engineer at Malvern Instruments 1-10-2014. Additive manufacturing: 3D printing and building-block particles (co-presenter) https://www.linkedin.com/in/sarah-macdonell-30a18791/
Prof. Malcolm Macleod	Chief Scientist, Research and Innovation, & Dean of Fellows at QinetiQ 27-6-2020. Opening remarks (virtual Malvern Science in the Park) https://www.linkedin.com/in/malcolm-macleod-1b386828/
Mike MacIntyre	Chief Scientist at Panaseer 9-10-2015. Implementing the security data lake in the real world https://www.linkedin.com/in/mike-macintyre-panaseer/
Dr Jamie Mackrill	Lecturer in the Faculty of Engineering at the Dyson School of Design Engineering, Imperial College London 7-10-2016. Design engineering: linking design thinking and engineering thinking https://www.linkedin.com/in/jamie-mackrill-68424a64/
Dr Alex Malm	Senior Development Scientist at Malvern Panalytical 6-10-2020. Tour of Malvern Panalytical laboratories (virtual) https://www.linkedin.com/in/alex-malm-45691048/

Prof Louise Manning	Director of Knowledge Exchange, Royal Agricultural University, Cirencester 9-10-2020. Smart food systems: challenges and benefits for greater transparency in the food supply chain (virtual) https://www.linkedin.com/in/louise-manning-a120745/
Eleanor Matthews	MD of WorkFutures 12-10-2018. Demystifying blockchain for supply chain https://www.linkedin.com/in/eleanorwinn/
Jon Matthews	Stand-up Comedian 8-10-2021. Comedy sketch https://www.facebook.com/JonMatthewsUK/
Prof Sir John McCanny CBE	Entrepreneur and emeritus Regius Professor at Queen's University Belfast 11-10-2018. Accelerating economic growth through research and innovation in cybersecurity https://en.wikipedia.org/wiki/John_McCanny
Nick McCloud	Managing Director at Handy Little Modules Ltd 3-10-2017. Up, up and away . . . launching a Raspberry Pi with a weather balloon https://www.linkedin.com/in/nick-mccloud/
Prof Mark Miodownik MBE	Professor of Materials and Society at University College London 9-11-2013. Stuff matters https://en.wikipedia.org/wiki/Mark_Miodownik
Benjamin Milsom	UK MD at Echosec Systems Ltd 9-10-2015. Social engineering – an underrated threat? https://www.linkedin.com/in/benjamin-milsom-12045856/
Animesh Mishra	CEO of Quickbird Making farming cool again: one byte at a time https://www.linkedin.com/in/siranimesh/
Hazel Moore OBE	Chairman at FirstCapital 8-11-2013. Pitching your innovative business to investors 8-11-2013. Panel member at pitching session https://www.linkedin.com/in/hazelmoore/
Tim Moran	CEO of LuJam Cyber 10-10-2019. Eliminating commodity cyber threats in SMEs https://www.linkedin.com/in/morantim/
Romeo Morgado	Business Development Manager at Industry 4.0 Solutions (I4S) 7-10-2021. Pitch about I4S https://www.linkedin.com/in/rom%C3%A9o-morgado-mba-b3059a5b/
Charles Morgan	Chairman of the Morgan Motor Company 9-11-2012. Innovation in the British motorcar industry https://en.wikipedia.org/wiki/Charles_Morgan_(automaker)
Prof Philip Moriarty	Professor at University of Nottingham's School of Physics & Astronomy 8-10-2019. Universal harmonies: when physics meets music meets maths https://en.wikipedia.org/wiki/Philip_Moriarty
Imogen Mornemont	Founder of Penny and a Pearl 7-10-2019. Creativity-filled packs delivered to your door
John Morton	CEO of CPM 6-10-2017. Entrepreneur: second mover advantage https://www.linkedin.com/in/jfmorton/
Philip Mossop	COO of Pentatonic 11-10-2019. Opportunities to be creative in the circular economy https://www.linkedin.com/in/philipmossop/
Jim Murphy	Cofounder of Malvern Hills Electric Automobile Association (electrAA) 11-10-2015. Opening and closing remarks

Orla Murphy	Acoustic and Audio Engineer at Jaguar Land Rover, 2015 IET Young Woman Engineer of the Year. 4-10-2016. The future of infotainment, and a career that brings together music & engineering https://www.linkedin.com/in/orla-murphy-cork/
Dr Jayne Nation	Business Development Director at Wynne Jones IP 7-10-2016. Panel member at pitching session https://www.linkedin.com/in/jayne-nation-72500a56/
Janina Neumann	Business Owner of Janina Neumann Design 8-10-2019. Creative thinking to tackle Grand Challenges workshop (co-host) 6-10-2020. Creating social impact through design (virtual) https://www.linkedin.com/in/janinaneumann/
Michael Newnham	Director at Systematic Innovation 7-11-2013. The predictability of product development and how to exploit it https://www.linkedin.com/in/michaelnewnham/
Dr Maddy Nichols	Chief Operating Officer of Spin Up Science 6-10-2021. Spinning-up science and tech to go commercial https://www.linkedin.com/in/drmaddynichols/
Beverley Nielsen	Associate Professor / Executive Director of Institute for Design & Economic Acceleration at Birmingham City University 11-10-2019. Building success on design and innovation https://www.linkedin.com/in/beverley-nielsen-3636a515/
Dr Mark O'Dell	Principal IT Analyst at QinetiQ 1-7-2017. Science busking at Malvern Science in the Park on fossils 30-6-2018. Science busking at Malvern Science in the Park on fossils 29-6-2019. Science busking at Malvern Science in the Park on fossils 27-6-2020. A look back in time: Fossils from the Malverns and the Cotswolds (virtual, in two parts) 26-6-2021. Science busking at Malvern Science in the Park on fossils https://www.linkedin.com/in/mark-o-dell-a221941a/
Tonya O'Donnell	Marketing & Sales Director of RIFT Technology 10-10-2018. Energy efficient actuators to save the world https://www.linkedin.com/in/tonyaodonnell/
Dr Colin O'Halloran	Technical Director at D-RisQ 7-11-2013. Cyber security, Turing's legacy 6-10-2016. Verifying cyber attack properties 5-10-2017. Cyber defence by swarm intelligence 11-10-2018. Swarm intelligence to enhance cyber security https://www.linkedin.com/in/colin-o-halloran-9887975/
Melanie Oldham OBE	CEO of Bob's Business 10-10-2019. Cybersecurity is getting personal https://www.linkedin.com/in/melanieoldham/
Dionne Oliver	Principal Innovation Consultant at QinetiQ 7-10-2016. An engineer's career at the cutting-edge of the defence industry https://www.linkedin.com/in/dionne-oliver-157a6a22/
Tim Onions	STEM Ambassador 27-6-2020. Do try this at home: science with a washing line (pre-record)
Hilarie Owen	Chief Executive of The Leaders' Institute 9-10-2019. Leading your business in a changing world 'fireside chat' https://www.linkedin.com/in/hilarieowen/
David Page	CEO of business mix 9-10-2019. How organisations can thrive in a connected world 'fireside chat' 10-10-2019. After dinner speech https://www.linkedin.com/in/david-page-6787731/

Rich Palk	UK Cyber Engagement Lead at Lockheed Martin 2-10-2014. Lockheed Martin's approach to cyber security https://www.linkedin.com/in/rich-palk-66138751/
Dr Chris Parker	Head of GeoVation Outreach at Ordnance Survey 8-11-2013. GeoVation and the next challenge 3-10-2014. Ordnance Survey GeoVation open innovation workshop https://www.linkedin.com/in/chrisjparker1/
Carolyn Parkinson	Technology Transfer Specialist at International Institute for Product and Service Innovation (WMG, University of Warwick) 9-11-2012. Exploiting academic links for innovation https://www.linkedin.com/in/carolyn-parkinson-1389ab17/
Rashik Parmar MBE	IBM Technical Executive – Europe & IBM Distinguished Engineer 6-10-2017. Finding your space in digital disruption https://www.linkedin.com/in/rashikparmar/
Dr Vassilis Pelekanos	Senior Research Fellow at University of Nottingham 27-6-2020. Tricking our brain and how we research it (virtual)
Dr Neil Pennington	Strategic Advisor at Energy Web Foundation & Founder Pennovate Ltd. 12-10-2018. A personal journey through blockchain: energy to fintech and back again https://www.linkedin.com/in/theneilpenners/
Professor John Perkins CBE	Chief Scientific Advisor at BIS 1-10-2014. The future of UK manufacturing https://www.linkedin.com/in/john-perkins-cbe-05660532/
Rhys Phillips	Research Engineer at Airbus Group 3-10-2017. Thunderbolts and lightning – are they really frightening? https://www.linkedin.com/in/rhysphillips/
Dr Emma Philpott MBE	CEO of The IASME Consortium Ltd 8-10-2015. Protecting your business from cyber crime 11-10-2018. Community SOC to offer affordable Internet protection for the most vulnerable 9-10-2019. Leading your business in a changing world 'fireside chat' 10-10-2019. Small company certifications and the skills gap https://www.linkedin.com/in/emphilpott/
Chris Pinder	Chris Pinder, Founder HDANYWHERE and OneAV 7-10-2020. Entrepreneurship in high definition (virtual) https://www.linkedin.com/in/chris-pinder-b3b3471b3/
Ellis Pitt	Design Associate at Design Council 8-11-2013. Designing for future success 6-10-2015. Hands-on product design workshop 4-10-2016. Hands-on product design workshop https://www.linkedin.com/in/ellis-pitt-07ab2512/
Dr Anna Ploszajski	Materials Scientist, Writer, and freelance Science Communicator 5-10-2021. Handmade: a scientist's search for meaning through making https://www.linkedin.com/in/anna-ploszajski-a9381144/
Dr Andrew Powell	CEO of Asia BioBusiness 9-11-2012. Innovation and the role of risk communication https://www.linkedin.com/in/andrew-d-powell-b542b83/
Dr Louise Pryor	Director of Callund Consulting Ltd 10-10-2018. Addressing issues of risk and insurance with climate change https://www.linkedin.com/in/louisepryor/
Tim Pullen	Operational Cyber Technical Authority at BAE Systems Applied Intelligence 5-10-2017. Keynote on cybersecurity & AI https://www.linkedin.com/in/t1m-p/

Dr Ilija Rašović	Lecturer at University of Birmingham 27-6-2020. A chat about carbon (virtual) https://www.linkedin.com/in/ilijarasovic/
Emma (Kirby) Reading	Schools Engagement Manager at SANS Institute 6-10-2020. Discover cyber security (virtual) https://www.linkedin.com/in/emma-reading-03452093/
Jeremy Redfern	Partner and Head of Commercial Department at QualitySolicitors Parkinson Wright 7-11-2013. Commercial law and commercialisation https://www.linkedin.com/in/jeremy-redfern-24676811/
Modwenna Rees-Mogg	Founding CEO of Angel News and Pitching4Management 7-10-2016. Pitching for business success 7-10-2016. Panel member at pitching session https://www.linkedin.com/in/modwenna/
Ross Renton	Pro Vice Chancellor Students, University of Worcester 25-4-2018. What students of the future will expect from their University education (TEDxMalvern) https://www.linkedin.com/in/rossrenton/
Dr Mark Reilly	Business Development Director at IP Group 9-11-2012. Planning and strategies for the exit 9-11-2012. Panel member at pitching session https://www.linkedin.com/in/markreilly/
Andrew Reith	Business Events Manager at Intellectual Property Office 7-11-2013. Every business owns IP. What do you own? https://www.linkedin.com/in/andrew-reith-217a8b70/
Paul Rhodes	Managing Director of Green Gorilla Apps Ltd 7-10-2021. Pitch about WellGiving https://www.linkedin.com/in/ukwebdevelopment/
Neill Ricketts	CEO of Versarien Plc 6-10-2017. Lessons learnt pitching an innovative technology company 6-10-2017. Panel member at pitching session https://www.linkedin.com/in/neillricketts/
Prof Gina Rippon	Emeritus Professor of Cognitive Neuroimaging at the Aston Brain Centre, Aston University, Birmingham 10-10-2020. Sexing the brain: is your brain female or male? Or are we asking the wrong question? (virtual) https://en.wikipedia.org/wiki/Gina_Rippon
Dr Alisdair Ritchie	Impact Champion, University of Warwick and PETRAS 5-10-2017. How will connected technologies change the world that we live in? https://www.linkedin.com/in/alisdairritchie/
Jim Robertson	Partner & Patent Attorney at Wynne Jones IP 7-10-2016. Intellectual property: the best kept secret in business strategy (co-speaker) https://www.linkedin.com/in/jim-robertson-ip/
Mark Robinson	Independent IT consultant 12-10-2018. Blockchain – what is it good for? https://www.linkedin.com/in/markrobinsonuk/
Christian Rogan	VP Business Development at Abatis (UK) Ltd 9-10-2015. Host integrity technology; how & why this complements an enterprise security framework https://www.linkedin.com/in/crogan/

Prof Chris Rogers	Professor of Geotechnical Engineering in the Department of Civil Engineering at the University of Birmingham 10-10-2018. Liveable cities & iBUILD – innovative approaches to future-proofing our cities https://www.birmingham.ac.uk/staff/profiles/civil/rogers-christopher.aspx
Dr Lucy Rogers	Science writer, maker & presenter 7-10-2017. Wiring the Internet of Things https://en.wikipedia.org/wiki/Lucy_Rogers
Peter Rogers	CEO of GBR14 Ltd 5-10-2017. Securing information in multi-user databases https://www.linkedin.com/in/peter-rogers-5a98177/
Bob Rose	Director Security at ADS Group 2-10-2014. Supporting SMEs – sovereign capabilities, innovation and growth https://www.linkedin.com/in/bob-rose-26318a12/
Pete Rose	Account Executive at HP Enterprise Services 1-10-2014. Telemetry & IoT: innovation in the 'big data' society (Deceased)
David Rowan	Founding Editor-in-Chief of WIRED magazine's UK edition 7-10-2021. Non-bullshit innovation: radical ideas from the world's smartest minds https://www.linkedin.com/in/mailrowan/
Ellie Runcie	Director of the Design Council's Design Leadership Programmes 9-11-2012. Innovation in design https://www.linkedin.com/in/ellie-runcie-9221723/
Gemma Ryall	Independent consultant & Associate at business mix 9-10-2019. Top 5 people tips as you scale your business 'fireside chat' https://www.linkedin.com/in/gemmaryall/
Ebrima Sallah	Engineering doctorate student at Swansea University 26-6-2021. Science busking at Malvern Science in the Park on shock and awe https://www.linkedin.com/in/ebrima-sallah-0125a6147/
Coco Sato	Founder and CEO of Studio Sato 26-6-2021. Science busking at Malvern Science in the Park on giant origami https://www.linkedin.com/in/cocosato/
Dr Frances Saunders DBE CB	President of Institute of Physics 8-11-2013. Translating innovative technology into business https://www.linkedin.com/in/frances-saunders-dbe-cb-2a861444/
Thomas Seidling	Partnership Manager at CyberSmart 5-10-2017. Our startup journey & the GCHQ Accelerator (co-speaker) https://www.linkedin.com/in/thomas-seidling-433aa244/
Sue Shackleton	Director of EasyRead Time Teacher Ltd 4-10-2017. Time is of the essence https://www.linkedin.com/in/sueshackleton/
Dr Janaki Shanmugam	Scientist I at Institute of Materials Research & Engineering (IMRE), Singapore 6-10-2020. A visit to Singapore – materials research facilities the other side of the world! (virtual) https://www.linkedin.com/in/janakishanmugam/
Dr Carl Shaw	Co-founder and CEO of MathEmbedded Ltd 6-10-2016. The vulnerability of things https://www.linkedin.com/in/shawcarl/
Dr Jennifer Sheridan	Chief Executive Officer at Togeva 8-11-2012. Live sharing: my journey from digital artist to technology entrepreneur https://www.linkedin.com/in/drjsheridan/

Paul Sherwood	Chief Executive Officer at Codethink 9-10-2015. Software engineering the gangrene in your supply chain (co-speaker) 9-10-2015. Panel member of cyber security session https://www.linkedin.com/in/paul-sherwood-9493291/
Dr Azar G. Shirazi	Research Fellow in the Energy Materials Group at University of Birmingham 27-6-2020. Battery quiz (virtual) https://www.linkedin.com/in/azarmidokht-g-shirazi-67361614b/
Kristo Shivachev	Founder of Simple Design Works 6-10-2021. In conversation with Dan Barker https://www.linkedin.com/in/kristo-shivachev-35b58445/
Alastair Shortland	Chief Executive Officer at TextLocal, later exited 8-11-2012. Why every business should embrace mobile messaging 8-11-2013. SMS, mobile marketing and how to engage the visitor 5-10-2016. Startup success one SMS at a time 9-10-2018. From bedroom coding to global business https://www.linkedin.com/in/alshortland/
Prof Ravi Silva CBE	Director of Advanced Technology Institute, University of Surrey 8-11-2013. The green energy challenge https://www.linkedin.com/in/professor-ravi-silva-cbe-05134696/
Etienne Smith	CTO of Mohara 9-10-2019. The challenges and approach of taking a product to market 'fireside chat' https://www.linkedin.com/in/etienne-smith/
Giles Smith	Deputy Director for Cyber Security and Resilience at Department for Business, Innovation and Skills 7-11-2013. Cyber Security: A global challenge with local solutions
Kevin Smith	Author & CEO of AWS International Business Development 8-11-2015. Financing innovation in your business https://www.linkedin.com/in/kevin-r-smith-msc/
Linda Smith	Head of International Trade at UKTI Herefordshire & Worcestershire 9-11-2012. Exporting for global growth 8-11-2013. Successfully growing your business through exports 7-10-2021. Host of Innovation Showcase pitches and delivered BetaDen pitch https://www.linkedin.com/in/linda-smith-1b380210/
Phil Smith CBE	Chief Executive UK & Ireland at Cisco International Ltd & Chair of Innovate UK 9-10-2015. The digital effect https://www.linkedin.com/in/phil-smith-cbe-a2332220/
Damian Mark Smyth	International consultant, speaker & author 24-4-2019. Understanding your mind to solve problems, overcome depression and be more entrepreneurial (TEDxMalvern) https://www.linkedin.com/in/damianmarksmyth/
Evie Snedker	Student at University of Leeds 27-6-2020. Nasty microbes! (virtual) https://www.linkedin.com/in/evie-snedker/
Melissa Snover	CEO of Get Nourish3d 9-10-2019. The sweet smell of business success https://www.linkedin.com/in/melissa-snover-84276920/
Don Southey	Chairman, Hereford & Worcester Branch of The IET 1-7-2017. Science busking at Malvern Science in the Park as Sir Isaac Newton https://www.linkedin.com/in/donald-southey-2470611/
Prof Tim Spiller	Director of York Centre for Quantum Technologies & Director of Quantum Communications Hub 11-10-2018. Quantum technologies and their implications for cyber security https://www.york.ac.uk/physics/people/spiller/

Hugo Spowers MBE	Chief Engineer and Founder of Riversimple Movement Ltd 4-10-2017. Hydrogen-fuelled cars and progress eliminating the environmental impact of personal transport https://www.linkedin.com/in/hugo-spowers-5a614a/
Prof. Andy Stamford-Clark	Chief Technology Officer, IBM UK and Ireland 5-10-2020. AI takes to the high seas (virtual) https://en.wikipedia.org/wiki/Andy_Stanford-Clark
Mark Stanger	Commercial Director at Serious Games International 8-11-2012. Games . . . for the serious minded https://www.linkedin.com/in/marknstanger/
Mark Stansfeld	Chairman of Giffgaff & Chair of Worcestershire Local Enterprise Partnership 7-11-2015. Telecommunications innovation that drives industries like agri-tech forward https://www.linkedin.com/in/mark-stansfeld-8098553/
Del Stark	Chief Executive Officer of Del Stark Technology Solutions 9-11-2012. Nanotechnology and other material science innovations https://www.linkedin.com/in/delstark/
Ella Stearn	Entrepreneur, Author, Speaker & Social Media Influencer 10-10-2018. Entrepreneurship in a social whirl https://www.linkedin.com/in/ellastearn/
Ian Sterritt	Scaleup Director at Innovate UK EDGE 6-10-2021. An entrepreneur's commercial reality of intellectual property https://www.linkedin.com/in/iansterritt/
Henrietta Stock	Director of Peak Time Consulting 10-10-2018. Innovation in demand side response (pre-recorded) https://www.linkedin.com/in/henrietta-stock-48935723/
Lorraine Stone	Independent consultant at Pragmatic1 Ltd 6-10-2017. Innovation supported by a connected county https://www.linkedin.com/in/lorraine-stone-52a19016/
Lee Strafford	Founder of Plusnet 3-10-2014. Building the UK's biggest (yet) bootstrapped start-up https://www.linkedin.com/in/leestrafford/
Dr Clive Summerfield	CTO of Auraya Systems 7-10-2019. Using your voice as a password https://www.linkedin.com/in/clive-summerfield-092b3a1/
Duncan Sutcliffe	Director of Sutcliffe & Co Insurance Brokers 6-10-2016. Launch of a specialist insurance package for UK cyber security SMEs https://www.linkedin.com/in/duncan-sutcliffe-b815664/
Edmund Sutcliffe	Thinker at Opus Novum 9-10-2015. Software engineering the gangrene in your supply chain (co-speaker) 9-10-2015. Panel member of cyber security session https://www.linkedin.com/in/edmundjsutcliffe/
Hilary Sutcliffe	Director of SocietyInside 11-10-2018. Will AI & robotics learn from the mistakes of past tech introductions? https://www.linkedin.com/in/hilary-sutcliffe-01235220/
Peter Sutton	Managing Director of Fox Dog Studios Ltd 11-10-2019. Science Comedy Night act https://www.linkedin.com/in/peter-sutton-204936165/

Christine Swan	Visiting Lecturer at Birmingham City University 9-10-2018. Ada Lovelace talk, alongside Charles Babbage 29-6-2019. Science busking at Malvern Science in the Park as Ada Lovelace 8-10-2019. Ada Lovelace talk, alongside Charles Babbage 26-6-2021. Science busking at Malvern Science in the Park as Ada Lovelace https://www.linkedin.com/in/christine-swan-a353aa31/
Marvin Tabi	CEO of WESAF Energy 11-10-2019. New technology and the African energy transition https://www.linkedin.com/in/wesafmarvin/
Melissa Tate	Head of Commercial at DOVU 12-10-2018. Blockchain applications in transportation https://www.linkedin.com/in/melissatateuk/
Prof. Harold Thimbleby	Professor of Computer Science at University of Swansea 2-10-2014. Cyber security for medical devices https://www.linkedin.com/in/haroldthimbleby/
James Thomas	CEO of JET Engineering System Solutions 7-10-2021. Pitch about JET Engineering https://www.linkedin.com/in/jamesetthomas/
Nicky Thomas	Teacher of Physics 30-6-2018. Science busking at Malvern Science in the Park on fun with dry ice 29-6-2019. Science busking at Malvern Science in the Park on physics 27-6-2020. Exploring space (pre-record) 26-6-2021. Science busking at Malvern Science in the Park on physics https://www.linkedin.com/in/nicky-thomas-ba-oxon-cphys-minstp-frsa-pgce-584ba826/
Revathi Timms	Managing Director at Avatar 3D 4-10-2016. 3D scanning and 3D printing workshop 25-4-2018. My extraordinary career falling in love with engineering (TEDxMalvern) 29-6-2019. Science busking at Malvern Science in the Park on 3D printing https://www.linkedin.com/in/revathi-timms-60b85728/
Dr Aphrodite Tomou	Technical Manager of Goodfellow Cambridge Ltd 8-10-2019. Advanced materials to facilitate innovation https://www.linkedin.com/in/aphrodite-tomou-664a2047/
Craig Tonge	Founder of Renault Zoe & ZE Owners Club (RZOC) 11-10-15. Migrating from petrol to electric https://www.linkedin.com/in/craig-tonge-b86b04146/
Nick Tudor	Business Director, later Chief Executive Officer, at D-RisQ 8-11-2012. The assurance chain for systems and software 9-10-2015. Can networks ever be secure? 9-10-2015. Panel member of cyber security session 4-10-2017. Testing complex software systems in future advanced transportation 7-10-2019. Proving software systems work 6-10-2021. Innovating in a high-tech business where cash is king https://www.linkedin.com/in/nick-tudor-beng-msc-ceng-fiet-6375556/
Jamie Turner	Co-founder of Postcode Anywhere (now PCA Predict) 4-10-2017. From postcode lottery to well-addressed exit https://www.linkedin.com/in/pcajt/
John Turvill	Director at Czero 9-11-2012. Sustainable biomethane production from annual lifecycle carbon sources https://www.linkedin.com/in/john-turvill-56517b30/
Andrew Tyrer	Digital Lead Specialist at Technology Strategy Board 8-11-2013. Innovation vouchers & competitions to fuel your business growth https://www.linkedin.com/in/andrew-tyrer-a04ab94/

Sibghat Ullah	PhD student at Leiden Institute of Advanced Computer Science 27-6-2020. Artificial Intelligence now and in the future (virtual) https://www.linkedin.com/in/sibghatkhancs/
John Unsworth	Chief Executive of the London Digital Security Centre 5-10-2017. Working with the London Digital Security Centre
Chris Vagges	Product Design Manager at Gtech 8-10-2015. The design challenge: making a game changer https://www.linkedin.com/in/chris-vagges-98993410/
Paul Verdeyen	Education Ambassador at Ultimaker GB Create Education Project 6-10-2016. 3D printing workshop https://www.linkedin.com/in/paul-verdeyen-54968410/
Cevn Vibert	Industrial Cyber Security Consultant and Evangelist 6-10-2016. Securing industrial control / SCADA systems within critical national infrastructure https://www.linkedin.com/in/cevnvibert/
Nigel Walker	Access to Finance at Technology Strategies Board 9-11-2012. Finance options for growth https://www.linkedin.com/in/nigel-walker-702ba43/
Paul Walker MBE	Non-Exec Director of Malvern Hills Science Park and former Managing Director of Malvern Instruments 29-6-2019. Opening remarks at Malvern Science in the Park https://www.linkedin.com/in/paul-walker-mbe-265730b/
Robin Walker MP	MP for Worcester 1-10-2014. Opening remarks https://www.linkedin.com/in/robin-walker-255044a/
Russell Walker	Managing Director at Atwell International 7-11-2013. Final destination: how to make lifts safer (co-presenter) https://www.linkedin.com/in/russell-walker-5303a610/
Chris Walklett	Partner at Bishop Fleming 8-11-2013. The life cycle of a technology business through the prism of tax 8-11-2013. Panel member at pitching session 3-10-2014. Panel member at pitching session https://www.linkedin.com/in/chriswalkletttaxandvaluation/
Prof Allan Walton	Professor of Critical and Magnetic Materials in the School of Metallurgy and Materials at the University of Birmingham 10-10-2018. Critical materials and the circular economy https://www.birmingham.ac.uk/staff/profiles/metallurgy/walton-allan.aspx
Dr Gary Wan	Postdoctoral Researcher, School of Physics, University of Bristol 6-10-2020. Laboratory Tour of the nanoESCA analysis laboratory (virtual) https://www.linkedin.com/in/gary-wan-619a5ba7/
Matt Ward	Junior Research Physicist at Queen Elizabeth Hospital Birmingham 30-6-2018. Science busking at Malvern Science in the Park on medical physics
Stephen Ward-Smith	Key Account Manager, Malvern Panalytical 26-4-2017. Size really matters (TEDxMalvern) https://www.linkedin.com/in/stephen-ward-smith-41a53711/
Richard Watson	Author and futurist 2-10-2014. After dinner speaker on future innovation https://www.linkedin.com/in/richard-watson-883b1327/
Mike Webster	Creative Director at TheOverworld 7-10-2016. Bringing Ideas to Life https://www.linkedin.com/in/michael-webster-a2b1874/

Jonathan Wells	Head of Design at Morgan Motor Car Company 7-11-2013. The view from Morgan – Morgan design vs. traditional manufacture https://www.linkedin.com/in/mrjonwells/
Dr Linde Wester	DPhil student in Quantum Computing at the University of Oxford 3-10-2017. Does Schrodinger's cat live in a multiverse? https://www.linkedin.com/in/linde-wester-099b4216/
Neil Westwood	Managing Director at Magic Whiteboard Limited 5-10-2016. Snatching success with the help of the jaws of Dragons – the magic in Magic Whiteboard Ltd https://www.linkedin.com/in/magicwhiteboard/
Jon Whitbread	Partner at Harrison Clark Rickerbys 6-10-2017. Raising funds to start and scale https://www.linkedin.com/in/jon-whitbread-55782b7/
Ian Whiting	Managing Director at Titania 8-11-2012. Cresting the cyber wave https://www.linkedin.com/in/ian-whiting-40813a5/
Nicola Whiting MBE	COO at Titania 6-10-2016. VIP Breakfast panel session on cyber skills https://www.linkedin.com/in/nicola-whiting-mbe-40069b14/
Marc Wickenden	Technical Director at 4ARMED 6-10-2016. Defending against an attack of the drones https://www.linkedin.com/in/marcwickenden/
Dan Wild	Cofounder of Malvern Hills Electric Automobile Association (electrAA) 11-10-2015. Tax breaks in buying an electric car
Stuart Wilkes	Content Writer at National Cyber Skills Centre 9-10-2015. Chair of cyber security panel session https://www.linkedin.com/in/stuartjwilkes/
Tim Wilkinson	UK Sales Leader at Avast Business 10-10-2019. Securing the changing workforce https://www.linkedin.com/in/tim-wilkinson189/
Andy Williams	International Business Head at Titania 7-11-2013. Small is beautiful: how SMEs are helping accelerate innovation in the transatlantic cyber security market https://www.linkedin.com/in/andy-williams-a677b159/
Jon Wills	Business Development Officer at Worcester Scientific 7-10-2019. Worcester Scientific: developing nano-sensors for future markets 7-10-2021. Pitch about Worcester Scientific https://www.linkedin.com/in/jon-wills/
Dr George Windsor	Senior Policy Researcher at Nesta 7-10-2016. Innovation analytics: Nesta's mapping and measurement work to support policy and practice https://www.linkedin.com/in/windsorgeorge/
Dr Simon Wiseman	Chief Technology Officer at Deep-Secure 8-11-2012. Innovating to meet cyber threats https://www.linkedin.com/in/simon-wiseman-56111024/
Dr David Wood	Chair of London Futurists 8-10-2015. The future of innovation – visions and nightmares https://www.linkedin.com/in/dw2cco/
Jon Wood	Science Presenter & Byrne Outreach Fellow at University of Birmingham 27-6-2020. Why do we breathe (pre-record) https://www.linkedin.com/in/jonwoodscience/

Mike Woollacott	Managing Director of Greenwatt Technology 9-11-2012. Innovation in renewable energy technology 7-10-2015. Farm energy monitoring and the promise of smart rural grids https://www.linkedin.com/in/mike-woollacott-952b965/
Dr Mark Yeadon	Chartered UK and European patent attorney at Yeadon IP 9-11-2012. Patent protection of your idea https://www.linkedin.com/in/mark-yeadon-507b732/
Dennis Yeates	Director of Business Development at Artwork Creative 9-11-2012. Branding and marketing https://www.linkedin.com/in/dennis-yeates-8222a01b8/
Matt Young	Head of Growth Partnerships at Plinx 7-10-2021. Pitch about Plinx https://www.linkedin.com/in/mattyoung901/
Vicky Young	COO at business mix 9-10-2019. The business of intellectual property (IP) 'fireside chat' https://www.linkedin.com/in/vicky-young/
Dr Ioanna Zafeiri	Research Fellow in the School of Chemical Engineering at the University of Birmingham 27-6-2020. Food science for thought! (virtual) https://www.birmingham.ac.uk/research/activity/chemical-engineering/microstructure-engineering/people/zafeiri-ioanna.aspx

APPENDIX D – EXPOSITION

An alphabetical list of the various organisations that
have exhibited over the years.

Name	Details
1% Studio https://www.onepercentstudio.com/	2016: Business of Innovating exhibition
3SDL (Now Meta Mission Data) https://meta.aero/mmd/	2013: Innovative Technology & Service Organisations 2015: Next Generation Innovators exhibition 2015: Cyber security exhibition
4ARMED https://www.4armed.com/	2016: Cyber security exhibition
Aardvark Marketing Consultants https://aardvarkmarketingconsultants.co.uk/	2012: Organisations Supporting Innovation
Accelero Digital –	2015: Cyber security exhibition
Acsoft https://acsoft.co.uk/	2014: Innovative Technology & Service Organisations
Activereach https://activereach.net/	2017: Cyber security exhibition
Advent IM https://www.advent-im.co.uk/	2019: Cyber security exhibition
Amphilogic –	2012, 2013: Innovative Technology & Service Organisations 2015: Agri-tech exhibition
APMG International https://apmg-international.com/	2017: Cyber security exhibition
Areca Design (now Abbey Gate Media) https://www.abbeygatemedia.co.uk/	2013: Innovative Technology & Service Organisations 2016: Next Generation Innovators exhibition
Armour Communications https://www.armourcomms.com/	2017: Cyber security exhibition
Army (STEM team) https://stemview.co.uk/	2021: Malvern Science in the Park
Artwork Creative https://artwork-creative.com/	2012, 2013: Organisations Supporting Innovation
Ash Wireless https://www.ashwireless.com/	2013: Innovative Technology & Service Organisations
Aspire Academy –	2015, 2016, 2017: Next Generation Innovators exhibition
Assimilate https://www.assimilate-ltd.co.uk/	2012: Organisations Supporting Innovation
Assure Technical https://assuretechnical.com/	2014: Innovative Technology & Service Organisations
Assuria https://assuria.com/	2016: Cyber security exhibition 2016: Business of Innovating exhibition

Aston Martin https://www.astonmartin.com/	2014, 2015, 2017, 2019: Creative Careers exhibition
Aston University https://www.aston.ac.uk/	2014: Organisations Supporting Innovation 2017, 2019: Next Generation Innovators exhibition 2014: Family day exhibition 2018: Cyber security exhibition
AuraQ https://www.auraq.com/	2016: Cyber security exhibition
Auraya https://aurayasystems.com/	2019: Cyber security exhibition
Avast https://www.avast.com/	2019: Cyber security exhibition
Avatar3D –	2015, 2016, 2017: Next Generation Innovators exhibition 2017, 2018: Family day exhibition
Babble IT –	2014: Innovative Technology & Service Organisations
Babcock Prime –	2016, 2017: Next Generation Innovators exhibition
BAE Systems https://www.baesystems.com/en/cybersecurity/home	2017, 2018: Cyber security exhibition
Barclays https://www.barclays.co.uk/digital-confidence/eagles/	2015: Next Generation Innovators exhibition
BatchBuild (now 4E Technology) https://4e-technology.co.uk/	2013: Innovative Technology & Service Organisations
Batfast https://batfast.com/	2019: Next Generation Innovators exhibition
BCS (Chartered Institute for IT) https://www.bcs.org/	2017, 2018, 2019: Malvern Science in the Park 2018, 2019: Next Generation Innovators exhibition 2018, 2019: Family day exhibition 2019: Cyber security exhibition
BetaDen https://www.beta-den.com/	2021: Innovation on the Hills exhibition
Biotronics –	2012: Innovative Technology & Service Organisations
Birmingham Institute for Forest Research (BIFoR) https://www.birmingham.ac.uk/research/bifor/index.aspx	2018: Next Generation Innovators exhibition
Bishop Fleming https://www.bishopfleming.co.uk/	2013, 2014: Organisations Supporting Innovation 2014: Family day exhibition
Black Country Atelier https://www.blackcountryatelier.com/	2013: Family day exhibition
BlockMark Technologies https://blockmarktech.com/	2019: Cyber security exhibition 2021: Innovation on the Hills exhibition
Bob's Business https://www.bobsbusiness.co.uk/	2015, 2017, 2018, 2019: Cyber security exhibition
Bloodhound SSC https://www.bloodhoundssc.com/	2013: Innovative Technology & Service Organisations 2013: Family day exhibition 2014, 2019: Next Generation Innovators exhibition
Bonwyke https://www.bonwyke.co.uk/	2014: Innovative Technology & Service Organisations

Borwell https://borwell.com/	2012: Innovative Technology & Service Organisations 2017: Cyber security exhibition
BPH Training -	2017: Cyber security exhibition
Brand Refinery https://www.brandrefinery.co.uk/	2013: Organisations Supporting Innovation 2021: Innovation on the Hills exhibition
BT Local Business -	2013: Organisations Supporting Innovation
Bugs & Beasties http://bugsandbeasties.co.uk/	2014: Next Generation Innovators exhibition
Business & Innovation Magazine https://www.businessinnovationmag.co.uk/	2017: Business of Innovating exhibition 2018: Cyber security exhibition
Business & IP Centre Worcestershire https://www.worcestershire.gov.uk/bipc	2021: Innovation on the Hills exhibition
business mix https://business-mix.com/	2019: Next Generation Innovators exhibition 2019: Business of Innovating exhibition 2019: Startup Stories exhibition 2019: Cyber security exhibition
C2B2 (now Payara) https://www.payara.fish/	2014: Innovative Technology & Service Organisations
C3IA https://c3ia.co.uk/	2014: Innovative Technology & Service Organisations
Cancer Research UK https://www.cancerresearchuk.org/	2018, 2019: Malvern Science in the Park
Cargill https://www.cargill.co.uk/	2014, 2015: Next Generation Innovators exhibition
Catshill Learning Partnership https://catshill.com/	2014, 2015, 2016, 2017: Next Generation Innovators exhibition
Centre For Entrepreneurs https://centreforentrepreneurs.org/	2014: Organisations Supporting Innovation
Charlton Networks https://www.charltonnetworks.co.uk/	2017: Business of Innovating exhibition
Cheltenham Science Group https://www.cheltenhamsciencegroup.co.uk/	2017, 2018, 2019, 2021: Next Generation Innovators exhibition 2018: Malvern Science in the Park
Circle2Success https://www.circle2success.com/	2017: Business of Innovating exhibition
CNS Group https://www.cnsgroup.co.uk/	2016: Cyber security exhibition
Cob House https://cobhouse.org/	2014: Next Generation Innovators exhibition
Cocidius Defence https://cocidius.co.uk/	2018: Cyber security exhibition
Code Club https://codeclub.org/en/	2015, 2016, 2018: Next Generation Innovators exhibition
Cognition https://www.cognitionagency.co.uk/	2015: Agri-tech exhibition
Cognore -	2017: Cyber security exhibition

COHO
https://coho.life/

2021: Innovation on the Hills exhibition

Collate Loop
–

2019: Next Generation Innovators exhibition

Compare Hospitality
–

2014: Innovative Technology & Service Organisations

Computer Network Defence
https://www.cndltd.com/

2015: Cyber security exhibition

Coomber
https://www.coomberaudio.com/

2014: Next Generation Innovators exhibition

Corsaire
–

2017: Cyber security exhibition

Corvid
https://www.corvid.co.uk/

2016: Cyber security exhibition

Cotswold TV
https://www.cotswoldtv.com/

2013: Organisations Supporting Innovation

Coventry University Enterprises
https://www.cuebusinesssolutions.com/

2012, 2013: Organisations Supporting Innovation
2016: Business of Innovating exhibition

Crossword Cybersecurity
https://www.crosswordcybersecurity.com/

2018, 2019: Cyber security exhibition
2021: Innovation on the Hills exhibition

CSP
https://www.csp.partners/

2016: Cyber security exhibition

Cyber Discovery
https://joincyberdiscovery.com/

2019: Next Generation Innovators exhibition

Cyber Security Challenge
https://cybersecuritychallenge.org.uk/

2014, 2015, 2016: Next Generation Innovators exhibition
2015: Family day exhibition

CyberAware (Cyber Apprenticeship Development
Scheme, CADS)
–

2016: Next Generation Innovators exhibition

Cybercorre
–

2018: Cyber security exhibition

Cyberis
https://www.cyberis.com/

2012: Innovative Technology & Service Organisations

Cyberlytic
–

2017: Cyber security exhibition

CyberSmart
https://cybersmart.co.uk/

2017, 2018, 2019: Cyber security exhibition

Cysure
https://www.cysure.net/

2017: Cyber security exhibition

D-RisQ
https://www.drisq.com/

2012, 2013, 2014: Innovative Technology &
Service Organisations
2015, 2016, 2017, 2018, 2019: Cyber security exhibition
2021: Innovation on the Hills exhibition

Daden
https://www.daden.co.uk/

2016, 2017: Next Generation Innovators exhibition

Data2Vault
https://data2vault.com/

2016: Cyber security exhibition
2016: Business of Innovating exhibition

David Prosser Chartered Surveyor
https://www.dpsurveys.co.uk/

2016, 2017: Family day exhibition

Deep Secure (now Forcepoint) https://www.forcepoint.com/	2012: Innovative Technology & Service Organisations
Design Council https://www.designcouncil.org.uk/	2012, 2013: Organisations Supporting Innovation
Department for International Trade (formerly UK Trade & Investment) https://www.great.gov.uk/	2012, 2013, 2014: Organisations Supporting Innovation 2019: Business of Innovating exhibition
Dephrisk –	2015: Cyber security exhibition
Digital Shadows https://www.digitalshadows.com/	2015: Cyber security exhibition
Discover Materials https://discovermaterials.co.uk/	2019: Next Generation Innovators exhibition 2021: Family day exhibition 2021: Malvern Science in the Park
Dod-dle https://dod-dle.co.uk/	2016: Business of Innovating exhibition
DooUp https://thedooup.com/	2013: Innovative Technology & Service Organisations
Drone Prep https://droneprep.uk/	2021: Innovation on the Hills exhibition
Drum Smart https://drumsmartapp.com/	2014: Next Generation Innovators exhibition 2014: Innovative Technology & Service Organisations
DTS Bromsgrove –	2012, 2103: Innovative Technology & Service Organisations
Dytecna –	2013: Innovative Technology & Service Organisations
E-cycle https://www.ecyclegroup.co.uk/	2015: Cyber security exhibition
e-fossils https://e-fossils.co.uk/	2017, 2018, 2019, 2021: Malvern Science in the Park
e-skills UK –	2014: Next Generation Innovators exhibition
Echosec https://www.echosec.net/	2015: Cyber security exhibition
Eco-lighting-life –	2013: Innovative Technology & Service Organisations 2013: Family day exhibition
Edwards https://www.edwardsvacuum.com	2014: Next Generation Innovators exhibition
ElectrAA (Electric Automobile Association, formerly the Malvern Hills Electric Automobile Association) https://www.electraa.org.uk/	2014: Organisations Supporting Innovation 2014: Family day exhibition 2015, 2016, 2017, 2018, 2019: Next Generation Innovators exhibition 2015: Electric Vehicle Innovation Showcase
Elemensus http://elemensus.com/	2018: Next Generation Innovators exhibition 2018: Family day exhibition
Elysium Communications –	2013: Organisations Supporting Innovation
Embedded Rail Technology	2018: Next Generation Innovators exhibition
EN Start-Ups	2013: Organisations Supporting Innovation

Encription (now Blackberry Cybersecurity Consulting)
https://www.blackberry.com/us/en/services/blackberry-cybersecurity-consulting

2012, 2013: Innovative Technology & Service Organisations

Energy Simple
–

2014: Innovative Technology & Service Organisations
2014, 2015: Next Generation Innovators exhibition
2014: Family day exhibition

Engineers Without Borders UK
https://www.ewb-uk.org/

2014: Next Generation Innovators exhibition

English Braids
https://www.englishbraids.com/

2012: Innovative Technology & Service Organisations

Enterprise Europe Network Midlands
–

2014: Organisations Supporting Innovation

Entrepreneur Coworking
–

2017: Business of Innovating exhibition

Ericom Software
https://www.ericom.com/

2018: Cyber security exhibition

Estatom Systems
–

2015: Cyber security exhibition
2015: Family day exhibition

Fab Foundation UK
https://www.fabfoundationuk.org/

2015: Next Generation Innovators exhibition

Fizz Pop Science
https://fizzpopscience.co.uk/

2017, 2018, 2019: Malvern Science in the Park

Fleet Innovations (now CleanCar)
https://cleancar.io/

2014: Innovative Technology & Service Organisations

Flowide
https://flowide.net/

2021: Innovation on the Hills exhibition

Flux Moving Science
https://www.fluxdancetheatre.com/

2017, 2018, 2019: Malvern Science in the Park

Foreseeti
https://foreseeti.com/

2017: Cyber security exhibition

Fortitude
–

2017: Cyber security exhibition

Fresh Skies (Mkryptor)
–

2015: Cyber security exhibition
2016: Cyber security exhibition
2016: Business of Innovating exhibition

FSB (formerly Federation of Small Businesses)
https://www.fsb.org.uk/

2013: Organisations Supporting Innovation
2016: Business of Innovating exhibition

GardPass Cyber
https://www.gpc.work/

2016: Cyber security exhibition
2016: Business of Innovating exhibition

GBR14
–

2017: Cyber security exhibition

GCHQ
https://www.gchq.gov.uk/

2014: Next Generation Innovators exhibition

GE Aviation
https://www.geaviation.com/

2017, 2018, 2021: Next Generation Innovators exhibition
2017, 2018, 2021: Family day exhibition

Genus One
https://www.genusone.co.uk/

2015: Cyber security exhibition

GeoLang
https://geolang.com/

2014: Innovative Technology & Service Organisations
2014: Next Generation Innovators exhibition
2015, 2016: Cyber security exhibition

GeoVation
https://geovation.uk/

2013, 2014: Organisations Supporting Innovation
2013, 2014: Family day exhibition

GFC Diagnostics
http://www.gfcdiagnostics.com/

2017: Next Generation Innovators exhibition

Girlguiding
https://www.girlguiding.org.uk/

2019: Malvern Science in the Park

Glassfull
https://www.glassfull.info/

2021: Innovation on the Hills exhibition

Glideology
https://www.glideology.co.uk/

2017: Next Generation Innovators exhibition
2017: Business of Innovating exhibition

Global Cyber Alliance
https://www.globalcyberalliance.org/

2019: Cyber security exhibition

Goodfellow
https://www.goodfellow.com/

2019, 2021: Next Generation Innovators exhibition

Gordon Coppock
–

2017: Malvern Science in the Park
2017, 2018: Next Generation Innovators exhibition

Great Malvern Route to the Hills project
–

2016, 2017: Family day exhibition

Green Gorilla Software
https://ggapps.co.uk/

2021: Innovation on the Hills exhibition

Greenwatt
https://www.greenwatt.co.uk/

2015: Agri-tech exhibition

GRG Engineers
–

2014: Innovative Technology & Service Organisations

Growth Accelerator
–

2014: Organisations Supporting Innovation

H&W Chamber of Commerce
https://hwchamber.co.uk/

2014: Organisations Supporting Innovation

Harrison Clark Rickerbys
https://www.hcrlaw.com/

2013, 2014: Organisations Supporting Innovation
2017: Business of Innovating exhibition

HDAnywhere
https://hdanywhere.com/

2015: Next Generation Innovators exhibition

Heart of Worcestershire College
https://www.howcollege.ac.uk/

2016: Next Generation Innovators exhibition
2016: Cyber security exhibition

Heber
https://www.heber.co.uk/

2012: Innovative Technology & Service Organisations

Herefordshire & Ludlow College
https://www.hlcollege.ac.uk/

2016, 2017, 2018, 2019: Next Generation
Innovators exhibition

Herefordshire & Worcestershire Earth Heritage Trust
https://earthheritagetrust.org/

2017, 2018, 2019, 2021: Malvern Science in the Park
2018, 2019, 2021: Next Generation Innovators exhibition

Hewett Recruitment
https://www.hewett-recruitment.co.uk/

2012, 2013, 2014: Organisations Supporting Innovation

HP
https://www.hp.com/

2014: Innovative Technology & Service Organisations
2014, 2015: Next Generation Innovators exhibition
2014, 2015: Family day exhibition

IASME Consortium https://iasme.co.uk/	2012, 2013, 2014: Innovative Technology & Service Organisations 2015, 2016, 2017, 2018, 2019: Cyber security exhibition 2016, 2017: Business of Innovating exhibition 2021: Malvern Science in the Park 2021: Next Generation Innovators exhibition 2021: Innovation on the Hills exhibition
ID Cyber Solutions https://idcybersolutions.com/	2021: Innovation on the Hills exhibition
Ident Computer https://www.ident-online.co.uk/computer/	2016: Next Generation Innovators exhibition
IDS Indata https://www.idsindata.co.uk/	2015: Cyber security exhibition
Igence Radar https://www.igenceradar.com/	2012: Innovative Technology & Service Organisations
Imagineering https://imagineering.org.uk/	2014, 2015, 2016, 2017, 2018, 2019: Next Generation Innovators exhibition
Imaginify https://www.imaginify.co.uk/	2017: Next Generation Innovators exhibition
Immersive Theatres https://immersive-theatres.com/	2015, 2016, 2017, 2018, 2019, 2021: Next Generation Innovators exhibition
In-Lode –	2012: Innovative Technology & Service Organisations
Indra https://www.indra.co.uk/	2015, 2016, 2019, 2021: Next Generation Innovators exhibition 2015: Electric Vehicle Innovation Showcase
Industry 4.0 Solutions https://i4s.ai/	2021: Innovation on the Hills exhibition
Infirmary Museum (now Worcester Medical Museums) https://medicalmuseum.org.uk/	2018: Next Generation Innovators exhibition
Infinite Precision –	2014: Innovative Technology & Service Organisations
InfoSec People https://www.infosecpeople.co.uk/	2018: Cyber security exhibition
InfoSec Skills –	2017: Cyber security exhibition
Innova Engineering (now The Packet Company) https://packet.company/	2013: Innovative Technology & Service Organisations
Innovate UK (formerly Technology Strategy Board), inc. as KTN (Knowledge Transfer Network) https://www.ukri.org/councils/innovate-uk/ https://www.innovateukedge.ukri.org/	2013: Organisations Supporting Innovation 2017: Cyber security exhibition (as KTN) 2021: Innovation on the Hills exhibition (as Innovate UK Edge)
Institute for Advanced Motorists (now IAM RoadSmart) https://www.iamroadsmart.com/	2015: Electric Vehicle Innovation Showcase
Institute of Biomedical Science (IBMS) https://www.ibms.org/	2016: Next Generation Innovators exhibition
Institute of Materials, Minerals & Mining https://www.iom3.org/	2014, 2015: Next Generation Innovators exhibition

Institute of Physics https://www.iop.org/	2013, 2014: Organisations Supporting Innovation 2014, 2015, 2016, 2017, 2018, 2019, 2021: Next Generation Innovators exhibition 2015, 2018: Cyber security exhibition 2013, 2014, 2015, 2016, 2017, 2018, 2019, 2021: Family day exhibition 2017, 2018, 2019, 2021: Malvern Science in the Park
Institution of Engineering & Technology https://www.theiet.org/	2013, 2014: Organisations Supporting Innovation 2013, 2014, 2015, 2016, 2017, 2018, 2019, 2021: Next Generation Innovators exhibition 2013, 2014, 2015, 2016, 2017, 2018, 2019, 2021: Family day exhibition 2017, 2018, 2019, 2021: Malvern Science in the Park
Institution of Mechanical Engineers https://www.imeche.org/	2013, 2014: Organisations Supporting Innovation 2014, 2015, 2016, 2017, 2018, 2019, 2021: Next Generation Innovators exhibition 2015: Agri-tech exhibition 2013, 2014, 2015, 2016, 2017, 2018, 2019, 2021: Family day exhibition 2016: Cyber security exhibition 2016, 2017: Business of Innovating exhibition 2017, 2018, 2019: Creative Careers exhibition 2017, 2018, 2019: Malvern Science in the Park
IntaForensics https://www.intaforensics.com/	2017: Cyber security exhibition
IntaPeople https://www.intapeople.com/	2016: Cyber security exhibition
Integrity Assured https://www.integrityassured.co.uk/	2017: Cyber security exhibition
Intel https://www.intel.co.uk/	2019: Cyber security exhibition
Intellectual Property Office https://www.gov.uk/government/organisations/ intellectual-property-office	2012, 2013, 2014: Organisations Supporting Innovation 2013: Family day exhibition
Intelligent Privacy Solutions -	2016: Cyber security exhibition 2016: Business of Innovating exhibition
Inventory Matters https://www.inventorymatters.co.uk/	2013: Organisations Supporting Innovation
Invizio (and formerly Little Pi Shop, The Pi Shop) https://invizioproductdesign.co.uk/	2013, 2014: Next Generation Innovators exhibition 2014: Innovative Technology & Service Organisations 2014: Family day exhibition 2021: Innovation on the Hills exhibition
iOra https://www.iora.com/	2016: Cyber security exhibition
IQHQ https://www.iqhq.co.uk/	2015: Agri-tech exhibition
Jaguar Land Rover https://www.jaguarlandrover.com/	2018: Creative Careers exhibition
JEMI-UK -	2012, 2013, 2014: Organisations Supporting Innovation
JET Engineering System Solutions https://jet-eng.co.uk/	2021: Innovation on the Hills exhibition

John Bibby (STEM Ambassador) -	2017, 2018, 2019, 2021: Malvern Science in the Park
Just2easy https://www.just2easy.com/	2015: Next Generation Innovators exhibition
Key IQ https://www.key-iq.com/	2012, 2013, 2014: Organisations Supporting Innovation 2013, 2014: Family day exhibition
Kissed Off Creations -	2013: Organisations Supporting Innovation 2013: Family day exhibition
Komatsu https://www.komatsu.com/	2017: Malvern Science in the Park 2017, 2018: Next Generation Innovators exhibition
Lantra https://www.lantra.co.uk/	2015: Agri-tech exhibition
LaserLines https://3dprinting.co.uk/	2015, 2016, 2017, 2021: Next Generation Innovators exhibition
Legrand https://www.legrand.co.uk/	2017, 2018, 2019: Next Generation Innovators exhibition 2021: Malvern Science in the Park
LineOn -	2017: Cyber security exhibition 2017: Business of Innovating exhibition
Lockheed Martin https://www.lockheedmartin.com/	2014: Innovative Technology & Service Organisations
Low and Behold https://www.lowandbehold.co.uk/	2014: Next Generation Innovators exhibition
Low Carbon Opportunities Programme https://www.business-central.co.uk/locopinnovation/	2017: Business of Innovating exhibition 2021: Innovation on the Hills exhibition
LuJam https://www.lujam.com/	2015, 2017, 2018, 2019: Cyber security exhibition 2017: Business of Innovating exhibition
Lumeta (now Firemon) https://www.firemon.com/products/lumeta/	2015: Cyber security exhibition
Magic Whiteboard https://www.magicwhiteboard.com/	2014, 2015: Next Generation Innovators exhibition
Make:Bromyard https://www.makebromyard.org.uk/	2016: Family day exhibition
Make IT Simple https://www.makeitsimple.co.uk/	2017: Business of Innovating exhibition
Malvern Book Cooperative https://www.malvernbook.coop/	2019: Business of Innovating exhibition 2021: Embarkation
Malvern Business Academy https://www.26steps.co.uk/	2016: Business of Innovating exhibition
Malvern Cyber Security Cluster https://malvern-cybersecurity.com	2012, 2013, 2014: Organisations Supporting Innovation 2015, 2016, 2017, 2018, 2019: Cyber security exhibition
Malvern Cycles -	2012, 2013: Innovative Technology & Service Organisations
Malvern For All -	2015: Family day exhibition
Malvern Hills Business Forum (formerly Malvern Small Business Forum) -	2013, 2014: Organisations Supporting Innovation 2014: Family day exhibition 2015: Cyber security exhibition
Malvern Hills District Council https://www.malvernhills.gov.uk/	2015: Agri-tech exhibition 2018, 2019, 2021: Next Generation Innovators exhibition

Malvern Hills Radio Amateurs Club https://www.mhrac.org/	2014: Next Generation Innovators exhibition
Malvern Inventors Club https://www.malvern-inventors.co.uk/	2012: Innovative Technology & Service Organisations
Malvern Panalytical (formerly Malvern Instruments) https://www.malvernpanalytical.com/	2012, 2013, 2014: Innovative Technology & Service Organisations 2014, 2015, 2016, 2017, 2018, 2019, 2021: Next Generation Innovators exhibition 2019, 2021: Malvern Science in the Park
Malvern Radar and History Society (MRATHS) https://mraths.org.uk/	2015, 2016, 2017, 2018, 2019: Family day exhibition 2018, 2019: Malvern Science in the Park 2018, 2019, 2021: Next Generation Innovators exhibition
Malvern Hills Raspberry Jam club https://www.innovatemalvern.com/family-pi-jams	2016, 2017, 2018, 2019, 2021: Next Generation Innovators exhibition 2016, 2017, 2018, 2019, 2021: Family day exhibition 2018, 2019, 2021: Malvern Science in the Park
Malvern Technology Network https://the-mtn.co.uk/	2021: Innovation on the Hills exhibition
MathEmbedded https://mathembedded.com/	2016: Cyber security exhibition
Manufacturing Advisory Service (MAS) https://www.mymas.org/	2013, 2014: Organisations Supporting Innovation
Mazak https://www.mazakeu.co.uk/	2014: Innovative Technology & Service Organisations 2014, 2015, 2016, 2017, 2018, 2019, 2021: Next Generation Innovators exhibition 2014, 2015, 2016, 2017, 2018, 2019: Family day exhibition
Medeis https://www.medeisltd.co.uk/	2012, 2013: Organisations Supporting Innovation
Medilink West Midlands https://www.medilinkwm.co.uk/	2012, 2013, 2014: Organisations Supporting Innovation
Mercian Events https://www.mercianevents.com/	2016: Business of Innovating exhibition
Met Office https://www.metoffice.gov.uk/	2018, 2019: Malvern Science in the Park
METCloud https://www.metcloud.com/	2019: Cyber security exhibition
Metnet -	2012: Organisations Supporting Innovation
Metrasens https://www.metrasens.com/	2014: Innovative Technology & Service Organisations 2016: Business of Innovating exhibition
Midlands Cyber https://www.midlandscyber.com/	2021: Innovation on the Hills exhibition
Midven https://midven.co.uk/	2014: Organisations Supporting Innovation
ML Electronics -	2013: Innovative Technology & Service Organisations
Morgan Motor Company https://www.morgan-motor.com/	2012, 2013, 2014: Innovative Technology & Service Organisations 2013, 2014: Family day exhibition 2014, 2016, 2018: Next Generation Innovators exhibition 2017: Automotive Advances exhibition

Modus https://www.modusagency.co.uk/	2016: Business of Innovating exhibition
Modux https://www.modux.co.uk/	2016: Cyber security exhibition
Neoperl https://www.neoperl.com/	2019: Next Generation Innovators exhibition
National Cyber Skills Centre –	2014: Organisations Supporting Innovation 2015, 2016, 2017: Cyber security exhibition 2016: Business of Innovating exhibition
National Space Academy https://nationalspaceacademy.org/	2014, 2016: Next Generation Innovators exhibition
Nesta https://www.nesta.org.uk/	2016: Business of Innovating exhibition
Net Consulting https://www.netconsulting.co.uk/	2016: Cyber security exhibition
Nimbox https://www.nimbox.co.uk/	2017: Cyber security exhibition
NMITE (New Model Institute for Technology & Engineering) https://nmite.ac.uk/	2019: Next Generation Innovators exhibition 2019: Formal Dinner exhibition 2019: Creative Careers exhibition
North Hill Software https://northhillapps.com/	2013: Innovative Technology & Service Organisations
Nottingham Trent University https://www.ntu.ac.uk/	2012: Organisations Supporting Innovation
Novaro Publishing (formerly Adam Jolly) https://novaropublishing.com/	2014: Organisations Supporting Innovation 2019: Business of Innovating exhibition
Nquiringminds https://nquiringminds.com/	2016: Cyber security exhibition
Omniscope https://www.omniscope.uk/	2017: Cyber security exhibition
Origone https://origone-group.com/	2016, 2017: Cyber security exhibition 2016, 2017: Business of Innovating exhibition
Panaseer https://panaseer.com/	2015: Cyber security exhibition
Pepperneck https://www.pepperneck.com/	2012: Organisations Supporting Innovation
Pervade Software https://pervade-software.com/	2014: Innovative Technology & Service Organisations 2015, 2016: Cyber security exhibition 2021: Innovation on the Hills exhibition
Peter Jones Foundation https://www.peterjonesfoundation.org/	2016, 2017: Next Generation Innovators exhibition
PGI https://pgitl.com/	2016: Cyber security exhibition
PiBot –	2014: Innovative Technology & Service Organisations 2014, 2015, 2017: Next Generation Innovators exhibition 2014: Family day exhibition
PixelPin https://www.pixelpin.io/	2014: Innovative Technology & Service Organisations
Plinx https://plinx.io/	2021: Innovation on the Hills exhibition

Protect Centre
–

2014: Innovative Technology & Service Organisations

PrivacySolved
https://www.privacysolved.com/

2015: Cyber security exhibition

Prizm
https://prizsm.co.uk/

2021: Innovation on the Hills exhibition

Public Health England e-Bug initiative
https://e-bug.eu/

2019: Next Generation Innovators exhibition

QinetiQ
https://www.qinetiq.com/

2012, 2013: Innovative Technology & Service Organisations
2015, 2016, 2017, 2021: Next Generation Innovators exhibition
2015, 2017: Cyber security exhibition
2015: Family day exhibition
2017, 2021: Malvern Science in the Park

QualitySolicitors Parkinson Wright
https://www.qualitysolicitors.com/parkinsonwright

2013: Organisations Supporting Innovation
2013: Family day exhibition

Quantum R&D Tax
https://www.quantumtax.co.uk/

2019: Business of Innovating exhibition

Quickbird
https://quickbird.uk/

2015: Agri-tech exhibition

Randall & Payne
https://www.randall-payne.co.uk/

2016: Business of Innovating exhibition

Raspberry Pi Foundation
https://www.raspberrypi.org/

2013: Innovative Technology & Service Organisations

Regency IT Consultancy
–

2015: Cyber security exhibition

Renault UK
https://www.renault.co.uk/electric-vehicles.html

2013: Innovative Technology & Service Organisations
2013: Family day exhibition

Ripjar
https://ripjar.com/

2014: Innovative Technology & Service Organisations

Risk-X
–

2016: Cyber security exhibition
2016: Business of Innovating exhibition

Riversimple
https://www.riversimple.com/

2017: Automotive Advances exhibition

Ross Robotics
https://www.ross-robotics.co.uk/

2016: Family day exhibition

ROCU (Regional Organised Crime Unit for West Midlands)
https://www.wmrocu.org.uk/

2018, 2019, 2021: Next Generation Innovators exhibition
2018: Cyber security exhibition
2018: Family day exhibition
2021: Malvern Science in the Park

Rotaire Dryline
–

2012, 2014: Innovative Technology & Service Organisations

Royal Agricultural University
https://www.rau.ac.uk/

2019: Next Generation Innovators exhibition

Royal Air Force
https://www.raf.mod.uk/

2017: Malvern Science in the Park
2017, 2018: Next Generation Innovators exhibition

Royal Microscopical Society
https://www.rms.org.uk/

2013, 2014: Organisations Supporting Innovation
2013, 2014, 2015, 2017: Family day exhibition
2014: Next Generation Innovators exhibition

Royal Society of Chemistry https://www.rsc.org/	2014: Organisations Supporting Innovation 2014, 2015: Next Generation Innovators exhibition 2016: Next Generation Innovators exhibition 2014, 2016: Family day exhibition 2018: Malvern Science in the Park
Santander Corporate & Commercial https://www.santandercb.co.uk/	2013, 2014: Organisations Supporting Innovation 2013, 2014: Family day exhibition
Saturn Bioponics https://www.saturnbioponics.com/	2015: Agri-tech exhibition
SB Print https://www.sbprint.co.uk/	2014: Organisations Supporting Innovation
Scattermedia https://scattermedia.com/	2016: Business of Innovating exhibition
Schoolasaurus -	2018, 2019: Malvern Science in the Park
Science Gecko https://www.sciencegecko.co.uk/	2017: Malvern Science in the Park
Senseye https://www.senseye.io/	2015: Agri-tech exhibition
Serious Games International (now CUEi) https://cueinteractive.co.uk/	2012: Innovative Technology & Service Organisations
Sidaway Technologies https://www.sidaway.com/	2021: Innovation on the Hills exhibition
Sight Designs -	2012, 2013, 2014: Innovative Technology & Service Organisations 2013, 2014: Family day exhibition
Smart Actuator Company (now RIFT Actuators) https://www.riftactuators.com/	2016: Next Generation Innovators exhibition
Smartbox Assistive https://thinksmartbox.com/	2014, 2015: Next Generation Innovators exhibition
SME Solicitors https://www.smesolicitors.co.uk/	2013, 2014: Organisations Supporting Innovation
Social Presence http://alasdairmunn.com/	2013: Organisations Supporting Innovation
Solar Solutions Malvern -	2012: Innovative Technology & Service Organisations
SomerData -	2014: Innovative Technology & Service Organisations
Spa Telecoms -	2012: Organisations Supporting Innovation
SpreadServe -	2014: Innovative Technology & Service Organisations
StartUp Britain -	2014: Organisations Supporting Innovation
STEM Ambassadors Hub (formally STEMNet), part of STEM Learning https://www.stem.org.uk/commercial/stem-ambassadors-supporting-community-groups	2014: Organisations Supporting Innovation 2015, 2016, 2017, 2018, 2019, 2021: Next Generation Innovators exhibition 2014, 2015, 2016, 2017, 2018, 2019: Family day exhibition 2014, 2015, 2016, 2017, 2018, 2019: Creative Careers exhibition 2017, 2018, 2019, 2021: Malvern Science in the Park

Surevine https://www.surevine.com/	2014: Innovative Technology & Service Organisations 2016: Cyber security exhibition 2016: Business of Innovating exhibition
Sutcliffe & Co. https://www.sutcliffeinsurance.co.uk/	2012, 2013, 2014: Organisations Supporting Innovation 2015, 2016, 2017: Cyber security exhibition 2021: Innovation on the Hills exhibition
System Simulation https://www.ssl.co.uk/	2012: Innovative Technology & Service Organisations
TCG (now Boxspring Media) https://www.boxspringmedia.com/	2012: Organisations Supporting Innovation
Tek Microsystems -	2012: Innovative Technology & Service Organisations
Tento -	2015: Cyber security exhibition
TextLocal https://www.textlocal.com/	2012, 2013: Innovative Technology & Service Organisations
Tharsus https://tharsus.com/	2014: Organisations Supporting Innovation
The Bugatti Trust https://www.bugatti-trust.co.uk/	2021: Next Generation Innovators exhibition
The Cleaning Faerie https://thecleaningfaerie.com/	2014: Family day exhibition
The Development Manager (TDM) https://thedevelopmentmanager.com/	2018: Next Generation Innovators exhibition
The Friday Beer Company https://thefridaybeer.com/	2016, 2017, 2018, 2019: Startup Stories evening
The Friendly Nerd -	2015: Cyber security exhibition
The Hive https://www.thehiveworcester.org/	2019: Family day exhibition
The Quekett Microscopical Club https://www.quekett.org/	2017: Next Generation Innovators exhibition
The Royal Institution https://www.rigb.org/	2019: Next Generation Innovators exhibition
The Royal Society https://royalsociety.org/	2018: Next Generation Innovators exhibition
The Trust Bridge https://www.thetrustbridge.co.uk/	2019: Cyber security exhibition
TheOverworld -	2016: Business of Innovating exhibition
Think On! -	2012: Organisations Supporting Innovation
Three Counties Showground https://www.threecounties.co.uk/	2016: Next Generation Innovators exhibition
Thursfields Solicitors https://thursfields.co.uk/	2012: Organisations Supporting Innovation
Titania https://www.titania.com/	2012, 2013, 2014: Innovative Technology & Service Organisations 2015, 2016, 2017: Cyber security exhibition

Today's Security -	2019: Cyber security exhibition
Tomorrow's Engineers https://www.tomorrowsengineers.org.uk/	2016: Next Generation Innovators exhibition
Tranchulas https://tranchulas.com/	2016, 2017, 2019: Cyber security exhibition 2016: Business of Innovating exhibition
Transition Malvern Hills https://transitionmalvernhills.org.uk/wp/	2012, 2013: Innovative Technology & Service Organisations 2013: Family day exhibition
Transition Worcester https://www.transitionworcester.org.uk/	2018: Malvern Science in the Park
UBRacing https://ubracing.co.uk/	2014, 2015, 2016, 2017, 2018: Family day exhibition 2016, 2017: Business of Innovating exhibition 2015, 2017, 2019: Creative Careers exhibition 2018, 2021: Next Generation Innovators exhibition
Ultimaker https://www.ultimaker.com/	2014: Innovative Technology & Service Organisations 2014, 2015: Next Generation Innovators exhibition 2014, 2015: Family day exhibition
Utilize https://www.utelize.co.uk/	2021: Innovation on the Hills exhibition
UK Cyber Security Forum https://www.ukcybersecurityforum.com/	2014: Organisations Supporting Innovation 2015, 2016, 2017, 2018, 2019: Cyber security exhibition
UK Electronics Skills Foundation https://www.ukesf.org/	2017: Next Generation Innovators exhibition
UK Flood Barriers -	2012: Innovative Technology & Service Organisations
UKTI DSO (now UK Defence and Security Exports) https://www.gov.uk/government/organisations/uk-defence-and-security-exports	2012, 2013, 2014: Organisations Supporting Innovation
Unipart Security https://www.unipart.com/security/	2015: Cyber security exhibition
University of Bath https://www.bath.ac.uk	2012: Organisations Supporting Innovation
University of Birmingham https://www.birmingham.ac.uk/	2013: Organisations Supporting Innovation 2017, 2018, 2019, 2021: Next Generation Innovators exhibition 2013, 2019: Family day exhibition 2021: Malvern Science in the Park
University of Bristol https://www.bristol.ac.uk/	2014, 2016, 2017, 2019: Next Generation Innovators exhibition
University of Buckingham https://www.buckingham.ac.uk/	2017: Business of Innovating exhibition
University of Gloucestershire https://www.glos.ac.uk/	2013: Organisations Supporting Innovation 2016, 2017, 2019: Next Generation Innovators exhibition
University of Nottingham https://www.nottingham.ac.uk/	2015: Next Generation Innovators exhibition 2019: Family day exhibition
University of Oxford https://www.ox.ac.uk/	2018, 2019: Malvern Science in the Park
University of Surrey https://www.surrey.ac.uk/	2012: Innovative Technology & Service Organisations

University of Warwick (inc WMG) https://warwick.ac.uk/	2012, 2013: Organisations Supporting Innovation 2014: Organisations Supporting Innovation
University of Wolverhampton (STEM Response Team) https://www.wlv.ac.uk/schools-and-institutes/faculty-of-science-and-engineering/stem-response-team/	2021: Malvern Science in the Park 2021: Next Generation Innovators exhibition
University of Worcester https://www.worcester.ac.uk/	2012, 2014: Organisations Supporting Innovation 2014, 2015, 2016, 2017, 2018, 2021: Next Generation Innovators exhibition 2016: Family day exhibition 2017: Cyber security exhibition 2017: Business of Innovating exhibition 2021: Malvern Science in the Park
UnLtd https://www.unltd.org.uk/	2013, 2014: Organisations Supporting Innovation 2013: Family day exhibition
Usborne https://usborne.com/	2019, 2021: Malvern Science in the Park
Usecure https://www.usecure.io/	2017: Cyber security exhibition
UTC Aerospace (now Collins Aerospace) https://www.collinsaerospace.com/	2015: Next Generation Innovators exhibition 2016: Next Generation Innovators exhibition
Venture Cyber Security -	2012: Organisations Supporting Innovation
Veritherm https://veritherm.co.uk/	2021: Innovation on the Hills exhibition
Verity Furniture https://www.verityfurniture.com/	2014: Innovative Technology & Service Organisations 2014: Family day exhibition
Versarien https://www.versarien.com/	2012: Innovative Technology & Service Organisations
Video Interactive -	2012: Organisations Supporting Innovation
VipSeal -	2013: Family day exhibition
Virtual Experience Company https://virtualexperience.co.uk/	2012, 2013, 2014: Innovative Technology & Service Organisations
Vollmer Engineering https://www.vollmer-engineering.co.uk/	2012: Innovative Technology & Service Organisations
WCG Malvern Hills College (formerly South Worcestershire College) and Pershore College	2014: Organisations Supporting Innovation 2015: Agri-tech exhibition 2017: Next Generation Innovators exhibition 2014, 2017: Family day exhibition
Wembley Partners https://www.wembleypartners.com/	2021: Innovation on the Hills exhibition
Western Power Distribution https://www.westernpower.co.uk/	2015: Next Generation Innovators exhibition 2016: Next Generation Innovators exhibition
Westgate Cyber (now Enclave Networks) https://enclave.io/	2014: Innovative Technology & Service Organisations
WhiteBox https://whitebox.systems/	2021: Innovation on the Hills exhibition
Willans https://www.willans.co.uk/	2016: Business of Innovating exhibition

WINN Worcestershire https://winn-hub.com/	2016, 2019: Business of Innovating exhibition 2017, 2018: Startup Stories evening 2021: Innovation on the Hills exhibition
Winton https://www.winton.com/	2015: Cyber security exhibition
Worcester Astronomical Society https://worcesterastro.weebly.com/	2017, 2018, 2019, 2021: Malvern Science in the Park
Worcester Bosch Group https://www.worcester-bosch.co.uk/	2017: Next Generation Innovators exhibition
Worcester Enterprise https://www.worcesterenterprise.org/	2017, 2018: Startup Stories evening
Worcester Roots Foundation -	2014: Next Generation Innovators exhibition
Worcester Scientific https://worcesterscientific.com/	2021: Innovation on the Hills exhibition
Worcestershire Beekeepers' Association -	2014, 2015: Next Generation Innovators exhibition
Worcestershire Business Central https://www.business-central.co.uk/	2013, 2014: Organisations Supporting Innovation 2014: Family day exhibition 2015: Agri-tech exhibition 2015, 2018, 2019: Cyber security exhibition 2016: Business of Innovating exhibition
Worcestershire County Council inc Worcestershire Skills Central and Worcestershire Libraries & Learning Services https://www.worcestershire.gov.uk/	2012: Organisations Supporting Innovation 2014, 2015, 2016: Next Generation Innovators exhibition 2014: Creative Careers exhibition 2014, 2015: Family day exhibition 2016: Business of Innovating exhibition 2019: Malvern Science in the Park
Worcestershire LEP https://www.wlep.co.uk/	2013, 2014: Organisations Supporting Innovation 2017: Business of Innovating exhibition
Worcestershire Litfest & Fringe https://worcestershirelitfestfringe.wordpress.com/	2016: Family day exhibition
Worcestershire Regulatory Services https://www.worcsregservices.gov.uk/	2014, 2015: Next Generation Innovators exhibition
Workspace Technology https://www.workspace-technology.com/	2015: Cyber security exhibition
World Class Worcestershire -	2016: Business of Innovating exhibition
Wright Solutions https://www.wrightsolutionsltd.com/	2013, 2014: Organisations Supporting Innovation
WSI Internet Marketing -	2013: Organisations Supporting Innovation
Wyche Innovation Centre https://www.wyche-innovation.com/	2012, 2013, 2014: Organisations Supporting Innovation 2013, 2014: Family day exhibition 2015: Agri-tech exhibition 2015, 2016, 2017, 2018, 2019: Cyber security exhibition 2015: Electric Vehicle Innovation Showcase 2016, 2017: Business of Innovating exhibition
Wynne Jones IP https://www.wynne-jones.com/	2016: Next Generation Innovators exhibition 2016: Business of Innovating exhibition 2017: Next Generation Innovators exhibition

X Kommunications –	2016: Cyber security exhibition 2016: Business of Innovating exhibition
Xitek https://www.xitek.co.uk/	2013, 2014: Innovative Technology & Service Organisations
Yeadon IP https://www.yeadonip.com/	2012, 2013: Organisations Supporting Innovation
YorCyberSec https://www.yorcybersec.co.uk/	2019: Cyber security exhibition
Yoti https://www.yoti.com/	2017: Cyber security exhibition
Young Enterprise https://www.young-enterprise.org.uk/	2014: Next Generation Innovators exhibition
Your Green Future https://www.yourgreenfuture.org.uk/	2014: Next Generation Innovators exhibition
Zybert Computing https://www.zybert.co.uk/	2012, 2013: Innovative Technology & Service Organisations

APPENDIX D – PRESS RELEASES

A record of most of our press releases over the years tells the story of how the Malvern Festival of Innovation and Malvern Science in the Park events evolved, referring to highlights of each edition.

CELEBRATING THE BEST OF BRITISH IDEAS
Malvern Festival of Innovation 8th-9th November 2012, Malvern Theatres and Malvern College

1st October 2012, Malvern UK. Today, Key IQ Ltd released more news about the inaugural Malvern Festival of Innovation which will take place on the 8th–9th November 2012 at the Malvern Theatres and Malvern College in Great Malvern, UK.

The festival, organized in association with the Malvern Hills District Council and supported by numerous sponsors, including the Platinum Sponsor QinetiQ, is free to attend. The event will be open to general public, and will particularly appeal to business professionals, entrepreneurs and students. The aim is to promote innovation in both technology and business, helping cutting-edge companies showcase their products and services and offer a platform for companies that assist innovation to explain their initiatives.

Several high-profile plenary speakers have agreed to participate. These include Luke Johnson, Chairman of Risk Capital Ventures and StartUp Britain, and former Chairman of Channel Four Corporation, Andrew Humphries from the Global Entrepreneur Programme at the UKTI and London's Tech City, Paul Farrer an accomplished TV and film music composer, and Professor Peter Dobson from the Begbroke Science Park at the University of Oxford.

During the two days, there will be themed symposia covering cyber security, digital media, materials and devices, as well as sustainability and the environment. These sessions will be augmented with an exhibition; already more than forty organisations have signed up, with more in the pipeline.

During Friday lunchtime, there will be a dragons' den style elevator pitching session in which entrepreneurs will present their idea to a panel of financial experts and investors for constructive feedback, and even the possibility of an investment. This will be an opportunity for the audience to listen to the presentations and learn some useful tips on making effective pitches of a business idea to potential backers.

Dr Adrian Burden, Technical Director of Key IQ and Founder of the Malvern Festival of Innovation, explained "The Festival will be a platform to learn about some of the latest ideas in areas where rapid innovation is happening. Innovation is a deliberately broad theme, spanning all technical disciplines and social-economic themes. As such, the event will be a melting pot where insight and perspective from one area can spark an idea in someone involved in a totally different activity. The festival will inspire creativity as much as it showcases innovation."

On the Thursday evening, there will be a formal dinner at Malvern College, with tickets priced at £50.00 per head for a drinks reception and three course meal with wine. During the evening, Tim Harper, managing director of Cientifica Ltd and technology advisor to the World Economic Forum, will deliver a keynote address called "21st Century Innovation: leveraging the new golden age of science". This will be an eye-opening tour of the some of the world's recent innovations, their impact on society, and what might be coming next.

*****

THE INAUGURAL MALVERN FESTIVAL OF INNOVATION A GREAT SUCCESS

The event attracted over 400 people to the Malvern Theatres

26th November 2012, Malvern UK. The inaugural Malvern Festival of Innovation was held in Great Malvern on the 8th and 9th of November 2012 with 35 invited speakers attracting more than 60 exhibitors and over 400 attendees. In addition, more than 125 people attended the Formal Dinner at Malvern College.

Multicoloured footprints on the pavements, balloons on the lampposts, and fully booked hotels accompanied the two-day event, with some visitors extending their stay when they saw the local beauty of Malvern.

In addition to the extensive exhibition, the excellent speakers made the event particularly enjoyable. Peter Urey from London based Fearless Innovation Management commented "The list of guest speakers was a Who's Who of luminaries from the world of innovation in business." Mark Yeadon from Leeds based Yeadon IP said "The Festival was a gem of a conference. An enviable line-up of speakers with very meaningful insights into the world of innovation."

The festival was organized by Key IQ Ltd in association with the Malvern Hills District Council and supported by numerous sponsors, including the Platinum Sponsor, QinetiQ. This enabled the event to be free of charge for exhibitors and visitors, and enabled it to be open to a wide audience including students and members of the public.

Chris Bocock, Chief Executive of the Malvern Hills District Council was pleased with the festival and said "Malvern Hills District Council were delighted to be able to support Key IQ in delivering the first Malvern Festival of Innovation. We believe that this year's event provides a strong basis for a successful annual event for Malvern that will help to promote the Malvern area and inspire future innovation within our businesses and community."

The aim of the festival was to promote innovation in both technology and business, encouraging people to interact with others from outside their usual working community. Four technology themes and a parallel business symposium encouraged companies from these different sectors to exhibit alongside each other. The themes this year were cyber security, digital media, materials and devices, and environment and sustainability.

One of the most popular sessions of the two days was a *Dragons' Den* like opportunity for brave entrepreneurs to pitch to a panel of real investors. Of the four that did this, at least two have now had offers of support for their businesses. Dr Adrian Burden, Technical Director of Key IQ and Founder of the Malvern Festival of Innovation explained "Such outcomes are a key reason why we wanted to organise this Festival. Malvern, and the surrounding region, have many creative entrepreneurs and we wanted to provide a platform for them to showcase their ideas and to get constructive feedback about their innovations."

The Malvern Festival of Innovation will be an annual event, attracting visitors from around the UK to listen to high quality presentations and see first-hand some of the latest new technology. Key IQ has fixed the next year's Festival to run Thursday 7th to Friday 8th November 2013. Online registration for exhibiting and attendance will open in January 2013.

*****

STUDENTS ATTENDING THE MALVERN FESTIVAL OF INNOVATION'S SCHOOLS FRINGE EVENT WILL EACH RECEIVE A FREE RASPBERRY PI STARTER KIT

4th November 2013, Malvern UK. Each student that is participating in the "Next Gen. Innovators" workshop on Friday 8th November as part of the Malvern Festival of Innovation will be able to take away a Raspberry Pi Starter Kit courtesy of Google and the Raspberry Pi Foundation.

This schools' fringe event is being hosted at Malvern College with the kind support of The Institution of Engineering and Technology (The IET), Malvern College, The Chase School, and the Herefordshire and Worcestershire regional partner of the Science, Technology, Engineering and Mathematics Network (STEMNET).

The event will allow over 100 students from schools around the region to participate in a series of workshops that will showcase engineering and hopefully inspire the attendees to pursue a career in science and technology. The morning session is primarily aimed at Year 6 students who will be going on to senior school next year and will be exposed to broader science-based subjects. The afternoon session is for Years 7, 8 and 9 who will be thinking about their career choices and starting to select their GCSE subjects.

Dr Adrian Burden, Founder of the Malvern Festival of Innovation and Technical Director at Key IQ Ltd stated "This year we wanted to introduce a schools' element to the Festival. Through this workshop, we aim to enthuse students about science and engineering and encourage them to consider it as an exciting career choice. The supporters of this event and sponsors of the main Festival have enabled the workshop to be offered free-of-charge, encouraging all schools to register and come along. The workshops have been many times oversubscribed, demonstrating that more of these kinds of opportunities could and should be offered to our regional schools."

The workshop will comprise of three parts. The Design Department at Malvern College is providing a Computer Aided Design (CAD) session to give students the opportunity to use an industry standard software design package. This will show students how ideas are drawn-up ready for prototyping and manufacturing.

The second session will involve an introduction to coding on a Raspberry Pi, a compact low-cost computer circuit designed to make computer programming accessible and exciting. Clive Beale, the Director of Educational Development at the Raspberry Pi Foundation, will help lead this session and give both the teachers and students a firsthand insight into these fascinating devices.

Moreover, the participating students will each be able to take a Raspberry Pi Starter Kit home with them and continue experimenting in their own time. This fantastic opportunity has come about as a result of the initiative announced earlier this year in which Google and the Raspberry Pi Foundation will be giving away 15,000 devices to school children around the UK to promote computer science and encourage children to learn about coding.

Clive Beale will also be talking at the main Festival on Thursday afternoon, highlighting the innovative work of the Raspberry Pi Foundation and its plans for the future.

The final aspect of the workshop will be a Ball Launching Challenge, led by the IET, in which children will attempt to engineer and build a system to throw a ball over the longest distance, demonstrating creativity within a tight time constraint.

For those not attending the schools' event, part of the festival that will be of particular interest to both students and their families is the Family Show on Saturday 9th November morning. This is a double-bill featuring television broadcasters and scientists Dr Jonathan Hare (from the BBC / OU *Rough Science* series) and Professor Mark Miodownik (as seen on BBC's *Dara O'Briain's Science Club*), and will be opened by Harriet Baldwin MP. The show will illustrate how innovation in materials science is impacting how we live and work, and promises to be an exciting tour of the stuff that makes up the universe around us. There is a small charge for this event, and tickets can be booked directly with the box office at the Malvern Theatres.

There will also be a free exhibition of some of the companies from the main Festival continuing on the Saturday morning in the foyer of the Malvern Theatres. Highlights on show will include the University of Birmingham's Student Formula Racing car and a 3D Printer demonstration.

*****

TIME ONCE AGAIN TO CELEBRATE THINKING-OUTSIDE-THE-BOX

Malvern Festival of Innovation returns for its third successive year with symposia, exhibition, family show, and an extensive schools' outreach

15th September 2014, Malvern UK. The nationally acclaimed Malvern Festival of Innovation is set to return to Great Malvern from 1st–4th October 2014 for its third successive year. The event continues to grow; this year spanning four full days at the Malvern Theatres and including parallel events around the town.

The festival, organized by Malvern-based Key IQ in association with the Malvern Hills District Council and supported by numerous sponsors, including the Platinum Sponsor Lockheed Martin, is largely free to attend. This year will see the themes of Advanced Engineering & Manufacturing, Cyber Security, and the Business of Innovating explored, with keynote speakers descending on Malvern from around the UK.

Dr David Bott, former Director of Innovation Programmes at the Technology Strategy Board and currently non-executive Chairman of Oxford Biomaterials will open the Festival on Wednesday 1st October with a talk titled The Epidemiology of Innovation. Professor John Perkins CBE, the Chief Scientific Advisor for the UK Government's Department for Business Innovation and Skills will talk after lunch about the importance of innovation to the UK's economy. The day will also include talks from local firms Malvern Instruments and Mazak, and from a former engineering apprentice at RSRE Malvern who is now Director of Software Engineering at Raspberry Pi in Cambridge; Gordon Hollingworth.

The Cyber Security Innovation Showcase on Thursday 2nd October underlines the importance of this industry to the region. Presentations from Lockheed Martin, the Civil Aviation Authority and the University of Swansea will highlight cyber security issues in defence, aviation and medical devices. After lunch, the winners of Technology Strategy Board's Severn Valley Cyber Launchpad competition will present their cutting-edge technologies to win support from potential customers and investors.

Friday's session focuses on the broader topic of innovating in business; taking new ideas to market, protecting intellectual property, and successfully exporting to grow. Festivalgoers will hear from Lee Strafford, entrepreneur extraordinaire who founded Plusnet and took it through to an exit of £67m when it was sold to BT. Lee will explain what he learnt during this journey and some of the initiatives he is now involved in to promote entrepreneurship in the UK. Later that afternoon, local entrepreneurs will have an opportunity to pitch their own ideas to a panel of experts and the audience to gain constructive feedback and maybe even some investment!

Dr Adrian Burden, the Founder of the Malvern Festival of Innovation stated "The Festival is a really good opportunity for people interested in business and technology innovation from around the region to come together and hear from world experts in their field. It is also a unique chance to network with like-minded individuals and come away inspired and invigorated."

Each day also includes a focused exhibition of innovative companies alongside organisations that can help you develop and grow your own enterprise. Exhibitors this year include HP, Santander, Bishop Fleming,

UKTI, Worcestershire Business Central, and Worcestershire Local Enterprise Partnership. It is free to attend both the symposia and exhibition, with the event open to business professionals, students, and members of the public alike.

After the success of last year's Family Show, Saturday 4th October will see a full day's exhibition including displays from the Institute of Physics, The IET, Royal Microscopical Society, Institute of Mechanical Engineers, Little Pi Shop and Ordnance Survey's GeoVation Challenge. A ticketed Family Show will also take place in which Mark Champkins, Inventor in Residence of the Science Museum and former winner on Dragon's Den will talk about what makes for a creative mind. This will be followed by Quentin Cooper, the entertaining broadcaster from BBC Radio's *Material World*, exploring the nature and reputation of great scientists and technologists in a talk titled 'Geeks, Freaks & Eggheads: the Pervasive Image of Scientists, Inventors & Innovators'.

For those coming from London and the South West, First Great Western will once again be naming their early morning train service out of London Paddington as *The Innovation Express*, arriving in Great Malvern in time for the opening talks each day.

Richard Watson, futurist and author of *What's Next?* will be the guest speaker at the Formal Dinner held on the Thursday evening at Malvern College. Richard travels the world advising executive at multinational companies about how to spot disruptive technologies and how to predict future developments. This is a rare opportunity to hear his thoughts on the future and how we made some incorrect predictions in the past. Those wishing to buy tickets for the dinner can even pay online this year with Bitcoins!

"Celebrating present-day innovations is one thing, but we must also be mindful that we need school students to be enthused about a career as a scientist, engineer, technologist or entrepreneur", add Dr Burden. "This year we have an expanded schools' outreach programme kindly supported by the Three Counties Showground called Next Generation Innovators. Numerous companies and organisations are coming along to provide hands-on exhibits, workshops, talks and careers advice to school students visiting from Years 7, 8 and 9. This is precisely the age that career choices start to be made ahead of selecting GCSE subjects."

In addition, Aston Martin are coming to Malvern College during the Festival to give an audio-visual presentation about the development and testing of their sports cars. This event alone will involve over 150 students in Years 10–13 from numerous local schools.

*****

DRONES AND ROBOTS COMING TO A FIELD NEAR YOU

28th September 2015, Malvern UK. Robots and drones will play an increasingly important role in the production of food according to the founder of the Malvern Festival of Innovation.

Dr Adrian Burden said agriculture was going through a second significant revolution but rather than being based on new farming techniques, as it was in the 1600s, it will be led by autonomous vehicles, big data and artificial intelligence instead.

The subject will be explored in detail at a free agri-tech day on Wednesday, 7 October at Malvern Theatres as part of this year's Malvern Festival of Innovation.

Dr Burden said: "Herefordshire and Worcestershire are both predominantly rural counties with huge opportunities to capitalise on agricultural technology. Both the Marches Local Enterprise Partnership (LEP) and the Worcestershire LEP have identified this sector as a key focus area for the region.

"This is an opportunity for farmers, food and drink producers, business professionals and students to find out more about the state of play in agri-tech and how we as a region can compete globally."

Keynote speakers include Mark Stansfield, Chairman of Giffgaff and Chair of the Worcestershire LEP and who started his career at Cadbury and Kraft Foods.

Prof Simon Blackmore, from Harper Adams, will speak on the subject of robotic agriculture and will argue autonomous tractors equipped with advanced technology will prepare, tend and harvest crops with very little human intervention whilst improving yield and quality.

Those attending will also hear how advanced connected sensors will continuously feed information about the environment to farmers, taking the guesswork out of farming, while energy use and sustainability will also be discussed.

Alexander Fisher, from award winning Midlands firm Saturn Bioponics, will also demonstrate how his business is using new techniques such as vertical growing to tackle the issue of a shortage of land for growing.

*****

AWARD-WINNING PARTICLE PHYSICISTS LAUNCH A NEW INTERACTIVE SCIENCE SHOW AT THE MALVERN FESTIVAL OF INNOVATION

Dr Sam Gregson will present Hunting the Higgs as part of the Small Particle, Big Impact! Family Show at the Malvern Theatres on Saturday 10th Oct. 2015.

5th October 2015, Malvern UK. The Malvern Theatres has a tradition of being the venue where new and innovative plays debut. As far back as 1929, George Bernard Shaw premiered a number of his famous plays in Malvern. Today, the practice continues in earnest as we announce that award winning scientists and science communicators Dr Sam Gregson, Dr Aidan Randle-Conde, Dr Ben Still, Dr Claire Lee, Dr Suzie Sheehy and Dr Djuke Veldhuis and renowned science communicators/entertainers Helen Arney and Jonny Berliner will be launching their revolutionary new science comedy show at the Malvern Festival of Innovation this year.

The Ministry of Sense: Hunting the Higgs show will be the first show of its kind and suitable for children (11+), family and adult audiences. The highly interactive and comedic show will see audience members exploring their own thinking biases, forming their own ideas to solve problems, collecting and analysing data from the Large Hadron Collider using their own smart phones and tablets, and even Skyping an active physicist at CERN live!

Dr Sam Gregson explains "The event puts the public in charge of making one of science's greatest and most exciting discoveries. The audience will be at the cutting edge of science and the progress of the field will rest in their hands as the Large Hadron Collider's latest recruits. Most shows don't want you to have your phones with you but we aren't like most shows, so please bring your smartphone or tablet to take part in the interactive games throughout the show."

The new initiative has been produced on the back of the highly successful CERN stand-up comedy evening "LHComedy: CERN after Dark" which saw CERN affiliated scientists and professional science communicators take to the stage to explain high-level research through informal stand-up. The event successfully engaged a live audience of 300 extra-CERN Geneva locals as well as 10,000 international online viewers in more than 100 countries.

In addition, at the Family Show in Malvern, the programme will also feature a talk from Dr Kate Lancaster on the promise of nuclear fusion as a future source of energy. Dr Lancaster is another renowned science communicator who will explain in layman's terms the technical challenges of building a star here on Earth.

"This is a fantastic double-bill for families interested in science and technology to enjoy. It is made all the more exciting having the launch of the new interactive show *Hunting the Higgs* as it begins its UK tour." states Dr Adrian Burden, founder of the Malvern Festival of Innovation.

The Family Show is ticketed via the Malvern Theatres box office and will run alongside a free hands-on exhibition in the foyers of the Malvern Theatres running from 10am to 4:30pm on the day. The exhibition will feature Raspberry Pis, microscopy demonstrations, physics demonstrations, 3D Printers, robot demonstrations and an exhibit of historical artefacts showcasing Malvern's scientific heritage.

*****

THOUSANDS INSPIRED BY FESTIVAL OF INNOVATION

12th October 2015, Malvern UK. More than 2,500 people were inspired by this year's Malvern Festival of Innovation to invent the future.

The six-day event offered a range of free activities, exhibitions and workshops including an event attended by 800 school pupils aimed at inspiring the next generation.

Different themes were explored each day focusing on the increasing need for Cyber Security, the use of robotics and drones in agriculture, and the role of creative design in product development. The business and technology days attracted more than 400 business professionals.

There were also keynote talks from industry heavyweights including renowned British designer Sebastian Conran, Phil Smith, CEO of Cisco UK & Ireland and Mark Stansfeld, Chairman of GiffGaff Chair of Worcestershire Local Enterprise Partnership.

The weekend programme included a family fun day during which 180 people attended the Family Show to hear Dr Kate Lancaster explain nuclear fusion and Dr Sam Gregson entertain with a comedic presentation about experimental design and the world of particle physics.

The final day of the festival saw an impressive fleet of current and future electric vehicles on display in Priory Park, with talks explaining the advantages of owning an electric car.

The festival is organised by the social enterprise Innovate Malvern CIC, supported by Malvern Hills District Council and with additional support from numerous sponsors including Cisco, IDS INDATA and QinetiQ.

Dr Adrian Burden, founder and curator of the festival, said: "During the festival it was wonderful to see so many students enthused by science and technology and so many families engaging with hands-on exhibits. "This is the fourth time the festival has been held and it gets bigger every year and we had speakers come from across the country to showcase new ideas, creativity, advanced technologies and entrepreneurship."

*****

ENTHUSING THE NEXT GENERATION TO THINK OUT-OF-THE-BOX

Malvern Festival of Innovation's Next Generation Innovators day returns to the Three Counties Showground this October

24th August 2016, Malvern UK. Over 800 students from schools around the counties of Herefordshire and Worcestershire have registered to attend the popular Next Generation Innovators day on Tuesday 4th October 2016 that features during the week-long Malvern Festival of Innovation.

Held at the Three Counties Showground, the event aims to enthuse students in the first three years of secondary school about the STEM subjects (science, technology, engineering and mathematics) as well as the role of product design and entrepreneurship in making a commercial success of ideas.

Numerous exhibitors will be providing hands-on demonstrations, workshops, and careers advice to the students, including local companies such as QinetiQ, Mazak and Malvern Instruments as well as organisations from further afield such as the Royal Society of Chemistry, the Peter Jones Foundation and the UK Electronics Skills Foundation.

Coinciding with World Space Week, the local branch of the Institute of Mechanical Engineers is kindly supporting an immersive 360-degree show called Future Moon, highlighting the engineering challenges to travel to and colonise our orbiting neighbour in the future. The National Space Academy will also be delivering workshops about the value of space exploration.

Ken Nottage, Chief Executive of Three Counties said "We are delighted to be supporting the Next Generation Innovators school focused day held at the Three Counties. It is a fantastic opportunity for students to explore different career opportunities which they may not have considered previously."

Students will also hear from keynote speakers including Professor Marcus du Sautoy OBE about the mystery of numbers and other mathematical curiosities, Orla Murphy the 2016 IET Young Woman Engineer of the Year who is an acoustic and audio engineer at Jaguar Land Rover (JLR), and Professor Adam Hart about the role of helpful bacteria in a range of important real-world applications.

Dr Adrian Burden, founder of the Malvern Festival of Innovation and Managing Director of the social enterprise Innovate Malvern CIC that organises the event explained "It is free for students to attend this event and so it is only possible for us to put this on with the kind support of our festival sponsors. If any organisations would like to join us as exhibitors to engage with students or indeed as sponsors to help us deliver an even more memorable event, please do get in touch."

This year, the Malvern Festival of Innovation will run 3rd–8th October 2016, with other events aimed at business and family audiences. For those wishing to hear further thoughts about innovation from Marcus du Sautoy, he will also be speaking about his new book What We Cannot Know at the launch event in Malvern College on Monday 3rd October evening. The festival is organised the social enterprise Innovate Malvern CIC with the assistance of the Malvern Hills District Council and numerous other supporters and sponsors.

*****

LEGAL AND FINANCE EXPERTS SHARE ONE OF THE BEST KEPT SECRETS IN BUSINESS STRATEGY

Hear more at the Malvern Festival of Innovation

19th September 2016, Malvern UK. Three local businesses are combining their expertise for a day to benefit business owners and entrepreneurs by talking about R&D tax credits and how to use intellectual property (IP) to make money for your business.

Leading professionals from Randall & Payne accountants, Willans LLP solicitors and Wynne Jones IP are on the main stage at the Business of Innovating day on Friday 7 October, part of the internationally-known Malvern Festival of Innovation.

Topics covered include; how to get cash back from HMRC via R&D tax credits, how to protect your brands and inventions to capture market share, how to license IP to make money, how to enforce your legal rights against infringement and how to combat counterfeit goods relatively cheaply.

Dr Adrian Burden, Malvern Festival of Innovation founder, said: "This is an opportunity to learn from experts about real-life business case studies which could apply to your own situation. Hear about the value of protecting your IP; you will leave this session aided with practical tips on how to go about it successfully, how to defend your portfolio, and how it can actually make money rather than cost you money."

The symposium is free for all to attend and will also feature talks about the UK's innovation landscape and tech clusters from keynote speakers from Innovate UK and Nesta, helping regional businesses of all kinds understand how they fit into our changing ecosystem and where opportunities may lie.

During the day, there will also be a range of exhibitors showcasing their innovative products and services as well as offering helpful advice and support to successfully scale your business. With networking opportunities and an entrepreneurs' pitching session, this could be a day that positively improves your bottom line.

Dr Adrian Burden explained that this symposium, at the Malvern Theatres, is suited to entrepreneurs, managers and business leaders keen to understand what drives the innovation economy in the UK and how to start and grow new businesses to succeed. He shared: "The day is devoted to instilling innovation in the heart of your business. Whether you need to protect intellectual property, secure funding, start a new venture, grow an existing enterprise or expand overseas, this festival day focuses on how to think creatively about your business operations and will include case studies and a popular elevator pitching session from brave entrepreneurs facing the audience and panel."

*****

NEW ROUTE POINTS THE WAY TO INNOVATIVE FUTURE

22nd September 2016, Malvern UK. Malvern is to get its own version of the London Underground map as part of this year's Festival of Innovation.

A specially designed *Get Around Route* has been created on the streets of Malvern by Spring Lane based Fleet Line Markers. The route has been created using more than 130 foil stickers and will help guide visitors to the festival around the various venues and discover more of what the town has to offer. Just like the 'Tube' map each route is in a different colour but the lines have been named after famous people with a link to Malvern including scientist Charles Darwin and authors CS Lewis and JRR Tolkien.

This year's Malvern Festival of Innovation takes place from Monday to Saturday, 3 to 8 October. The programme launches at Malvern College on the Monday evening with a talk by Oxford professor Marcus du Sautoy OBE, who will be discussing his new book *What We Cannot Know*, which explores the limits of the human brain to innovate.

Nick Holzherr, a finalist in hit BBC show *The Apprentice* and founder of smart grocery shopping tool Whisk, will appear on stage at the Coach House Theatre in Malvern on Wednesday, 5 October. He will be joined by Neil Westwood, founder of Magic Whiteboard which won investment on another BBC show *Dragons' Den*, and Alistair Shortland, who founded local mobile communications company TextLocal from his bedroom. All three will be sharing their stories of the trials and tribulations of being an entrepreneur.

Other highlights include a schools' event full of activities and demonstrations aimed at inspiring the next generation of entrepreneurs, a business support event to help companies and entrepreneurs deal with issues such as intellectual property and a day focusing on the latest developments in cyber security.

The festival ends on Saturday, 8 October, with a family fun day at Malvern Theatres. This will include free interactive exhibits where children can find out more about drones, Raspberry Pis and 3D Printers as well as two ticketed live shows on the benefits of stem cell research and how to use an electric guitar to explain string theory.

To set the tone for the festival there will be an open air showing of the film *The Matrix* on Sunday, 2 October in Priory Park.

The festival is being organised by the social enterprise Innovate Malvern CIC, supported by Malvern Hills District Council and with additional support from numerous sponsors. Dr Adrian Burden, founder and curator of the festival, said: "Today, more than ever, we all need to innovate. We need new ideas to stay competitive in business, new technologies to improve our lives, and we must be creative in how we use resources. This festival is a fantastic opportunity for businesses and the public to find out what's coming next and how others are innovating."

Cllr Phil Grove, Leader of Malvern Hills District Council, said: "We're delighted to be supporting the Festival of Innovation once again. It highlights how through innovation we can unlock a world of possibilities and hopefully someone will be inspired to go out and create the next big thing which will revolutionise our lives."

Tickets for *The Matrix* cost £8.50 and for the two family shows £7.84. Both are available from the Malvern Theatres Box Office. Most other events are free but places need to be registered.

*****

THOUSANDS GLIMPSE THE FUTURE AT MALVERN FESTIVAL OF INNOVATION

21st October 2016, Malvern UK. More than 2,000 people flocked to this year's Malvern Festival of Innovation to discover the emerging ideas, creative designs and new technology changing the future. Highlights of this year's week-long event included renowned mathematician and author Marcus du Sautoy discussing his new book *What We Cannot Know*, as he expanded the horizons of the 150 strong audience at Malvern College, in parallel with a live #WorcestershireHour 'tweet up'.

A new 'StartUp Stories' event at The Coach House Theatre saw celebrity entrepreneurs Nick Holzherr, a finalist in the 2014 television show *The Apprentice*, and *Dragons' Den* winner Neil Westwood, join forces with local entrepreneur Alastair Shortland of TextLocal to enthuse over an attentive auditorium about the trials and tribulations of being your own boss.

The packed programme also included the Next Generation Innovators Day at the Three Counties Showground. More than 750 students and teachers from nearly 20 schools across Herefordshire and Worcestershire attended the event which brought the world of science, technology and engineering alive through a series of interactive exhibits.

There was more fun for all ages at the Family Day held at Malvern Theatres, with Dr Emily Grossman talking about cloning and stem cells, and 'Rock Doctor' Dr Mark Lewney explaining Superstring Theory with his custom Ibanez electric guitar. An array of exhibitors provided hands-on demonstrations of chemistry, physics, electronics, and design technology in the foyers.

The customary series of themed business days held at Malvern Theatres focused on Cyber Security, the Internet of Things and the Business of Innovating, featuring keynote speakers from GCHQ and Innovate UK.

The whole programme kicked off on Sunday, 2 October with more than 130 people braving the October chill to watch an open-air screening of cult film *The Matrix* in Priory Park as part of the fringe festival.

Now in its fifth year, the festival is organised by the social enterprise Innovate Malvern CIC, supported by Malvern Hills District Council and with additional support from numerous sponsors including Palladium Sponsor Wynne Jones IP, and Gold Sponsors QinetiQ and the Three Counties Showground.

Dr Adrian Burden, founder and curator of the festival, said: "We had another fantastic week of fascinating insights and cutting-edge ideas from people that travelled to Great Malvern from around the UK. Of particular note was the cyber security symposium with a record-breaking attendance to the extent that we had to close registration early."

Cllr Phil Grove, Leader of Malvern Hills District Council said: "We will continue to support the Malvern Festival of Innovation as it focuses on the future opportunities for businesses and our young people. We want next year's festival to be even bigger and better, and welcome any proposals from local businesses or the community to run fringe events to bring the benefits of the festival out into the town and continue Malvern's legacy as the home of innovation."

*****

EXPERIMENT WITH SCIENCE IN THE PARK

16th June 2017, Malvern UK. A chance to hunt for dinosaurs, use pedal power to generate electricity and take a closer look at sun spots will be some of the activities on offer as part of a free science-themed fun day.

Malvern Science in the Park takes place on Saturday, 1 July between 10.30am and 4.30pm in Priory Park. The event aims to promote the wonders of science, technology, engineering and mathematics through a series of interactive experiments and games.

Activities include the chance to hunt out the prehistoric creatures hiding in the park as part of a special dinosaur trail and the opportunity to have a ride on an energy bike in a bid to power various household appliances. There will be science-related dance workshops to take part in, stories about the history of medicines, opportunities to blow giant bubbles, mini rocket launches, and the chance to get a closer look at sun spots with Worcester Astronomical Society.

A series of short fun talks from the bandstand will explain the scientific world around us, including appearances from Sir Isaac Newton, aka Don Southey, a local STEM Ambassador.

The event is being organised by the social enterprise Innovate Malvern and the local branch of the Institute of Physics, with support from Malvern Hills District Council and the Worcestershire Local Enterprise Partnership.

Dr Adrian Burden, Managing Director of Innovate Malvern, explains "Nationally there continues to be a shortage of scientists and engineers, and we know that here in Worcestershire there is high demand for these skills within our local businesses. Our aim is to show the younger generation and their parents that science is fun, and encourage them to continue to study sciences at school in the future."

Evidence shows the earlier you can get young children and teenagers involved in and enjoying the world of science, technology, engineering and mathematics (STEM), the more likely they are to pursue a career in those subjects in later life.

*****

SCIENCE IN THE PARK TO RETURN

20th July 2017, Malvern UK. Organisers of Malvern Science in the Park say they plan to make it an annual fixture in the district's social calendar after more than 900 people turned up to the first event.

Hundreds of people packed into Priory Park on Saturday, 1 July 2017 to enjoy a day of activities designed to promote the wonders of science, technology, engineering and mathematics (STEM).

It was organised by Innovate Malvern and the local branch of the Institute of Physics with support from Malvern Hills District Council, Worcestershire Local Enterprise Partnership, Malvern Town Council, The IET and the Institution of Mechanical Engineers.

During the day visitors were able to enjoy activities including hunting for dinosaurs, launching mini rockets, generating electricity with pedal power, blowing giant bubbles and looking at sun spots with Worcester

Astronomical Society. Numerous volunteer STEM Ambassadors assisted with hands-on demonstrations and fascinating science talks were delivered from the bandstand.

The day was partly organised in response to growing concerns that not enough young people are interested in STEM subjects, which could increase the skills shortage in these areas and hurt Britain's future economic growth. A report by the UK Commission for Employment and Skills (UKCES) revealed 43 per cent of vacancies in STEM roles are hard to fill due to a shortage of applicants with the required skills.

Dr Adrian Burden, Managing Director of Innovate Malvern, said: "Part of tackling the skills gap involves encouraging young people at an early age to discover the joys and exciting possibilities associated with science and engineering.

"This event was a trial to see how it was received and we're delighted with the attendance and many positive messages of support we have received since. We've now decided we want to make this an annual event and already have organisations showing an interest in being involved."

Cllr David Chambers, Leader of Malvern Hills District Council and portfolio holder for economic development, said: "It's wonderful to hear Science in the Park is to become an annual event. Malvern is the home of scientific innovation, so it's fitting that we lead the way in encouraging our young people to be part of the inventions and discoveries of the future."

FESTIVAL TO UNVEIL 5G TEST PLANS FOR COUNTY

21st September 2017, Malvern UK. Plans to use Worcestershire as a test site for the next generation of mobile communication technology are set to be unveiled as part of this year's Malvern Festival of Innovation.

Worcestershire Local Enterprise Partnership has successfully bid for the county to be included in the national test programme for the 5G network, which is set to revolutionise how people communicate and live their lives. Details will be outlined during a Business of Innovating event on Friday, 6 October at Malvern Theatres as part of the festival, which is organised by Innovate Malvern CIC and supported by Malvern Hills District Council and numerous sponsors. An as yet to be confirmed location in Malvern will be among the areas to try out the 5G network before it is rolled out nationally in 2020. This forms part of the council's commitment to encourage investment in the next generation of mobile technology as part of its Five Year Plan.

Gary Woodman, CEO of Worcestershire LEP, said: "The arrival of 5G will open up so many possibilities from a doctor performing robotic surgery on the other side of the world to a road that can identify when it needs gritting in bad weather. It will form the backbone of the industries and technologies of the future and I'm delighted Worcestershire is going to be at the forefront of that."

Other festival highlights include The Next Generation Innovators schools' day on Tuesday, 3 October at Three Counties Showground, which aims to inspire the 800 students taking part to become young entrepreneurs and inventors.

The day will also involve, conditions permitting, the launch of a helium weather balloon which will be tracked and monitored in real time from the exhibition hall.

Morgan Motor Company is hosting The Automotive Advances Morning on Wednesday, 4 October looking at driverless vehicles and environmentally friendly cars. The UK's leading cyber security firms will visit Malvern Theatres on Thursday, 5 October to showcase their research, products and services in a series of talks and exhibits.

The festival ends on Saturday, 7 October with a family fun day and show at Malvern Theatres including hands-on exhibits and a whistle stop tour of the universe in just an hour.

Dr Adrian Burden, founder and curator of the festival, said: "Once again we're looking forward to welcoming world-class speakers to Malvern to hear their take on the latest developments in a variety of industry sectors. At the Friday business session alone we have Emma Jones MBE from Enterprise Nation, Rashik Parmer MBE from IBM, Polly Barnfield OBE from Maybe and Neill Ricketts from Versarien sharing their thoughts and business experience."

*****

TOUR THE UNIVERSE AT FESTIVAL FAMILY DAY

2nd October 2017, Malvern UK. The chance to take a tour of the universe without leaving your seat is on offer as part of this year's Malvern Festival of Innovation Family Day. The event takes place on Saturday, October 7 at Malvern Theatres and will see professional astrophysicist and science communicator Dr Megan Argo take visitors on a whirlwind ride through the solar system and beyond in just an hour.

It is one of two shows being performed on the day. The other involves maker, engineer, problem solver and BBC *Robot Wars* judge Dr Lucy Rogers, discussing the wiring of the Internet of Things. She will be exploring all the fun, frivolous and even useful devices that can be made at home using Raspberry Pi computers. There will also be the opportunity to learn more about attempts to 3D print chocolate, the use of drones in surveying buildings, how Raspberry Pis can control multi-coloured LEDs, and how microscopes work through a series of free hands-on exhibits and demonstrations throughout the day. Companies exhibiting include GE Aviation and Mazak, alongside organisations such as the Institute of Physics, the University of Birmingham's Formula Student Racing team and Malvern Radar and Technology History Society.

The Malvern Festival of Innovation is organised by Innovate Malvern CIC and supported by Malvern Hills District Council and numerous sponsors.

Dr Adrian Burden, founder and curator of the festival, said: "Our Family Show this year will enthuse children and their parents about our connected planet and our extended universe. Kids need to be encouraged to become makers and inquisitive explorers. Dr Lucy Rogers and Dr Megan Argo are both fantastic role models for any budding engineer or scientist."

The day runs from 10am to 4.30pm and entry to the exhibition is free. Tickets for the shows cost £7.84 and can be booked by visiting Malvern Theatres online or calling the box office.

*****

FESTIVAL OF INNOVATION ENTHUSES YOUNG AND OLD

10th October 2017, Malvern UK. People from around the UK caught a glimpse of the future at the sixth edition of the annual Malvern Festival of Innovation last week. The six-day event, which ran from Monday to Saturday 2 to 7 October, offered a range of free activities, exhibitions and workshops including events for schools, business leaders and members of the public.

The weather balloon launch was prepared and watched by nearly two hundred students at the Next Generation Innovators schools' day. The conditions on the ground were near-perfect, but upper atmosphere winds blew the balloon south faster than hoped and led to the Raspberry Pi payload being lost at sea in the English Channel. Students were able to see the journey unfold in real-time with live telemetry to the exhibition centre.

Another highlight was the seeing Riversimple's Rasa car parked up at the Morgan Motor Company alongside classic Morgan models at the inaugural Automotive Advances symposium. The Rasa is a hydrogen-powered eco prototype vehicle built by Hugo Spowers and his team in mid Wales. During the session, he explained the pros and cons of the car and why he had embarked on its creation.

The cyber security day, full to capacity, showcased this burgeoning industry sector with presentations by experts from BAE Systems, Yoti, the UK's National Cyber Security Centre and numerous SMEs including Malvern's D-RisQ. In addition to the business delegates, the session attracted Masters students from the University of Warwick and undergraduates from the University of Worcester.

The weekend programme included a hands-on family fun day in the Malvern Theatres in which a live demonstration of 3D-printing chocolate from local company Avatar 3D caught the eye of many attendees. Other highlights included Raspberry Pi computer demonstrations from The IET and the Wyche Innovation Centre's Pi Jam club.

Dr Adrian Burden, founder and curator of the festival, said: "Once again we had a week of thought-provoking presentations and fascinating demonstrations of technology. Arranging an event like this is tiring, but it was all put into perspective at our Formal Dinner in Malvern College when extreme explorer Newall Hunter described how he had just a few days earlier returned from a fact-finding mission to Outer Mongolia. He was preparing for the first solo winter crossing of the Gobi Desert this November, explaining the kind of technology he will use (and avoid) on the journey."

The festival is organised by the social enterprise Innovate Malvern CIC, supported by Malvern Hills District Council and with additional support from numerous sponsors.

FINAL LINE-UP REVEALED FOR MALVERN'S SCIENCE IN THE PARK

22nd June 2018, Malvern UK. From exciting experiments to amazing astronomy, there will be something for everyone at the latest Malvern Science in the Park on Saturday, 30 June.

Running from 10.30am to 4.30pm, the free, family-fun event will see Priory Park transformed into an open-air laboratory for budding scientists to launch fizzy rockets, blow enormous bubbles and mix colourful chemicals. Organisers, social enterprise Innovate Malvern and the local branch of the Institute of Physics, have revealed the full line-up for the day and visitors won't be disappointed.

MP for West Worcestershire Harriett Baldwin will open the event which is aimed at providing an educational and entertaining insight into science, technology, engineering and mathematics.

For paleontologists and geologists, the Earth Heritage Trust will be displaying their hands-on collections of rocks, minerals and fossils, and local expert Dr Mark O'Dell will be on hand to crack open a few fossil nodules.

Science-buskers will also be demonstrating scientific principles and engineering concepts from the bandstand, including science communicator Sarah Cosgriff who will talk about physical forces and aerodynamic flight.

Children will be transported to prehistoric times with the Dinosaur Detective Trail, tour the park in search of planets with the Interplanetary Trail and learn more about viruses and bacteria with the Microbe Treasure Hunt.

Malvern Science in the Park is supported by Worcestershire Local Enterprise Partnership, Malvern Hills District Council, Worcester City Council, Institution of Mechanical Engineers, BCS The Chartered Institute for IT, The IET and Malvern Town Council.

Dr Adrian Burden, Managing Director of Innovate Malvern, said: "The late, great scientist Professor Stephen Hawking once said 'Science is beautiful when it makes simple explanations of phenomena . . .'

"We need people to appreciate this beauty so that more of our younger generation follow in his footsteps and become scientists or engineers in the future.

"Hopefully we'll sow some seeds of curiosity during the event in the park this year."

*****

FESTIVAL TO HIGHLIGHT CYBER SECURITY AND QUANTUM COMPUTING

7th September 2018, Malvern UK. The annual Malvern Festival of Innovation returns 8th–13th October 2018, this year highlighting, amongst other subjects, advances in cyber security and the emerging field of quantum computing.

Cyber security remains a key growth sector for the Worcestershire, but its implications and indeed implementation should be of interest to all types of business around the region. The festival offers a unique opportunity to connect with experts and thought-leaders for help, advice and insights.

Included in the line-up at this year's symposium on Thursday 11th October 2018 in the Malvern Theatres will be an update from the National Cyber Security Centre (NCSC) on how businesses large and small can get the basics of cyber security right in the face of evolving threats.

We will also hear from a number of SMEs active in the sector and at the forefront of technical research and development. Sir John McCanny will deliver a keynote about the Centre for Secure Information Technologies (CSIT) in Northern Ireland, its involvement with new London Cyber Innovation Centre, and how businesses in and around the Midlands can collaborate.

And for those with an eye on the future, the programme will include talks about quantum computing and how this technology will have a major impact on digital security and the way in which computers solve complex problems in general. Leading the discussion, Professor Tim Spiller Director of the York Centre for Quantum Technologies and Director of the UK's Quantum Communications Hub will argue that quantum technologies are disruptive and provide advantages over the current, conventional technology in use today.

Other festival highlights include the Environment and Sustainability symposium on Wednesday 10th October morning and the Startup Stories session later that evening. On Friday 12th October morning, the exciting new technology platform of blockchains and cryptocurrencies will be explored.

The festival ends on Saturday 13th October with a ticketed family show at Malvern Theatres and a free hands-on exhibition about science and technology for all to enjoy.

*****

MALVERN FESTIVAL TO CELEBRATE BOFFINS EVERYWHERE

30th September 2018, Malvern UK. Residents and businesses are being urged to join in a celebration of intelligence and creativity as part of this year's Malvern Festival of Innovation.

Tuesday 9 October is being declared Boffin Day by Malvern Hills District Council in honour of the term which is believed to have first been coined to describe the scientists that worked on radar in Malvern during the Second World War. The aim is to celebrate intelligence, invention and creativity to help inspire the next generation of scientists, mathematicians and engineers.

The day coincides with Malvern Festival of Innovation's Next Generation Innovators schools' day which will see about 800 students and their teachers descend on the Three Counties Showground to be inspired by the world of science, technology and entrepreneurship. Visitors will be invited to take a special quiz to find out which one of 12 famous boffins they are most like as well as take part in various workshops. The quiz will also be available through Malvern Hills District Council's social media channels and people are being encouraged to tweet their support on the day with the hashtag #BoffinDay.

There will also be an exhibition along Church Walk in Malvern designed by MRATHS to highlight the many inventions and discoveries made in the town.

Cllr David Chambers, Leader of Malvern Hills District Council, said: "Malvern has a rich heritage when it comes to invention and creativity and we want people to help us champion Boffin Day and help inspire the next generation to continue that proud tradition."

The festival runs from the 8 to 13 October and other highlights throughout the week include talks on how technological innovations will help cut household energy use and aid the fight against climate change. Entrepreneurs will also be telling their stories of success while help and support will also be on offer to those innovators looking to make their way in the world of business. The potential pitfalls and opportunities presented by quantum computing will be explored as will the applications of Blockchain technology, which is being described as the 'biggest thing since the internet'.

The festival ends with the popular Family Day at Malvern Theatres on Saturday, 13 October from 10am. There will be a number of free hands-on activities and exhibits to be explored as well as a ticketed event featuring Dr Sophie Kain, who appeared on *The Apprentice* in 2007, showing people how to take an idea and turn it into a successful business. This will be followed by adventurer and astronomer Huw James helping us to celebrate World Space Week by explaining how we are already sending probes far in to space and discussing where we might go next.

Huw explains, "I'm excited to speak at the Malvern Festival of Innovation! We've got an inspiring history of exploration and adventure in the UK and Space really is surprising us at every turn as we explore more. 50 years ago we put a person on the Moon, the next 50 could see us become a space fairing species!"

Dr Adrian Burden, organiser and founder of the Malvern Festival of Innovation, said: "We're looking forward to some fantastic speakers coming to our town once again to enthuse us all about the possibilities of the future. You don't have to be a boffin to enjoy it, but hopefully we'll inspire some to be become one in the future."

Most festival events are free but places must be booked. The exhibition on Family Day is free to attend but the show is ticketed and costs £8.40 via the Malvern Theatres box office.

*****

INSPIRATION, EXPLORATION AND ADVENTURE AT THE MALVERN FESTIVAL OF INNOVATION

10th October 2018, Malvern UK. Once again, the Malvern Festival of Innovation's Family Day will feature an exciting double-bill family show at the Malvern Theatres. This year's theme is Inspiration, Exploration and Adventure, highlighting our drive to solve problems, make discoveries and strike out on quests in to the unknown.

Dr Sophie Kain trained as a quantum physicist and found herself competing on BBC's *The Apprentice*, having to think quickly on her feet and make business decisions to win tasks. During this interactive show, Sophie will explore how to make money by turning innovative ideas into commercial reality and highlight ways to solve real-world problems.

"I am thoroughly looking forward to inspiring young minds to use their natural creativity to both see and solve problems.", states Sophie. "I will explain how to flex your creative thinking muscle and how to use this to benefit society and make yourself more wealthy. I will show you how to use what we learn in science to form new and better businesses."

After the break, adventurer and astronomer Huw James will help us celebrate World Space Week with an exciting journey through space, explaining how we are already sending probes far in to space and discussing where we might go next. Live demonstrations and science experiments will help explain the engineering principles of making space exploration a reality.

Huw explains, "I'm excited to speak at the Malvern Festival of Innovation! We've got an inspiring history of exploration and adventure in the UK and Space really is surprising us at every turn as we explore more. 50 years ago we put a person on the Moon, the next 50 could see us become a space fairing species!"

The Family Day will also include a host of hands-on exhibits in the Malvern Foyers, free for all to enjoy. Visitors will be able to interact with Raspberry Pi computers, 3D Printers, computer simulations, and engineering challenges to learn more about science and technology being applied in the real world. The day takes place on Saturday 13th October between 10am and 4:30pm at the Malvern Theatres, with the Family Show ticketed through the Malvern Theatres Box Office and running from 10:30am to 1pm.

*****

MARCUS CHOWN TO SPEAK AT FESTIVAL LAUNCH EVENING

3rd September 2019, Malvern UK. The annual Malvern Festival of Innovation returns 7th–12th October 2019, this year in collaboration with London-based business mix. The programme will highlight advances in science, technology and business practice to improve the way we live, work and play.

Award-winning writer and broadcaster Marcus Chown will speak at the opening evening on Monday 7th October in Malvern College. He will explore "Bonkers Things about the Universe", highlighting thought-provoking and profound science whilst providing a new perspective on life and the Universe in which we live.

Marcus was formerly a radio astronomer at the California Institute of Technology in Pasadena, where he studied under the renowned physicist Richard Feynman. Now he is cosmology consultant for *New Scientist* and has written a number of popular science books including *The Ascent of Gravity* which was *The Sunday Times* Science Book of the Year 2017. More recently he has written *Infinity in the Palm of Your Hand: 50 Wonders That Reveal an Extraordinary Universe.* Marcus has also been regular guest on the BBC 4 comedy-science show, *It's Only A Theory* with Andy Hamilton and Reginald D. Hunter, and often appears on Channel 4's *Sunday Brunch.*

Dr Adrian Burden, the founder of the Malvern Festival of Innovation states "We're really looking forward to welcoming Marcus to kick-start the festival this year. Creativity and discovery often occur with an open mind and fresh-thinking. Marcus will provide a fascinating perspective of the world in which we live; asking if babies are powered by rocket fuel, if we could fit the entire human race in the volume of a sugar cube, showing that 98% of the universe is invisible, and explaining why time travel is not ruled out by the laws of physics!"

The rest of the week will include a packed programme for school students, business professionals and families. Highlights include the Cyber Security day on the Thursday, the new Comedy Science Night on the Friday evening, and the Family Show on the Saturday. David Page, the CEO of business mix, will speak about his thoughts on the power of collaboration and innovation in business at Thursday evening's Formal Dinner.

*****

LAUGH OUT LOUD AT THIS YEAR'S FESTIVAL

23rd September 2019, Malvern UK. The annual Malvern Festival of Innovation, returning 7th–12th October 2019 in collaboration with London-based business mix, will this year feature a new Science and Technology Comedy Night.

To be held in Malvern Radio, Great Malvern's latest refurbished venue on the site of the old recon club at the top of Church Street, the evening will feature perhaps one of the highest qualified line-ups to take to the comedy stage.

Ria Lina will host the evening, having a BSc in experimental pathology, an MSc in forensic science, and a PhD in viral bioinformatics. She then worked as an IT Forensic Investigator for the Serious Fraud Office before embarking on her present career as a comedian. Ria has made numerous television appearances and was nominated for the Amused Moose Laughter Awards at the Edinburgh Fringe Festival.

Ria will be joined by The Bad Boy of Science Dr Sam Gregson who has a PhD from the University of Cambridge, worked on the Large Hadron Collider, and founded CERN's first comedy show LHComedy. He returns to Malvern having spoken about particle physics at the Family Show in 2015.

Microbiologist and science theatre performer Dr Martin Khechara will explore the nature of disease transmission through human faeces, vomiting and by breathing in each-others airborne secretions in a segment that will require the audience to have a strong stomach.

Scary Boots, aka Dr Kate Oliver, will perform physics stand-up comedy, herself warming-up ahead of her main billing at the Family Show the next day in the Malvern Theatres where she will speak about 3D printing and soft matter.

And the evening will round off with award-winning Foxdog Studios as computer programmers Lloyd Henning and Peter Sutton take to the stage with an interactive finale featuring games and gadgets.

Dr Adrian Burden, the founder of the Malvern Festival of Innovation quipped "This is an experiment to mix science and comedy in a notional round-bottomed flask, pass the evaporate through a Liebig condenser and determine if pure laughter comes out as distillate. Bring your lab book and safety specs."

The rest of the week will include a more serious programme for school students, business professionals and families. Highlights include the opening Monday evening lecture by science writer Marcus Chown, business and entrepreneur sessions on the Wednesday, Cyber Security day on the Thursday, an environment and sustainability symposium on the Friday, and the Family Show on the Saturday. David Page, the CEO of business mix, will speak about his thoughts on the power of collaboration and innovation in business at Thursday evening's Formal Dinner.

*****

FESTIVAL TO HELP BUSINESSES LEADERS ADDRESS ENVIRONMENT & SUSTAINABILITY ISSUES

2nd October 2019, Malvern UK. A free Environment and Sustainability business symposium forms a key pillar of the programme at the upcoming Malvern Festival of Innovation. Thought leaders from London and the Midlands will feature in the line-up that will take place at the Coach House Theatre in Great Malvern on Friday 11th October.

Anna Bright, Chief Executive of Sustainability West Midlands, will provide an overview of current regional innovation activity whilst sharing case studies of local sustainable innovation successes.

Professor John Bryson from the Department of Strategy and International Business at the University of Birmingham will speak about citizen-led innovation at a community level and how this can lead to new business opportunities.

Then Beverley Nielsen, an Associate Professor/ Executive Director of IDEA (Institute for Design & Economic Acceleration) at Birmingham City University (BCU) will highlight how small businesses can build success on design and innovation, being mindful of the need to scale sustainably and to offer products and services that do not exacerbate the environmental issues that we are all becoming acutely aware of.

This year, the festival is in collaboration with business mix, a consultancy based in London with a wealth of experience working with exciting new start-ups and scale-ups. One such company is WESAF Energy that is introducing appropriate new energy-generating and distribution technology into communities in Africa. Their CEO Marvin Tabi will highlight their work and the opportunities open to technology providers in the West Midlands keen to help address these emerging markets.

The day will round off with two further inspiring talks. Philip Mossop, the founder of WasteCollection.com, will speak about his passion for dealing with environmental issues and his latest venture that illustrates the potential of thinking in terms of a circular economy. And then Tom Levitt, consultant on responsible business and the author of *The Company Citizen: Good for Business, Planet, Nation and Community* will reinforce the role of business in tackling environmental and sustainability issues.

Dr Adrian Burden, Festival Founder, explains "With a growing need to address climate change, pollution and waste, businesses will need not only to do things differently in the future, but their leaders will need to foster a culture of both sustainability and innovation. The best way forward is to learn from others and so a symposium like this is a great way to share ideas, insights and opportunities."

Malvern-based consultancy Quest for Future Solutions have kindly helped to curate the Environment and Sustainability symposium and will also be on-hand to answer questions and steer the debate.

*****

KNOCKING SCIENCE OUT OF THE PARK

11th June 2020, Malvern UK. COVID-19 and social distancing is not going to put a damper on Malvern's annual alfresco celebration of hands-on science experiments that usually takes place in Priory Park, Great Malvern.

Instead, Innovate Malvern CIC has announced that it has organised a free virtual event to take place 10am to 4:30pm on Saturday 27 June 2020 with scientists presenting live from around the country alongside short pre-recorded videos and science discussions.

Aimed at primary and early secondary school students, and their families, people can register for a limited number of tickets on Zoom, enabling them to pose questions to the guest speakers about the subjects being presented. And others will be able to watch on the Facebook Live stream throughout the day.

Dr Adrian Burden, Managing Director of the social enterprise behind the event and host for the day, explains "We didn't want to simply cancel this year's event, particularly as schools have been so disrupted over the last few months. So, we're grateful that so many science communicators have agreed to jump on board with the new format and share their insights and enthusiasm for the subject from their own homes and gardens."

The science topics covered will be wide ranging; from Rockets to Raspberry Pis, Microbes to Möbius strips, Physics to Fossils, Bubbles to Batteries, Surfactants to Scurvy, Rocks to Radio, and more. There will also be demonstrations of experiments and projects that people can perform for themselves. And for those living in the Malvern area there will be a self-guided quiz around the town organised by The IET with prizes to be won.

This year, Malvern Science in the Park is kindly supported by the Institute of Physics, Institution of Mechanical Engineers, The IET, Worcester City Council, Worcestershire Local Enterprise Partnership, and Malvern Hills District Council.

*****

SCIENCE IS ONCE AGAIN A WALK IN THE PARK

15th June 2021, Malvern UK. Malvern Science in the Park is set to return to Priory Park in Great Malvern, running from 10:30am to 4:30pm on Saturday 26th June 2021.

Following the UK Government's announcement that, although Step 4 of the opening-up is being delayed, Step 3 restrictions are remaining unchanged, an in-person COVID-secure outdoor event will be able to take place that will enthuse visitors young and old about the wonders of science.

Dr Adrian Burden, Managing Director of the social enterprise Innovate Malvern CIC that organises the event states "After more than a year of disruption from the pandemic, we're all relying on science to better understand the virus and come up with effective vaccines and novel treatments so that life can one day return to normal. And we're going to need plenty more scientists across many disciplines in the future to reboot the economy and tackle climate change, so this will be a fun opportunity to perform some experiments and find out what being a scientist is all about."

The event is aimed at primary and early secondary school students, and their families. Planned activities will include rocket launching, physics experiments, materials analysis, computer science, geological investigations, meteorology, mathematical origami, imaging sun-spots, and more.

With the current pandemic restrictions in place, the event will proceed with additional safety precautions including zoning and ticketing. People who wish to attend are asked to visit www.innovatemalvern.com/science-in-park for the latest information, to reserve tickets, and to see the latest details of the full programme.

This year, Malvern Science in the Park is kindly supported by the Institute of Physics, Institution of Mechanical Engineers, The IET, West Midlands Railway, and Malvern Hills District Council.

*****

SCIENCE ENTHUSED MANY IN THE PARK

28th June 2021, Malvern UK. Malvern Science in the Park went ahead as planned on Saturday 26th June 2021 in Priory Park, Great Malvern.

The event was held, as usual, in the open air, but with additional COVID safety measures in place to ensure visitors could stay socially-distanced and engage with exhibits and speakers without the risk of virus transmission.

The event was kindly opened by Katy Gibson from the Institute of Physics Midlands, signalling the start of a day filled with science experiments, engaging demonstrations, and fascinating short talks delivered from the bandstand.

Dr Martin Khechara talked about tapeworms and poo, a subject that was of great appeal to the young audience. Renowned origami artist Coco Sato, visiting with the University of Birmingham School of Mathematics, had everyone folding paper with great precision, and Dr Chris Hamlett, representing the Discover Materials initiative, demonstrated the wetting properties of a giant lotus leaf before synthesising some foaming elephants' toothpaste.

Around the park, numerous science activities and experiments were taking place from over twenty organisations, including local businesses QinetiQ, Malvern Panalytical, IASME and Legrand, as well as learned organisations including the Institute of Physics, the Earth Heritage Trust and The IET. The University of Worcester, University of Wolverhampton, and the University of Birmingham were all represented as well.

Dr Adrian Burden, Managing Director of the social enterprise Innovate Malvern CIC that organised the event said "It was great to stage an in-person event in which families of all ages could once again learn about different sciences first-hand from enthusiastic experts. I think we managed to cover a good range: from geology to biology, from cyber security to chemistry, from physics to astronomy, and from environmental science to ballistics."

Malvern Science in the Park was kindly supported by the Institute of Physics, Institution of Mechanical Engineers, The IET, West Midlands Railway, and Malvern Hills District Council.

*****

RORY CELLAN-JONES TO OPEN THE TENTH MALVERN FESTIVAL OF INNOVATION

15th September 2021, Malvern UK. The annual Malvern Festival of Innovation returns 4th–9th October 2021 for its tenth successive year. The programme will once again highlight science, technology, engineering and mathematics (STEM) along with entrepreneurship and creativity.

To launch the festival week, its founder Dr Adrian Burden will be joined on stage by Rory Cellan-Jones, the BBC's principal technology correspondent and author of the book *Always On, Hope and Fear in the Social Smartphone Era*. Adrian will chat with Rory about his fascinating life travelling around the globe to report on emerging technology and meeting with some of the world's most influential tech entrepreneurs.

The event will be held at the Coach House Theatre in Great Malvern before moving next door to Bloom. Space for an opportunity to network over light refreshments and buy signed copies of Rory's book. The event is free for all to attend, but places are limited so people are encouraged to book tickets ahead of time on line.

Dr Burden states "Whilst we've been encouraging our local entrepreneurs and students to innovate over the last decade through the Festival, Rory has been meeting influential, innovative household names like Amazon's Jeff Bezos, Facebook's Mark Zuckerberg, Lastminute.com's Martha Lane Fox, and Tesla's Elon Musk. This will be a fascinating opportunity to hear what Rory thinks makes them tick and to understand his take on the impact of the mobile phone and associated rise of social media."

The rest of the week includes the enthusing Next Generation Innovators schools outreach day, an afternoon live with local Thriving Three Counties business podcaster Dan Barker, a showcase featuring numerous innovative local ventures many of whom have benefited from Worcestershire's BetaDen accelerator programme, the back-by-popular-demand Science and Technology Comedy Night, and finally the Family Day with its associated science show at the Malvern Theatres on the Saturday.

*****

INNOVATION ON THE HILLS SHOWCASE

30th September 2021, Malvern UK. The upcoming edition of the Malvern Festival of Innovation will feature a showcase of local innovators in the Malvern Theatres on the afternoon of Thursday 7th October 2021.

The exhibition will highlight the breadth of exciting technology companies around the region, including those associated with BetaDen; Worcestershire's dynamic launchpad for entrepreneurs. Free to attend, this event will provide ample opportunity to find out more about these ventures and their cutting-edge products and services.

The afternoon will include a keynote from David Rowan, the founding Editor-in-Chief of *WIRED* magazine's UK edition and the author of the informative book *Non-bullshit Innovation: Radical Ideas from the World's Smartest Minds*. David has travelled the world meeting technology entrepreneurs and understanding what makes ambitious start-ups succeed.

Dr Adrian Burden, the Festival founder states, "When I started the festival ten years ago, it was in my mind to be implicitly about innovation without the BS. Then David wrote the book! So, I'm delighted that he can at last join us in Malvern and share some of his fascinating insights. Moreover, he'll be selling signed copies of his book too, which I highly recommend reading."

During the afternoon, some of the exhibiting start-ups will be delivering lightening pitches in the auditorium, including BlockMark Technologies, FloWide, Green Gorilla Software, Invizio, JET Engineering System Solutions, Plinx, Prizm and Worcester Scientific.

IASME, the National Cyber Security Centre's Cyber Essentials Partner and the local company behind a range of other important certification schemes, will also be exhibiting. They will be alongside a number of their technical partners and a visit will provide a good opportunity for organisations keen to improve their cyber security to find out more information.

The rest of the week includes an afternoon live with local Thriving Three Counties business podcaster Dan Barker, an evening of Innovation Insights from Innovate UK, Spin Up Science and D-RisQ, and the Science and Technology Comedy Night.

*****

FESTIVAL SUCCESS

14th October 2021, Malvern UK. The tenth edition of the Malvern Festival of Innovation went ahead as planned as a live, in-person event in Great Malvern between 4th and 9th October.

Rory Cellan-Jones chatted on stage with Festival Founder Dr Adrian Burden about his life as a technology reporter with the BBC. He gave intriguing insights into some iconic moments such as the launch of the Apple iPhone, the switching on of 5G in the UK, and his televised interview with Elon Musk. The Malvern Book Cooperative was then on hand to sell signed copies of his recent book *Always On*.

Dr Burden adds "With all the uncertainty of the COVID-19 pandemic, we were both relieved and pleased that the Festival progressed as planned enabling people to meet safely in-person and benefit from the energy generated at live events. We also thank all our sponsors and supporters, including the cross-festival support of West Midlands Railway's 'Your Community, Your Fund'.

The Next Generation Innovators schools' day involved over 20 exhibitors show-casing science and technology to senior school students ahead of their GCSE subject choices. These included technology businesses like GE Aviation, QinetiQ, Malvern Panalytical, Mazak, IASME and Indra alongside outreach organisations like the Institute of Physics, Bloodhound Education, The IET and the Institution of Mechanical Engineers. Award winning scientist Dr Anna Ploszajski also travelled to the event from London to talk with students about everyday materials and their selection.

Dan Barker, the host of the popular Thriving Three Counties podcast took to the stage to interview leadership consultant Lucy Barkas, product designer Kristo Shivachev, and business operations manager Ruth Allsopp about their career and management insights. This was followed by a session highlighting the role of intellectual property, the nature of innovation ecosystems and the importance of cashflow management in a start-up business.

Another highlight of the week was the keynote from David Rowan, the founding Editor-in-Chief of *WIRED* magazine's UK edition and the author of the informative book *Non-bullshit Innovation: Radical Ideas from the World's Smartest Minds*. This formed part of a showcase of local tech ventures in association with

Worcestershire's technology accelerator BetaDen. Five comedians travelled from around the country to The Old Con Club on Church Street for an evening of hilarious and yet intellectual science comedy. This was hosted by Dr Steve Cross and rounded-off with live music from John Hinton's "Ensonglopedia" show.

Lucy Eckersley described her experiences as a wildlife conservationist at the Family Show on Saturday illustrating the different roles of scientists and non-scientists in this important work. And Alina Ivan educated everyone about their (more than five) sensors with on-stage demonstrations involving members of the audience.

For more information about the festival and its past editions over the last decade, please visit www.festival-innovation.com

*****

APPENDIX F – THE BLOGS

For several years I wrote a few blogs during the leadup to the festival in the hope they might attract readers that would translate into new event attendees. We also had some guest blogs by Stuart Wilkes. 2014 was a particularly fertile year.

CALM BEFORE THE STORM

23rd August 2014

As we approach the third annual edition of the Malvern Festival of Innovation, anyone who has organised an event will know that there is a nagging worry that no one will turn up. Today there are so many trade shows, public events and schools' activities that standing out from the crowd is not easy. And since the Festival was founded in Great Malvern, we have noticed a growing number of innovation festivals vying for attention.

But we have something that we believe others lack; a simply stunning location in the heart of the United Kingdom where innovation has been a key part of the local culture and heritage for hundreds of years. The Malvern Hills must have inspired creative thought, technical inventiveness, and entrepreneurial opportunity since humans first stumbled upon them.

The iPhone may have been designed in Silicon Valley, but the liquid crystal display chemistry came from Malvern, as in fact did the architecture of an Integrated Circuit, and the approach of using a capacitive touch screen to access content. Scientists in the defence research facility in Malvern were also responsible for Radar, passive infra-red detectors that now protect homes from intruders, and numerous other technical wonders; many of which remain esoteric or top secret! Today we are a recognised national hub for cyber security.

But innovation is not just about science and technology. Innovation must include new ways of creating business, new approaches to teaching, and creative novel ways of improving health. Malvern has seen plenty of this innovation too; England's oldest preparatory school, The Elms School, was established at the foot of the Malvern Hills and still educates today. This development paved the way for a new way to teach school-aged children and is a sector that remains very strong in Malvern today. Malvern's water is believed to be the first in the world to have been bottled commercially, and has since been drunk by royalty and continues to be bottled today from the original source. This spring water also played a key role in Victorian health with the renowned water cure that went on to establish Malvern as a key tourist destination for those wishing to escape city pollution and have a breath of fresh air. Today about one and quarter million people visit the Malverns each year!

Thankfully there is plenty of fresh air in Malvern. We are currently taking deep breaths of it ahead of what will be a busy few weeks leading up to the next edition of the Festival. Luckily, we know from past experience that plenty of people will turn up. But it would be super if you were one of them – see you there!

BOFFINS (GEEKS, FREAKS & EGGHEADS)

30th August 2014

We're looking forward to hearing from Quentin Cooper at the upcoming Family Show as he explores "why it is that for all they've done to radically change the world we live in, the popular image of scientists has hardly changed at all". There are many scientist stereotypes; people that wear socks with their sandals, adults who can't quite look you in the eye as they speak, brains the size of planets that are unable to function at the basic level needed to boil an egg, and so on.

But we have to be careful what we say here in Malvern because the town has an unusually high concentration of scientists for a rural settlement without a university. And it turns out that the word Boffin may well have originated from here!

If you check the Oxford English Dictionary, the derivation of the word is unknown but came into use around the time of the Second World War. An example given is "the boffins at the Telecommunications Research Establishment" which is now the QinetiQ site in Great Malvern. Consult Wikipedia and there is a citation of a pre-war use of the word; by J.R.R. Tolkien as a surname in *The Hobbit*. Interestingly, Tolkien was a frequent visitor to Malvern, travelling up to the town from Oxford with fellow author C.S. Lewis. It is said that Middle Earth and The Shire were inspired by his walks on the Malvern Hills, just as the Victorian gas lamps that still operate today in and around Malvern inspired the opening scene in *The Lion, The Witch and Wardrobe*.

Quentin refers to boffins as Geeks, Freaks and Eggheads in the title of his talk. Another common term in modern parlance is Nerd. Consult Roget's *Thesaurus*, and it also includes more complimentary terms such as Scientist, Technologist, Scholar, Expert, and Savant. Peter Roget published his collection of words well before the second world war in 1852, so in that first edition Boffin would not have been included. However, I think you might arguably now refer to Roget as a Boffin. Roget died in 1869 and happens to be buried in West Malvern, so he remains in good company!

*****

CYBER SECURITY: CAN WE INNOVATE FAST ENOUGH?

3rd September 2014

Some sectors seem to develop faster than others. The computer industry has always been a fast-track innovator fuelled by miniaturisation, a hunger for speed, and a creative community that has brought us the Internet, phone apps, tablets and now the promise of the Internet of Things. How many other industries have delivered so much and consistently managed to lower the price for a given level of performance in the way the IT industry has?

But in parallel we have had to deal with a darker side of innovation: viruses, hackers, phishers and fraud. Our reliance on all things silicon from running our business to running our social lives is now under threat from others who can defraud our business and take over our lives. The question is, can we keep up? The first challenge is that the industry needs to constantly develop new defences against cyber attacks, new algorithms to encrypt passwords, and new processes to plug vulnerabilities. Then we, as the users, have to keep up too.

We now have numerous accounts, numerous profiles, and a proliferation of data in cloud services and on devices. All of these are protected by our passwords that ideally need to be growing in complexity, changed frequently, and different for each service we use. And as this trend continues, we start to feel the fatigue of staying abreast of it all and wondering if we can continue to function in this fast-paced world.

Interestingly, as a species, we have probably been here before. I'm sure the Stone Age man wondered how he could live in a world as bronze tools emerged and accelerated the pace of change in all walks of life he was accustomed to; hunting, gathering, farming, and crafting. And at the same time he no doubt feared the bronze weapons being unleashed on his world and wondered if he could develop defences against them as they became sharper, longer, heavier and more accurate.

More recently we had the industrial revolution in which people feared the speed and capability of the motorcar, train, plane and robotic production line. As these new inventions allowed us to travel at high speeds across land and water, so too they enabled nations to engage in warfare and espionage. As a race, though, we pulled through again.

Cyber does offer its own new challenges however. In a way, it allows numerous layers of reality (or virtual reality) to be created, so things become very much more abstract. It is harder for our brains to rationalise abstract things like data. Is it valuable? how does it really affect our privacy and those around us? is it dangerous? and so forth.

The good news is that so far it looks like we can innovate fast enough. Our systems haven't melted down yet, and there are plenty of new services and interesting new defences emerging each day. We'll hear about some of these at the festival this year: the Internet of Things, cyber security, Big Data, assurance of complex systems, new approaches to passwords and encryption, etc. Assuming of course we're not out-paced in the next few weeks and everything starts to unravel. . . .

*****

SHOULD THERE BE ANOTHER E IN STEM?
14th September 2014

Promoting Science, Technology, Engineering and Mathematics (the STEM subjects) to school-aged children is an incredibly important activity if the goal is to generate a more creative and innovative future. Of course, the arts are creative and innovative in their own right, but wealth generation that fuels an economy (and in many ways funds art so that it can be enjoyed) is likely to come about through the application of STEM.

And that is where the other E comes in. STEM subjects on their own cannot lead to revenue. It is business acumen that turns a technical invention or scientific discovery into a viable commercial product or service. This relies on a firm understanding of Enterprise, or indeed that of being an Entrepreneur.

With this in mind, I think we are doing students a disservice if we encourage them to think STEM, but don't teach them about how to commercialise results. Not everyone wants to be a businessman or businesswoman (the Entrepreneur), but appreciating what's involved and understanding routes to market (Enterprise) that others may follow will help them focus on the overall importance of STEM.

At a recent panel session on the subject of STEM skills held in Birmingham as part of the Festival of Science, the point was made that the term 'knowledge economy' is an outdated concept. What is needed instead is 'clever makers or clever builders'. In other words, it is not good enough to just think good ideas, but you have to implement them into something tangible, usable and hence valuable. I would add 'clever exploiters'. I don't mean exploit in terms of abuse; I mean exploit in terms of capitalise. Yes, I know, another E.

Young Enterprise is an example of a school-based initiative that promotes business thinking in students. But my experience is that YE activities are largely done in isolation of the parallel, and equally good, work of the likes of STEMNet, CodeClub and their ambassadors. Part of the problem being of course that there are few people with experience from both sides of the fence to act as advisors or mentors.

So perhaps we should start promoting the other E in parallel with STEM. Let's call it Encouraging Science, Technology, Engineering, Enterprise and Maths: ESTEEM. How's that for creativity?

*****

ADDITIVE MANUFACTURING IS NATURE'S WAY

21st September 2014

3D printing is one of the latest technology trends to enthuse the public and excite the journalist. Universities are using them for research tools, manufacturers for rapid prototyping, and schools are starting to buy them for their design and technology classrooms. Indeed, earlier this year, Festival-alumnus Luke Johnson called for help in an *FT* article to place one in every UK school, rather than just the privileged few that could afford the investment.

And 3D printing is certainly worthy of attention. For once we are starting to consider building complex structures in an additive way; brick-by-brick on a much smaller scale. This is second nature to those brought up on Lego, and this is also second nature to Nature herself. We as humans grow by the slow but accurate deployment of new cells, seashells extend by the gradual deposition of mainly calcium carbonate, and striking geological formations build up by sedimentation of rock and debris.

We have been witness to additive manufacturing since the day we were born, yet we tend to manufacture most artificial things using subtractive techniques on moulded or extruded billets. This is a little wasteful of material, and not particularly elegant. Imagine if trees began life as solid 100-foot-tall blocks of wood and gradually eroded to reveal their structure with a large pile of waste shavings at their foot?

As we get to grips with 3D printing, one of the key milestones will be our ability to manipulate materials during the process to create continuously changing compositions. Look carefully at that tree again, and you will see that the deposited cells create a structure that transcends through root, wood, bark, softer wood, leaf, and fruit. And these themselves have complexities visible only on the micro-scale.

So our ability to slowly 3D print a lump of plastic, albeit in a complex shape, is not really enough to congratulate ourselves about. When we can control the self-assembly of a series of structures that seamlessly change from metal to polymer to ceramic so as to provide functional mechanical and electrical properties in just the right places, we are getting there. The test, for example, might be to 3D print the electric lightbulb. Any bright ideas?

*****

SO WHAT IS INNOVATION?

1st October 2014, by guest blogger Stuart Wilkes
The Malvern Festival of Innovation has kicked off, for the next 4 days in the beautiful hillside town of Malvern. There is a range of exciting speakers talking on everything from Cyber Security and the Internet of Things, through to manufacturing and bootstrapping. These are complemented with a diverse range of exhibitors such as Aston Martin and Lockheed Martin to small startups and entrepreneurs.

Everybody will talk 'innovation'! But hang on, exactly what is innovation? I'm sure if you ask half a dozen engineers, you will get half a dozen answers – it's the new, it's a device, it's a process, it's an application, it's a better solution . . . it's all of these and more.

Being innovative, being an innovator is seen as a very good thing. These are the people who break new ground, rip up the rules and try something new. Not encumbered by the past, but excited by the future. Convinced that things, no matter what they are can be better. The human race can be moved forward by innovation in whatever form it comes and in whatever subject it occurs. Innovators will fall, but they pick themselves up, dust themselves down and keep pushing forward, enthused by the fact that one day they will 'crack it'.

Innovators have given us smart phones, heart monitors, cars and planes; microwave ovens and digital cameras; They have delivered flat screens, HD, WiFi and more – and they are not done yet. With the world now more connected than ever innovators around the world can share and collaborate, they attack the big problems facing humanity as a collective.

It appears to me that innovation is not one thing, in fact innovation is a state of mind, and many of those minds are gathering for the next few days here in Malvern. . . .

*****

THE BIGGEST BIG DATA

1st October 2014, by guest blogger Stuart Wilkes
At the risk of sounding like a technical dinosaur, I still have neatly filed away some 3.5" floppy discs. Their capacity a tiny 1.44Mb. I remember well the days that I used to pop them in and out of my Mac and other devices at the time thinking that I would never need any more storage than that. Of course I was wrong, by a long way. Megabytes, became Gigabytes, Gigabytes have become Terabytes and today, whilst listening to

Pete Rose from HP talk at the Malvern Festival of Innovation about Big Data, I heard for the first time about Brontobytes – yep, 'brontobytes', like that huge dinosaur! This is a huge, huge number, this is almost the biggest of big data.

Just to bring you up to speed sequentially we have a gigabyte, then add three more zeros to get a terabyte, add 3 more zeros to get a petabyte, then you go exabyte, zettabyte, yottabyte and then the aforementioned brontobyte. This is 10 to the power 27, or more zeros than you can comfortably write down or even quantify. Just to put this into context 10 to the power 24, the yottabyte, is the total strange capability of 250 trillion DVDs. So a brontobyte is 1000 yottabytes, in other words – massive!

These are immense numbers and in order to access (never mind find!) data that will be stored in this quantity, new computing methods will be required. HP Labs are already innovating, developing and researching into photonics to replace the copper connections within today's computers, servers, and tablets with optical connections – the much heralded computing at the speed of light, literally. In order to do this, they have a research project called 'The Machine' to make computing more efficient by removing the 80% of time that computers spend on managing their environment – as in moving data from one place to another – and getting it to perform the task at hand. The technology and the new thinking (the innovation) needed to do this is immense, but with HP behind it and their enviable track record in innovation, it will no doubt come to market.

So will 'The Machine' be able to crunch through brontobytes at the speed of light? That's the aim, that's the dream, in fact that's the future market need. Oh and just in case you were wondering, the brontobyte will go the way of its dinosaur namesake, as the 'geopbyte' – that's 10 to the power 30, is already in HP's sights. Big Data will continue to get bigger!

*****

SMART CITIES: SMART STATES: SMART NATIONS
22nd October 2014

Innovating Together for the 21st Century was the subject of a UK / Singapore event today in Central London, and despite the rhetoric and back-patting from both sides about past creativity and success, this is actually likely to be a programme that will yield good results in the future.

And the reason is that Singapore is a very technologically progressive nation; and one for which I have strong affinity and a high regard. I lived and worked there for five years and was able to start, grow and exit a high technology company within that timeframe. My microcosm of activity stress-tested its research and development capability, its start-up mentality, its business support infrastructure, its logistics, its connectivity, and its resilience to global issues (SARS and economic meltdown in the western world, to name but two). And it all worked well for me. Of course there were frustrations, but there were also great rewards realised and strong friendships created.

That experience happened between 2002 and 2007, and although the term hadn't really been coined, Singapore was a pretty smart city even back then. I travelled with an RFID card (like London's Oyster card of today) seamlessly on both buses and the underground, traffic lights were fitted with LEDs to reduce energy consumption, the electronic road pricing (ERP) system reduced city centre traffic jams, wi-fi was free (and fast) at Changi airport, libraries and many fast food outlets, and taxis had seat-back displays giving you information as you travelled. And when SARS struck, free digital thermometers were distributed widely and body temperature was recorded and uploaded across the island.

But interestingly at the event today, a major panel discussion centred on smart cities and Singapore's aspiration to be not just a smart city, but a smart nation; and probably the first. Of course, this is semantics, because Singapore is a city state, so by definition if its city is smart, so is its nation. But actually, there is a real challenge in this ambition, because being a smart nation needs to embrace more than just the city infrastructure. It needs to include national policy, diverse public services, education, employment, entertainment, tourism, retirement, and healthcare across the country.

And although being contained in a city has its advantages, it is also a great opportunity to reap the benefits. Today, being smart involves much more than I witnessed a decade ago. It needs energy supply, water supply, air quality, movement of people, movement of vehicles, supply of food, deployment of security, scheduling of entertainment and so on to be monitored, controlled and optimised in real-time against data models and in-field feedback.

Steve Leonard of Singapore's Infocomm Development Agency (IDA) summed it up well: connecting everything and everyone all the time! The ramifications are enormous. Huge data, huge insights, huge efficiencies and a huge competitive edge.

And in Singapore where everyone lives on top of each other and there has arguably been a kind of "benevolent dictatorship", privacy is not seen as such a big deal as it is to us in the west. Whether this is morally right of wrong is another debate, but the point is that culturally Singapore is primed to embrace being a truly smart nation and many of the barriers we see in the UK are not so high in Singapore. As Lily Chan, CEO of NUS Enterprise explained in her talk: Singaporeans are a very pragmatic people.

So the UK would do well to collaborate on this ambition with Singapore as it could learn a lot, test a lot, and probably bring its own cities up to speed in smartness more quickly than it would in isolation.

The challenge for the UK is actually the part of being a smart nation. Firstly, there is more to the UK than London. Secondly, there is more to the UK than a dozen or so large cities. We have huge swathes of rural countryside with small towns and villages where even broadband is absent. Living in Malvern, I know all too well how being rural can put the brakes on growth and development. But significant things do happen in Malvern and we need to be part of the smart infrastructure too. Moreover, there are lots of other rural spaces like us where tourism, agriculture, education, energy production, niche commerce, etc. are contributing to the nation and can be done better in a smart integrated way.

So my view is that in this partnership, Singapore should focus on becoming the model smart city state, and the UK should focus on becoming the model smart nation beyond cities. What we learn from Singapore can be applied to our great cities, and what we learn from the rural challenge can be exported via Singapore to its Asian neighbours where indeed rural jungles, isolated islands, and lesser-developed suburbs proliferate. Meanwhile, we are ready here in Malvern to be the test-bed for the smart exo-city.

Postscript: As a case in point, this article would have been published more quickly had the wi-fi been working on my train home to the rural hinterland of our yet-to-be smart nation.

*****

THE BATCH OF ONE

10th December 2014

Branded fashion survives on exclusivity; limiting the supply and making something desirable and aspirational. Original paintings fetch more than the prints, and limiting the prints pushes up the value of both. But now more and more commoditised consumer products offer customisation, and customers have got used to demanding it: for example, cars come with a multitude of options from added equipment through to colour and upholstery.

Manufacturers achieve this range of choice by completing the production process after selling the concept. Just in time manufacturing becomes just-after-the-sale manufacturing. This has the advantage of reducing stock and wastage, but creates a headache for supply chain logistics which needs to ensure all the specific parts are available at that time.

The logical conclusion for this type of manufacturing is the batch of one, where each version of the product is unique and bespoke. Common components, but potentially no two creations the same. 3D Printing is an enabler for this type of production, because the process can be produced on demand and with the necessary variations.

The idea of batches of one is not new. Anything handmade, hand painted, or hand crafted is arguably a batch of one, but often these are created from a plan or template, so things are not so different overall. The trend, however, is for complex physical production processes to become more and more individual so as to specify the colour, shape, weight, functionality, and so on.

But is manufacturing the only place we are seeing the batch of one concept applied? Actually not. Medicine is heading that way too. In the future, as genome mapping and genetic engineering becomes prevalent, so too will treatments that are tailored to the individual. Already medicine is becoming personalised, with various cocktails of pharmaceuticals being prescribed on a case-by-case basis. However, the natural endpoint for this is for the actual drug molecules to be dispensed into a carrier pill, the carrier serum or directly into the body just when needed. Each concoction uniquely tailored to the genetic make-up and current metabolic state of the specific human body.

Then comes education. Whilst attending the NEF Innovisions 2014 conference in London last week, much emphasis was placed on the changes ahead in teaching and training. How education is delivered is changing with the advent of digital content. But soon, the course, the exercises, the references and even the final examination and qualification could be delivered as a batch of one. A specific set of materials presented in a way that the particular student will most efficiently adsorb, retain and learn from, so as to provide an optimised set of skills for a very specific job or task.

This could go full circle of course – the uniquely trained human being becoming capable to develop unique products many times over, helped by medical treatments that keep him or her not just healthy, but specifically adapted to the task; be it with provision of training, nutrition, or medicine.

*****

INNOVATION CAN SOMETIMES CAUSE A STIR . . .

22nd February 2015

The last few weeks have seen residents of Malvern, the home of the Festival of Innovation, gripped by a divisive proposal; that of building a cable car from the town of Great Malvern up the steep slopes of an Area of Outstanding Natural Beauty to the highest point in Worcestershire.

Those for the scheme cite the economic benefits that such an infrastructure project would bring to the town. It might provide a new activity for tourists, it would facilitate access for all onto the Hills, and it would create jobs and spin-off opportunities. Those against fear a ruining of unspoilt vistas, damage to wildlife and the creep of other buildings onto the Hills, an area protected by a unique historic Act of the UK Parliament.

Not to be drawn one way or another, this debate highlights one key aspect of innovation: that of change. Change is always met with resistance as it upsets the status quo. People have things to gain and to lose; the balance of power shifts, and the real outcome is generally unpredictable. Disruptive innovation, be it an idea, a concept, a device or a process, creates antagonism and concern. It also creates opportunities.

Sometimes, proposed solutions to problems can lead to other more compelling ideas. To me the idea of a cable car per se is not particularly creative, as it has been done before in many places, and the aerial structures they require can be rather ugly. As an example, one alternative suggestion has been made from residents to reintroduce donkey rides up the Hills; these are a green form of transport and have a quirkiness about them that sits well in the town! A bit retrograde, however.

So I think we can do better still. What about trialling a fleet of green all-electric (or hydrogen fuel cell) autonomous vehicle that does not require a cable in the first place? Despite the wilderness, the Malvern Hills are unusual because there is actually a narrow tarmac track via a shallower inclined route to the summit. It would make a great rural testbed for the technology that is now being trialled in some of our major cities.

*****

SOCIAL MEDIA OR SOCIAL TEDIA?

4th September 2015

As we race towards the next edition of the Malvern Festival of Innovation, we are stepping up our social media engagement to help market the event as widely as possible. Today this activity is a necessary part any campaign, and as all business owners will know, the spectrum of platforms available is daunting. Facebook, LinkedIn, Twitter, Pinterest, Blogger, What's App, Instagram, Flickr, MailChimp, to name but a few of the more well-known ones. Each has its nuances, each its own demographic, and each its own acceptable (n)etiquette.

Moreover, campaigns are no longer the monologue of a billboard or flier. They are two-way conversations in which the target audience responds, interacts and engages. This is a 24-7 activity requiring the stamina of a marathon runner to stay the course, the agility of a sprinter to respond quickly, and frankly the skills of a decathlete to navigate across all the platforms.

Just last week Facebook reported that it had over 1 billion users on line in a single day. That's a significant proportion of the world's population; especially when you remember that the global population must include some people who are very young, some who are very old, and some who are living in really quite remote and undeveloped areas of our planet.

Is it therefore all getting too much? Has innovation in this space finally surpassed the human brain's ability to cope with all this activity? And as was indicated in a BBC news piece this week, it's not so much that we are just overloaded, but rather that we are addicted to all the stimulation and won't switch off.

The good news is that at some point someone will come up with a new idea that eases the situation again for us all. Until that happens, your sanity may only be saved by pressing the off button and relishing the short-lived silence before switching it all back on again so you don't miss something important.

*****

CEREBRAL SECURITY & BIG BIG DATA

13th September 2015

Not a day goes by without news of a compromised website, a leakage of passwords, a loss of credit-card data, or a concern that someone has taken control of an online account. Cyber security and the associated issue of personal privacy are a scourge of modern times brought on by us humans relying on the connected world to live our lives; whether that's to manage our finances, do the shopping, communicate with friends, or grow a business. Pretty much everything we do, and even more so for the younger generation, involves digital data that can be leaked, eaves-dropped, harvested, or sold.

I suspect, however, things may be about to get a whole lot worse over the next decade! At the moment our brains are off-limits; they host our private memories, thoughts and intentions without others being able to interfere. The only clues are what we display with our emotions and choose to disseminate with our words and actions. And within each of our brains is a lot of data; this is big big data, typically a memory of about a million gigabytes each!

How different the world will be when we can interface directly with our brain, controlling things telepathically by merely thinking of the action. As with all innovations, there will be plenty of benefits; people with disabilities and illness will gain more control over their lives and daily tasks could be completed hands-free and efficiently from a distance. There is plenty of research going on at the moment to this end; already it is possible to control external objects with brainwaves, it's just that that the range of commands is rather limited and requires a fair bit of training and concentration to do repeatedly and accurately.

This will change, and one day it will be possible to download memories as both stills (like photographs) and sequences (like videos). It will be possible to back-up our personal memory bank so that learned facts, figures and insights are not forgotten over time, and then eventually it will be possible to upload data to augment your memory with new catalogues of information.

Soon we'll be into the realms of cerebral security. People around you may try to access your brain to see what you are really thinking about them, the police and security services will want to monitor your past actions and future intentions, criminals will want to know things with which to blackmail you or second-guess you, and terrorists may try to gain control of you so that you can perform actions on their behalf. Suddenly, the brain will be susceptible to new forms of viruses; hybrids of the biological and the computational.

Somehow, we'll have to rush to develop the equivalent of passwords, firewalls and anti-virus scans for our brain. There will be a need for memory back-up and data recovery (read personality recovery). This will be a whole new and exciting industry bridging the gap between biochemistry, neurology and the IT industry.

The difference between a neurone and a silicon transistor will be greyed, the keyboard and mouse will be no more, and things like smart phones, monitors and televisions will be replaced by direct interfaces to the retinal receptors of our brains. You will be both a source and a sink for direct data transfer. Google will collect street views from your own eyes, Amazon will ship on one-blink orders, and Facebook will become Brainbook as your timeline is thought-after-thought-after thought. . . .

Deep breath.

On Friday 9th October 2015 we discuss cyber security and big data at the Malvern Festival of Innovation. Will we be considering cerebral security and big big data at the same Festival in October 2025? Probably, and there will be no need for you to attend; we'll just beam it all straight to you whilst you are sleeping and extract a quick user survey to see what you thought of it all afterwards!

*****

DRONES, ROBOTS AND SENSORS COMING TO A FIELD NEAR YOU
1st October 2015
If you live in the countryside, you may feel a bit isolated from modern technology. Broadband speeds are often slow, mobile phone coverage poor, and the pace of life that little bit more relaxed. Oh, and getting stuck behind a tractor on the way to work is par for the course. This is all about to change. Although

investment in rural Internet connectivity is generally on the up, oddly enough it is in the fields themselves where the harnessing and crunching of data is probably increasing most quickly. This will also drive data connectivity in the countryside.

Farmers are gathering soil data to optimise which crops to plant when and where. Tractors are equipped with telemetry and GPS to log detailed information about the processes taking place during the preparation of fields, the sowing of crops, the application of chemicals, and the yield of the harvest. Satellite images are cross-correlated with soil condition, ground features and crop history. This is crop rotation from the Agrarian revolution taken to its next level.

Next come the sensors, monitoring weather, ground conditions, environment and pollution around the fields all in real time and alerting the farmer to adverse conditions on a hyperlocal scale.

Drones will systematically, and eventually autonomously, patrol acres of land, feeding back crop condition and scheduling the workload. Couple this with artificial intelligence and machine learning, and soon the land will be delivering improved yields and meeting the ever-increasing demands for sustainably produced food and bio-fuel whilst optimising the use of energy and water.

This is all good news for the society, and we'll hear more about it at the festival this year. The farmer will extract more value from his land, the consumer will benefit from affordable and nutritious food, and the countryside commuter will probably no longer get stuck behind a tractor being driven home for dinner.

⁂⁂⁂⁂⁂

CYBORG SECURITY & EMBEDDABLES

15th January 2016

Perhaps surprisingly, we as humans haven't gone down the road of embedding much technology in ourselves yet. Where we do, it tends to be for medical reasons, with many of these applications being passive technologies like hip replacements, stents, traction pins, etc.

Artificial hearts and pacemakers are good examples of embedded active technologies, and these are certainly becoming more sophisticated as they can be monitored and controlled externally. And this has just started to raise people's fears about the security of Medtech; could someone hack the implant and control the device independently? Can people read my health data and violate my privacy?

A few high-profile research cases have embedded other non-medical objects in humans. Like pets with RFID identity tags implanted, so too have humans tried this out. Professor Kevin Warwick's team at Reading University investigated this, with Kevin having an RFID chip embedded under his skin that allowed him to open his laboratory door without the need of a separate keycard. He and his team did a lot more since.

Well over a decade ago a pioneering nightclub in Barcelona allowed partygoers to pay for their drinks with an embedded microchip in their arm. But there haven't been many cases of this approach being adopted.

You don't see Londoners using embedded Oyster Cards to travel the Tube. You don't see people with Contactless credit cards embedded in their fingertip to pay for their M&S goods. You don't see skiers with their ski pass embedded in a limb.

Indeed, wearables or WearableTech are the current fashion. People have Fitbits and GoPros strapped to their body parts; Google Glass was a relatively short-lived accessory which may come round again as some kind of contact lens, and the mobile phone and smart watches are the ubiquitous tech about our bodies.

Bodyhacking or biohacking is the term given to hobby cyborgs that are experimenting at the in vivo technology frontier. People have embedded magnets in their fingertips and gained a 'sixth sense' in which they can feel the vibrations from a nearby electromagnetic field. The aforementioned Kevin Warwick has had microneedle chip arrays embedded in his arm to provide an interface with his nervous system. And Neil Harbisson embedded an antenna-like sensor through his skull and into his brain to help him overcome his colourblindness and 'hear' colours.

And this really is just the beginning because the next (un?!)natural step must surely be to take all our wearable tech and turn it into embeddable tech. The advantages will be many; the body could 'feed' the device with energy (heat if nothing else) and obviate the need for a battery. The nervous system could be used to interface with our visual cortex and dispense with the LCD display. The same approach could connect to the cochlear nerve and we'd hear the phone ring or the iTunes track without the need of a loud speaker or headphones; and no one else would be disturbed either.

Get this embedded interface right with our existing nervous system, and there will be many more ways to exploit sensors to help us navigate and communicate. We'll have embedded GPS, embedded Wifi, embedded 4G, and our bodies will join the Internet of Things; think Internet of Beings.

I wrote an earlier piece about Cerebral Security highlighting that all we know about the issues of cyber security will multiply once we start directly interfacing with our brain. But if our entire body starts to accommodate embeddables, then we're going to need to think about Cyborg Security.

People's appendages could start to house very valuable devices that generate even more valuable data. It's not just the ability to pay with a finger, or know where someone is because the chip is now within their arm, but it is also about health and status information being generated. Your internal systems will be streaming data like the telemetry from a rocket ship, and people around you may try to intercept it. If they knew you were hungry, they could sell you a snack. Feeling thirsty; can I sell you a drink? Feeling tired? then you might be a target worth abducting because you wouldn't have the energy to defend yourself.

Given this you'll also need to invest in other cyborg accessories; radar and infrared devices that can detect stalkers sneaking up behind you, bionic muscle-boosting devices that pack a heavier punch for improved defence, and exoskeletons that enable you to flee quicker.

As you can see, this will be disruptive technology that will make many of today's must-have devices obsolete and open up vast new markets where we'll feel compelled to spend money and keep an even closer eye on our security and privacy. Perhaps someone will create a third eye embeddable just for that task.

*****

ALL ABOARD THE BLOCKCHAIN

25th February 2016

We might just be about to witness the next 'industrial' revolution; one where societal interactions on all levels become completely decentralised (or peer-to-peer, as the saying goes). What does this really mean? It means cutting out the middleman so that people (and machines) can transact with each other in full trust and with high degrees of privacy. Doing so lowers cost, increases efficiency, and opens up lots of opportunities.

This might sound like an iterative change with little impact, and when I first started to look into this I wasn't particularly impressed with the hype. But, take a step back to look at the bigger picture and indeed the full potential, and it becomes apparent there might just be something disruptive and paradigm-shifting in it all.

The most cited example (and perhaps easiest situation to relate to) is that involving money. Blockchain is almost synonymous with Bitcoin, the virtual currency that most people have heard of but relatively few have dared buy or spend. Ironically it is Bitcoin's encrypted virtual autonomous being that seems to deter people from adopting it; can it be trusted? Will it just evaporate from my virtual wallet? Does it really have any value?

Yet it is designed precisely to allay these fears. It is also a way to send and receive money with someone directly anywhere in the world without involving a bank, a clearing house, or any one specific third party. It's like paying for cash without the need of a government regulated mint or central bank to issue and manage the currency.

But Bitcoin is more than this. It relies on multiple copies of a decentralised record book (a distributed ledger; the blockchain) to encrypt and record the transactions thus creating an immutable audit trail. It is this aspect that will very likely be incredibly disruptive. This is because the blockchain does not have to be limited to transacting Bitcoins. It can form the backbone for exchanging contracts and credentials; like any database or record book only with added security and in many ways greater transparency. Moreover, the contracts can be smart so that actions can follow automatically based on a set of software rules without human interference. An example is that the Bitcoin could be loaned automatically to a business, the business could pay interest automatically to the lender, and the loan could be repaid automatically when the business meets a set of agreed criteria. And if you are a bank, then you are no longer in the loop. And if you are a government, you may find it rather difficult to regulate. And if you are tax authority, you may well be avoided.

Looking into the details there are a few surprises along the way. The ledger is getting bigger by the second, and so as I write this, the blockchain associated with Bitcoins stands at just over 56 Gb. It takes a while to fully transact a Bitcoin (around about 10 minutes; considerably slower than a credit card payment, significantly faster than an international telegraphic transfer). It also requires a fair amount of energy; the Bitcoin and associated transactions require cryptography and consensus by many parties, and the system has built in this number-crunching cost to ascribe some value and rarity to the currency. There are other technical challenges as well around limitations and levels of security of the current blockchain, not to mention the issue of standardisation and the existence of alternative blockchains, other virtual currencies and a growing range of protocols.

But one thing is almost certain. The blockchain will start to creep into our everyday lives just as personal computers, the Internet and social networks have. Currently there are bits and pieces about you dispersed around the global network and before long some of these will become attached to blockchains. You may not ever understand the inner workings, but you'll probably wonder how you ever functioned without them.

Join us at the Malvern Festival of Innovation to find out more about cyber security, the Internet of Things and where blockchains fit into all of this. And when we go live with our Formal Dinner tickets, as in previous years you will be able to pay with Bitcoins. . . .

*****

JUMPING FROM SILICON TO CARBON

3rd April 2016

The artificial technology-based world that we have created around us contains a lot of silicon. Our computers, smart phones, cars, planes, medical devices, power stations, and infrastructure networks all rely on silicon chips to process 0's and 1's, and transistor-adorned central processing units are at the nucleus of every electronic device we deploy.

But this may be about to change. Our natural world is based on an element one level above in the periodic table; carbon. Life is built not on silicon wafers, but around carbon chains. DNA molecules define the form and function of organisms large and small, and this is a very different approach to the electronic technology we invented and developed over the last few decades.

Our silicon-based computational tools have been allowing us to analyse and decode carbon-based life for years, but only now are we starting to understand what might be needed, as a minimum, to create an autonomous organic device we term life. A recent news report outlined progress with creating a synthetic bug using what seems to be a minimum number of genes; 473 to be precise.

This is a leap beyond genetic modification because it is about creating a life form from the ground up rather than simply adjusting something that already exists. We still don't understand the full function and scope of each of the genes, but it won't be long before we do. And then it will be possible to create libraries of building-block genes rather like we create libraries of computer code modules, so that before long we'll have a programming language, compiler system and developer kits to create and prescribe forms of life itself.

This will almost certainly have much in common with how the silicon-based computer industry developed. There will be organic devices that perform new functions rather like the calculator and digital watch did in the early days of silicon. These will grow in complexity and value as we develop our knowledge around the systems. And our present-day silicon devices will start to look as outdated as thermionic valve technology did when silicon wafers started to emerge. But don't expect equivalent devices; an organic timepiece is not an appropriate use of this new carbon-based technology, whereas a swarm of bee-like reconnaissance drones may well be.

A major difference, however, is around self-replication. Silicon chips do not reproduce, but life has a habit of being able to do so. On the right substrate, simple organisms like bacteria can quickly generate a colony, and more complicated life creates seeds, spores, and eggs. It is a key requisite of life that it should be able to create younger selves. So, expect our drones, our algae-based batteries, and our leafy photosynthetic solar cell roof tiles to grow, replicate and die; and more interestingly to adapt in Darwinian fashion. No longer will we have centralised factories or vast landfills. Instead, our devices will grow in-situ and we'll throw them on the compost heap when they have completed their life cycle. And we'll use their children and their children's children to provide an on-going service.

This really is going to be a dramatic change to the way we live. It will throw us enormous challenges and probably provide serendipitous solutions. We will need to be careful that we don't create a species of a device that acts as a predator on something else we value, as they will almost certainly need to feed on something. Then again, one company may adopt this approach as a way to see off competition! But, equally something like our reconnaissance drones could also provide a pollination service as they go about their surveillance work. Honey may even be a by-product! These carbon-based devices may also photosynthesise and help capture carbon, reducing global warming as a by-product of their use. We may even legislate it as a prerequisite for any new such device on the market.

Our landscape around us will change. Life that has taken millennia to evolve on our planet will co-habit with life we seed in the laboratory. Oaks will stand alongside trees designed to behave as wind harnessing 'turbines', fields of pasture will butt up against plantations of device seedlings, and oceans will have shoals of fish that we designed to seek out mineral deposits for the few remaining electronic devices we still need.

*****

PETROLHEADS AND PISTON-HEADS, MAKE WAY FOR ELECTRODE-HEADS

2nd May 2016

Pop the bonnet on a Nissan Leaf, a Renault Zoe or a Tesla Model S, and you won't find any carburettors, plugs, sumps or turbochargers. No, these are fully electric cars without a piston in sight.

You can still talk torque and effuse efficiency, but you can't discuss displacement or exclaim over chrome exhaust manifolds. But the electric vehicle industry is certainly breeding equally enthusiastic proponents who will wax lyrical about range, cost of ownership, and electric charging networks.

Oddly enough, the UK used to have fleets of electric vehicles roaming the streets early each morning almost half a century ago. These were milk floats, whispering around neighbourhoods on defined rounds before breakfast, returning to be plugged in each day ahead of the next trip. Their Achilles' heel was the lead acid car battery that was needed in sizeable arrays that added weight, cost and range anxiety.

Today, the new breed of electric vehicles has replaced lead for lithium; a considerable weight saving, an improved energy density, and a better form factor. But still electric vehicles take time to charge, have a limited range, and come at a price.

Yet the advantages are also plain to see. The mechanics are much simpler with motors on each axle or wheel hub, thus dispensing with gearboxes, engines, differentials and exhaust systems. No more engine oil changes, no more oil filter changes, and significantly reduced brake disk wear as much of the stopping can be done regeneratively using the motor as a dynamo with its integral resistance to rotation.

Having recently attended the unveiling of the Tesla Model X in Birmingham, and travelled there as a passenger in a Model S, I have to say the real excitement with electric cars is the paradigm shift in how new arrivals in the automotive industry are turning the concept of motoring on its head. The idea that your car is an extension of your world of mobile apps, basically another Thing of the Internet, is intriguing. We're starting to see integrated navigation with your calendar of meeting appointments, the ability to have a defrosted and warmed car autonomously prepped at your front door as you step out to leave, and a system that receives updates, tweaks, improvements on your driveway without the need for costly product recalls.

Eventually it may only be fanatics that own cars; the rest of us will simply treat them as rentable pods that arrive on demand, drop us at our destination, and disappear off to recharge and transport someone else. Of course, cars don't need to be electric to do this, but the change of mindset around range, charging and cost models is driving innovation in how we will own and use vehicles. Tesla may be the vanguard at the moment, but expect Apple, Google and Microsoft to be in this space soon too; electric cars will just be hardware accessories built around software applications rather like an office printer or mouse.

In the future, the electric vehicle power plant may well be a lithium battery, a hydrogen fuel cell, or a biofuel jet generator. Pop the bonnet and you might catch sight of a gold-plated cathode or a silver coated anode. Polished and pimped, this will herald the age of the electrode heads . . .

*****

STILL A LOT OF WORK TO DO INGRAINING STEM
30th September 2016

Science, technology, engineering and mathematics (STEM) subjects are not easy to learn, as they require a good understanding of technical concepts and of course an interest in the topics being explained.

But let's take something as simple and ubiquitous as water; the liquid at room temperature that sustains life, the liquid that all of us are familiar with through drinking many times a day, the liquid that rains down much of the time here in the UK, and the liquid that covers about two-thirds of the planet that we live on.

You'd think, therefore, that everyone in the developed world would have a vague enough interest in the substance to know that it comprises of molecules that each contain two hydrogen atoms and one oxygen atom. Many of us are taught this at school at some point in our lives, and given how common the substance is, it crops up in not just chemistry, but also biology, physics (the anomalous expansion of water), geography (the water cycle) and even English Literature (*The Rime of the Ancient Mariner*).

However, being involved in a cafe at our business centre in Malvern, which we named Cafe H2O to celebrate the hydrological heritage of the town and hills, it has become apparent that there are some major misunderstandings of the simple chemistry of water out there.

We became aware when both an alternative Facebook page and an alternative Trip Advisor page appeared, linked to the cafe, that were both named Cafe H20 (yes, twenty, not 2-O). Do people really think we would call our outlet Cafe H-twenty, and if so, why? Do they think there is the possibility of a molecule, water or otherwise, that consists of twenty connected hydrogen atoms?

We were tempted to delete the erroneous social media pages, but before we could get around to it, people kept posting and referring to them. So, it wasn't a case of just one or two misinformed people finding them, people must actually have been searching using the wrong name. In fact, though it pains us to have the wrongly titled pages in existence, if we deleted them they would almost certainly reappear. We have decided to use the opportunity to provide a little STEM education, redirecting people to the correct pages with an explanation as to why they've found the wrong page. And now at the time of writing, Trip Advisor have realised we had effectively duplicate pages and have combined them. Now, we wait to see if another H20 is spawned by a patron using the wrong search term.

Fortunately, the Royal Society of Chemistry will be on-hand in a few days' time at both the Malvern Festival of Innovation's Next Generation Innovators schools' day and the weekend's Family Day. We'll take the opportunity to highlight that water is H2O not H2o, and explain why. And with that grounding, we'll then be able to talk about all the innovation around water technology; desalination, purification, de-ionising, wave power, nuclear fusion, and more.

Perhaps Samuel Coleridge should have written "Di-hydrogen-oxide everywhere, nor any drop to drink" and then there would be no excuse whether your studied sciences or not.

＊＊＊＊＊

ALEXA, PLEASE ORGANISE THE NEXT FESTIVAL . . .

2nd January 2018

As we enter 2018, we're starting to organise the seventh edition of the annual Malvern Festival of Innovation. It comes around quickly, and in reality no sooner has one finished, we start to think about the next. In many ways, each year gets a little easier, as we have a system in place to book the venues, plan the programme, raise the sponsorship, and encourage participation. But there is still a lot of legwork which seems to take an inordinate amount of time to complete.

How long, I wonder, before we can rely on digital assistants equipped with artificial intelligence to do the majority of the organising? Which event will be the first to claim it was organised entirely by Amazon's Alexa, Apple's Siri, Google's Assistant or Microsoft's Cortana? And will the event run smoothly, or will there be hiccups as it becomes clear that some of the detail was lost in translation; taxis booked instead of venues, catering ordered a week early, exhibitors given joining instructions for Malvern PA rather than Malvern UK. A lot can go wrong!

And yet, as we enter 2018, there is plenty of talk about robots and AI taking over our jobs and replacing human labour with silicon efficiency. Over the years we've captured some of these trends at the festival; autonomous vehicles, big data, Internet of Things, and smart agri-tech. And no doubt this year, as the programme crystallises, we'll be covering more of these disrupting technologies that will change the way we live and work.

But what makes an event like the festival appealing to us humans is more than just the organisation; it is the curated content and the friendly atmosphere which unfortunately digital assistants are probably not so good at prescribing. Maybe we'll see a few Alexi, or her cousins, in the audience as delegates first, before they are in a position to start being the organisers. In anticipation we may bring one along to start some in-field training early: Hey Google, fancy joining us at the next festival to see what you can learn?

*****